ALGEBRA I

Teacher's Resources and Assessments

VOLUME 1

Carnegie Learning™
THE COGNITIVE TUTOR® COMPANY

Carnegie Learning™
THE COGNITIVE TUTOR® COMPANY

Pittsburgh, PA
Phone 888.851.7094
Fax 412.690.2444

www.carnegielearning.com

Acknowledgements

We would like to thank those listed below who helped to prepare
the Cognitive Tutor® *Algebra I* Teacher's Resources and Assignments.

Karise Mace
Michael and Emily Amick
Claudine Thiem
Michele Covatto
The Carnegie Learning Development Team

ISBN 1-932409-64-5
Teacher's Resources and Assessments, Volume 1

Printed in the United States of America
1-2006-VH

Contents

Contents

Contents

Section I
Assessments
Chapters 1-6

Pre-Test

Name _____ Date _____

Find the next two terms of each sequence.

1.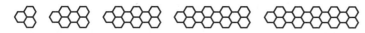

2. 2, 4, 8, 16, 32, _____ , _____

3. Use the nth term to list the first five terms of the sequence. Show your work.

    $a_n = 2n + 4$

    $a_1 = $ _____

    $a_2 = $ _____

    $a_3 = $ _____

    $a_4 = $ _____

    $a_5 = $ _____

Use the sequence below to answer Questions 4 through 6.

4. Complete the table by filling in the number of hexagons in each term of the sequence.

Term (n)	1	2	3	4	5
Number of hexagons					

5. Write an expression showing the relationship between the term and the number of hexagons in that term. Let n represent the term.

6. Use the expression from Question 5 to find the 10th term of the sequence. Show your work.

7. Write the power as a product.

    3^4

1

8. Write the product as a power.

    7(7)(7)(7)(7)(7)(7)(7)

9. Perform the indicated operations. Show your work.

    $4^2 + (8 - 3)6$

10. You and your classmates have set up a phone chain to call each other if school is cancelled due to bad weather. You call two classmates, then each of them calls two classmates, and so on until everyone in your class has been notified. There are 31 students in your class. Draw a diagram to show how each student would be reached to be notified of school cancellations.

11. Find the sum of the numbers from 1 to 10. Show your work.

12. Write an expression for the sum of the numbers 1 to n.

Name _____ Date _____

Read the scenario below. Use the scenario to answer Questions 13 through 16.

The Spanish Club at your school is selling animal piñatas to raise money for a trip to Mexico City. The club earns $3 for each piñata sold. The sale runs for five weeks. The number of piñatas sold each week are 15, 22, 8, 35, and 42.

13. Make a table to show the number of piñatas sold and the profit made for each week of the sale.

14. Create a bar graph to display the profit for each week of the sale.

(units)

(label)

1

15. Create a graph to display the relationship between the number of piñatas sold and the profit. First, choose your bounds and intervals. Be sure to label your graph clearly.

Variable quantity	Lower bound	Upper bound	Interval
Number of piñatas			
Profit			

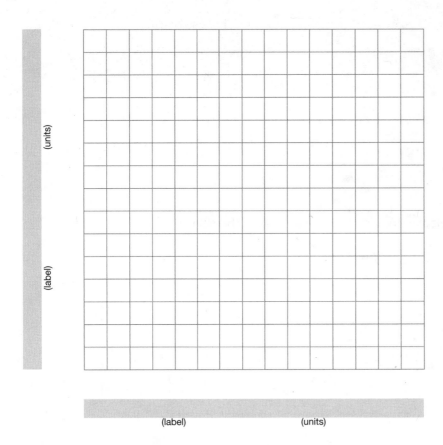

(units)

(label)

(label)   (units)

16. Write an algebraic equation that you could use to show the profit for any number of piñatas sold.

Name _____ Date _____

Read the scenario below. Use the scenario to answer Questions 17 and 18.

Two airlines offer special group rates to your school's Spanish Club for the trip to Mexico City. The Mexican Air airline offers a roundtrip airfare of $250 per person. The Fiesta airline offers a roundtrip airfare of $150 per person if the club agrees to pay a one time group rate processing fee of $1000.

17. Which airline offers the better deal if only nine students from the Spanish Club are able to fly to Mexico City? Show all your work and use complete sentences to explain your answer.

18. Which airline offers the better deal if 20 students are able to fly to Mexico City? Show all your work and use complete sentences to explain your answer.

Post-Test

Name _____ Date _____

Find the next two terms in each sequence.

1.

2. 4, 7, 10, 13, _____ , _____

3. Use the *n*th term to list the first five terms of the sequence. Show your work.

$a_n = 3n + 5$

$a_1 =$ _____

$a_2 =$ _____

$a_3 =$ _____

$a_4 =$ _____

$a_5 =$ _____

Use the sequence below to answer Questions 4 through 6.

4. Complete the table by filling in the number of triangles in each term of the sequence.

Terms	1	2	3	4	5
Number of triangles					

5. Write an expression showing the relationship between the term and the number of triangles in that term. Let *n* represent the term.

6. Use the expression from Question 5 to find the 10th term of the sequence. Show your work.

7. Write the power as a product.

5^6

1

8. Write the product as a power.

   3(3)(3)(3)(3)(3)(3)(3)(3)

9. Perform the indicated operations. Show your work.

   $(2 + 1)^3 - 5(2)$

10. You and your classmates have set up an email chain to notify each other if school is cancelled due to bad weather. You email three classmates, then each of them emails three classmates, and so on until everyone in your class has been notified. There are 31 students in your class. Draw a diagram to show how each student would be reached to be notified of school cancellations.

11. Find the sum of the numbers 1 to 200. Show your work.

12. Write an expression for the sum of the numbers 1 to *n*.

Name _____ Date _____

Read the scenario below. Use the scenario to answer Questions 13 through 16.

A local ballet company is selling tickets for their upcoming performances of Swan Lake. The company earns $8 on each ticket they sell. The first week that tickets are on sale, they sell 30 tickets on Monday, 27 on Tuesday, 18 on Wednesday, 6 on Thursday, and 41 tickets on Friday.

13. Make a table to show the number of tickets sold each day during the first week and the profit made on each of those days.

14. Create a bar graph to display the profit for each day of ticket sales in the first week.

(units)

(label)

1

15. Create a graph to display the relationship between the number of tickets sold and the profit. First, choose your bounds and intervals. Be sure to label your graph clearly.

Variable quantity	Lower bound	Upper bound	Interval
Number of tickets			
Profit (dollars)			

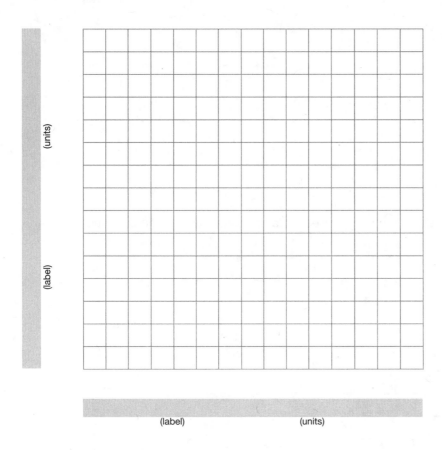

(units)

(label)

(label)   (units)

16. Write an algebraic equation that you could use to show the profit for any number of tickets sold.

Name _____ Date _____

Read the scenario below. Use the scenario to answer Questions 17 and 18.

The director of the local ballet company needs to print the programs for Swan Lake. Janet's Print Shop charges $.25 a program plus a $35 set-up fee. The Printing Press charges $.18 a program plus a $50 set-up fee.

17. Which printing company offers the better deal if 200 programs are printed? Show your work and use complete sentences to explain your answer.

18. Which printing company offers the better deal if 300 programs are printed? Show your work and use complete sentences to explain your answer.

Mid-Chapter Test

Name _____ Date _____

Read the scenario below. Use the scenario to complete Questions 1 through 8.

A local concrete company has hired you for the summer. Your first project is to help pour a driveway. Before you can pour the driveway, you must put wood forms in place to hold the concrete until it is dry. The first form in a driveway is made by constructing a square out of four 2 × 4's that are each ten feet long. The second form is made by using one side of the first form and three other 2 × 4's to make a second square. This process is continued to the end of the driveway. The diagrams show the first two steps in completing the form.

Step 1   Step 2

1. Draw a diagram that shows steps 3, 4, and 5 in the form construction.

   Step 3

   Step 4

   Step 5

2. The completed driveway will be 80 feet long. The company would refer to this as an eight-form driveway. Draw a diagram that shows what the completed form will look like. (Hint: Draw the eighth step in the form construction.)

1

3. The company needs to know the number of 2 × 4's needed to complete the driveway. They will also need to know the area of the driveway in order to properly bill their clients. Complete the table to help organize this information.

Number of forms	1	2	3	4	5	6
Number of 2 × 4's						
Area (square feet)						

4. Write the sequence of numbers formed by the area of one form, two forms, three forms, and so on. Use a complete sentence to describe the pattern produced by the area.

5. Use a complete sentence to describe the relationship between the number of forms and the number of 2 × 4's required to complete the forms.

6. Write an expression that gives the number of 2 × 4's needed to complete a driveway with *n* forms.

7. Use your expression from Question 6 to determine the number of 2 × 4's needed for a 12-form driveway. Show your work.

8. **a.** Write the sequence of numbers formed by the number of 2 × 4's.

   b. Find the 10th term of this sequence. Show your work.

   c. Use a complete sentence to explain what the 10th term represents.

Mid-Chapter Test PAGE 3

Name _____ Date _____

Write each power as a product.

9. 7^4

10. 12^6

Write each product as a power.

11. 15(15)(15)(15)(15)

12. 6(6)(6)(6)(6)(6)(6)(6)

Perform the indicated operations. Show your work.

13. $(6 - 3)^3 + 2(1 + 4)$

14. $25 - (3 + 5) + 2^4$

Evaluate each expression for the given value of the variable. Show your work.

15. Evaluate $2r + 8$ when r is 12.

16. Evaluate $\dfrac{t}{4}$ when t is 36.

17. Use the nth term to list the first five terms of the sequence. Show your work.

$a_n = 20 - 2n$

$a_1 =$ _____

$a_2 =$ _____

$a_3 =$ _____

$a_4 =$ _____

$a_5 =$ _____

1

Read the scenario below. Use the scenario to answer Questions 18 through 20.

A local college has decided to build new sidewalks to connect the main administration building to the other buildings on campus. They can only build two new sidewalks a month. It will take 6 months to connect the administration building to all of the other buildings on campus. The diagrams show the number of sidewalks that have been built after 1, 2, and 3 months.

1 month   2 months   3 months

18. Draw diagrams that would represent the number of sidewalks after 4, 5, and 6 months.

19. Complete the table to show your results.

Number of months	1	2	3	4	5	6
Number of sidewalks						

20. The college wants to put in sidewalks connecting the library to the other buildings on campus. There is already a sidewalk connecting the library to the main administration building. How many more sidewalks will need to be built in order to connect the library to the remaining buildings on campus?

21. Write an algebraic expression to find the sum of the numbers from 1 to n.

22. Use your answer to Question 21 to find the sum of the numbers from 1 to 85. Show your work.

End of Chapter Test

Name _____ Date _____

For each sequence, find the next two terms and describe the pattern.

1. 3, 8, 13, 18, 23, _____ , _____

2. 3, 9, 27, 81, _____ , _____

3.

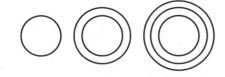

4.

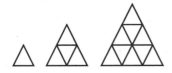

For each sequence, find the expression for the *n*th term and describe the pattern.

5.

Term (*n*)	1	2	3	4	5
Sequence	5	15	25	35	45

6.

Term (*n*)	1	2	3	4	5
Sequence	5	25	125	625	3125

© 2006 Carnegie Learning, Inc.

7. Write the power as a product.

5^4

8. Write the product as a power.

$8(8)(8)$

Use the _n_th term to list the first five terms of each sequence. Show your work.

9. $a_n = \dfrac{3(n + 1)}{2}$

$a_1 =$ _____

$a_2 =$ _____

$a_3 =$ _____

$a_4 =$ _____

$a_5 =$ _____

10. $a_n = (n - 1)^2 + 3$

$a_1 =$ _____

$a_2 =$ _____

$a_3 =$ _____

$a_4 =$ _____

$a_5 =$ _____

Read the scenario below. Use the scenario to answer Questions 11 through 23.

You are a volunteer for the school store. One of the most popular items is strawberry-banana-orange juice. There are two local vendors that will deliver the juice to the school store at the beginning of every month. Healthy Drinks, Inc. charges $.39 per bottle with a delivery fee of $25. The Squeeze charges $.18 per bottle with a delivery fee of $65.

11. You want to stock the store with juice at the beginning of the school year. How much will it cost to purchase 300 bottles of strawberry-banana-orange juice from Healthy Drinks, Inc.? Show your work and use a complete sentence in your answer.

12. How much will it cost to purchase 300 bottles of strawberry-banana-orange juice from The Squeeze? Show your work and use a complete sentence in your answer.

Name _____ Date _____

13. Complete the table summarizing the cost of purchasing strawberry-banana-orange juice from each vendor based on last year's actual monthly sales. Remember to label units.

Month	Number of bottles of juice purchased	Cost of purchasing from Healthy Drinks, Inc.	Cost of purchasing from The Squeeze
	bottles	dollars	dollars
September	187		
October	229		
November	162		
December	137		
January	171		
February	201		
March	192		
April	258		
May	214		
June	79		

14. Let C represent the cost of purchasing bottles of juice from Healthy Drinks, Inc. and b represent the number of bottles. Write an equation that relates C and b for this problem situation.

15. Let C represent the cost of purchasing bottles of juice from The Squeeze and b represent the number of bottles. Write an equation that relates C and b for this problem situation.

16. What was the average number of bottles of juice sold in a month last year? Show your work and use a complete sentence in your answer.

17. Create a bar graph to display the costs of purchasing strawberry-banana-orange juice from Healthy Drinks, Inc. each month.

(units)

(label)

18. Create a graph displaying the cost of purchasing strawberry-banana-orange juice from both Healthy Drinks, Inc. and The Squeeze. First, choose your bounds and intervals. Be sure to label your graph clearly.

Variable quantity	Lower bound	Upper bound	Interval
Juice			
Cost			

Name _____ Date _____

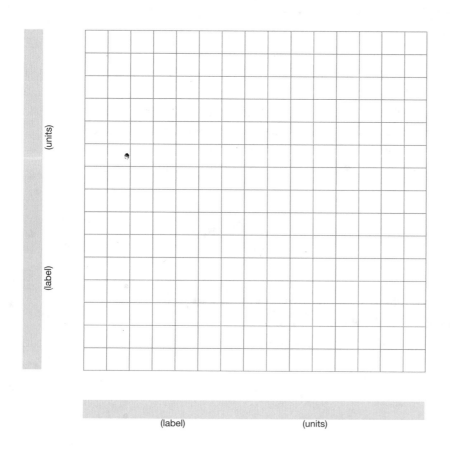

(units)

(label)

(label)   (units)

19. Estimate the number of bottles of juice for which the total costs for each company are the same and explain how you found your answer. Use complete sentences in your answer.

20. For how many bottles of juice is Healthy Drinks, Inc. more expensive to order from? Use a complete sentence in your answer.

1

21. For how many bottles of juice is The Squeeze more expensive to order from?
    Use a complete sentence in your answer.

22. The faculty sponsor who is responsible for the school store has asked you to write a
    report that compares the costs of ordering from each vendor. She would also like you to
    make a recommendation about which vendor you would choose if you had to order from
    the same vendor for the entire school year. Use complete sentences in your answer.

23. If you were able to choose a different vendor each month, would you?
    Explain your answer using complete sentences.

Standardized Test Practice

Name _____ Date _____

1. Which choice shows the next two terms in the sequence?

   1, 101, 2, 102, 3, 103, …

   a. 4 and 140

   b. 4 and 401

   c. 4 and 104

   d. 4 and 114

2. Which choice shows the next two terms in the sequence?

   a.

   b.

   c.

   d.

3. Which statement describes the pattern?

   −1, 10, −100, 1000, …

   a. Start with the previous term, and multiply by 10 to get the next term.

   b. Start with the previous term, and add a zero to get the next term.

   c. Start with the previous term, and multiply by 100 to get the next term.

   d. Start with the previous term, and multiply by −10 to get the next term.

4. Simplify $5^2 - (3 + 6) + \dfrac{14}{7}$.

   a. −1

   b. 3

   c. 14

   d. 18

1

5. Which expression is equivalent to 4^6?

a. 4(6)

b. 4(4)(4)(4)(4)(4)

c. 6(6)(6)(6)

d. 46

6. How many cups of flour are needed for 10 loaves of bread?

Loaves of bread	1	2	3	4	5
Cups of flour	2	4	6	8	10

a. 12

b. 16

c. 20

d. 24

7. Evaluate $3p + 5$ when $p = 6$.

a. 14

b. 18

c. 23

d. 41

8. Which expression represents the nth term of the sequence?

Term (n)	1	2	3	4	5
Sequence	6	13	20	27	34

a. $7n - 1$

b. $7n$

c. $6n$

d. $n + 7$

Name _____ Date _____

9. Which number represents a_4?

$a_n = 2n + 4$

   a. 6

   b. 8

   c. 10

   d. 12

10. A family of 8 has just signed a contract for a new cellular phone service so that they can call each other for free. To try it out, each person in the family calls every other person once unless that person has already called them. How many calls does the family make?

   a. 10

   b. 15

   c. 21

   d. 28

11. What is the sum of the numbers 1 to 300?

   a. 301

   b. 4515

   c. 45,150

   d. 300,001

12. The average speed of an airplane is 325 miles per hour. Which expression shows the distance in miles an airplane could travel in n hours?

   a. $\dfrac{325}{n}$

   b. $325n$

   c. $325 + n$

   d. $\dfrac{n}{325}$

13. James earns $6.25 an hour at work. The table shows his hours and earnings for each week in one month. Which graph correctly displays the relationship between hours worked and earnings?

Week	Time worked	Earnings
	hours	dollars
Week 1	15	93.75
Week 2	18	112.50
Week 3	12	75
Week 4	13	81.25

a.

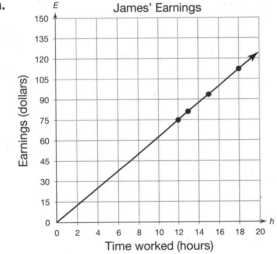

b.

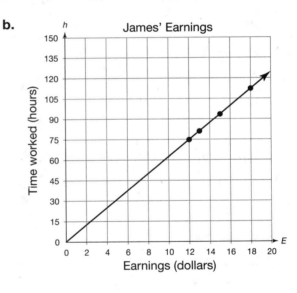

c.

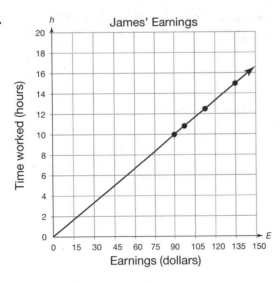

d.

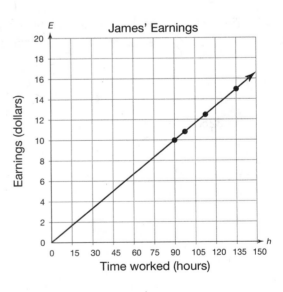

Name _____   Date _____

14. James earns $6.25 an hour at work. The table in Question 13 shows his hours and earnings for each week in one month. Which bar graph correctly displays the relationship between the week and the time worked?

a.

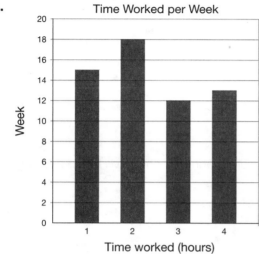

b.

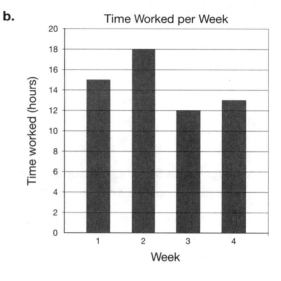

c.

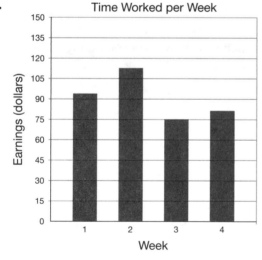

d.

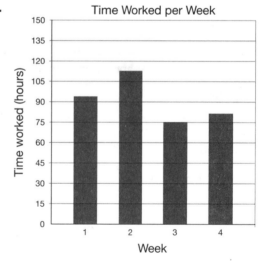

1

15. James earns $6.25 an hour at work. Which algebraic equation shows the amount of money E that James earns in n hours?

    a. $E = 6.25 + n$

    b. $E = \dfrac{6.25}{n}$

    c. $n = 6.25E$

    d. $E = 6.25n$

16. Angelica earns $7.50 each hour she works. How many hours will she have to work to buy a bicycle that costs $90?

    a. 6

    b. 9

    c. 12

    d. 15

17. Angelica earns $7.50 each hour she works. How much money will Angelica earn if she works for 6 hours and 12 minutes?

    a. $45

    b. $46.50

    c. $46.75

    d. $135

18. T-Shirts & More Print Shop will print any image on a Frisbee for a cost of $2 per Frisbee and a one-time charge of $12 to set up the Frisbee design. The total cost of an order was $562. How many Frisbees were printed?

    a. 47

    b. 275

    c. 281

    d. 550

Name _____ Date _____

19. T-Shirts & More Print Shop will print any image on a Frisbee for a cost of $2 per Frisbee and a one-time charge of $12 to set up the Frisbee design. Which algebraic equation shows the cost C of printing f Frisbees?

   a. $C = 2f$

   b. $C = 12f + 2$

   c. $f = 2C + 12$

   d. $C = 2f + 12$

20. T-Shirts & More Print Shop will print any image on a Frisbee for a cost of $2 per Frisbee and a one-time charge of $12 to set up the Frisbee design. You Say It, We Print It will print any image on a Frisbee for a cost of $5 per Frisbee and no set-up fee. Which statement is true?

   a. You Say It, We Print It is a better buy if you purchase more than four Frisbees.

   b. T-Shirts & More Print Shop is always the better buy.

   c. You Say It, We Print It is always the better buy.

   d. T-Shirts & More Print Shop is the better buy if you purchase more than four Frisbees.

Pre-Test

Name _____ Date _____

Use the table below to answer Questions 1 through 3.

Grade	Blue eyes	Brown eyes	Other
8	13	14	3
9	5	18	7
10	9	8	13
11	2	25	3
Total number of students	29	65	26

1. How many students were surveyed? Use a complete sentence in your answer.

2. Write the ratio of the number of blue-eyed students to the number of students surveyed. Write the ratio two different ways.

3. Write the ratio of the number of brown-eyed students in the 9th grade to the total number of brown-eyed students. Write the ratio two different ways.

Complete each proportion.

4. $\dfrac{4}{9} = \dfrac{\square}{54}$

5. $\dfrac{16}{52} = \dfrac{4}{\square}$

Solve each proportion using the products of the means and the extremes. Show all your work.

6. $\dfrac{2}{7} = \dfrac{x}{4221}$

7. $\dfrac{40}{576} = \dfrac{5}{x}$

2

8. To make the color orange using food coloring, you must mix 2 drops of red and 3 drops of yellow. Write a ratio that compares the number of drops of red to the total number of drops. Then simplify the ratio, if possible.

9. Write the given fractions in order from least to greatest. Show all your work and use a complete sentence in your answer.

$$\frac{3}{4}, \frac{5}{9}, \frac{1}{3}$$

10. Bethany can run 1600 meters in 10 minutes. Write a rate to determine the number of meters Bethany can run in one minute.

11. Triangle *ABC* is similar to triangle *DEF*. What is the length of *EF*? Show all your work and use a complete sentence in your answer.

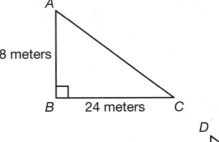

18 meters

24 meters

12 meters

x meters

12. One mile is equal to 5280 feet. Use a proportion to determine the part of a mile is equivalent to 3960 feet. Show all your work and use a complete sentence in your answer.

Name _____ Date _____

Use the data below for Questions 13 through 15.

Your school band has decided to sell pizza kits for a fundraiser. The table at the right lists the relationship between the selling price and the profit your band will make on those sales.

Selling price	Profit
dollars	dollars
6	4
9	6
12	8
15	10
18	12

2

13. Make a line graph that displays the relationship between the selling price of pizza kits and the profit.

Variable quantity	Lower bound	Upper bound	Interval
Selling price of pizza kits	0	30	2
Profit	0	15	1

(units)

(label)

(label)   (units)

14. Write an equation that shows the relationship between the selling price s and the profit p.

2

15. Use your equation to predict the profit for a pizza kit that has a selling price of $24 dollars. Show all your work and use a complete sentence in your answer.

16. Solve the equation for a.

$$\frac{a}{b} = \frac{4}{9}$$

Write each percent as a fraction and as a decimal.

17. 30%

18. 78%

Write each fraction as a decimal and as a percent.

19. $\dfrac{29}{100}$

20. $\dfrac{37}{50}$

Name _____ Date _____

21. Your bill at a restaurant is $36. You leave a 15% tip. How much do you leave for a tip? Show all your work and use a complete sentence in your answer.

Your gross pay is $450, and your net pay is $315.

22. How much do you pay in taxes? Show all your work and use a complete sentence in your answer.

23. What is the tax rate? Show all your work and use a complete sentence in your answer.

Post-Test

Name _____ Date _____

Use the table below to answer Questions 1 through 3.

Grade	Brunette	Blonde	Other
8	27	8	15
9	15	21	14
10	33	11	6
11	20	23	7
Total number of students	95	63	42

1. How many students were surveyed? Use a complete sentence in your answer.

2. Write the ratio of the number of blonde students to the number of students surveyed. Write the ratio two different ways.

3. Write the ratio of the number of brunette students in the 10th grade to the total number of brunette students. Write the ratio two different ways.

Complete each proportion.

4. $\dfrac{27}{63} = \dfrac{3}{\boxed{}}$

5. $\dfrac{3}{5} = \dfrac{\boxed{}}{20}$

Solve each proportion using the products of the means and the extremes. Show all your work.

6. $\dfrac{297}{x} = \dfrac{3}{11}$

7. $\dfrac{35}{90} = \dfrac{x}{18}$

2

8. To make pink paint, Tamika mixes 2 parts white paint and 5 parts red paint. Write a ratio that compares the number of parts of red paint to the total number of parts of paint. Then simplify the ratio, if possible.

9. Write the given fractions in order from least to greatest. Show all your work and use a complete sentence in your answer.

$$\frac{4}{9}, \frac{2}{5}, \frac{3}{7}$$

10. Donald can ride his bicycle 63 miles in 3 hours. Write a rate to determine the number of miles Donald can ride in one hour.

11. Triangle *JKL* is similar to triangle *MNO*. What is the length of *MN*? Show all your work and use a complete sentence in your answer.

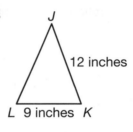

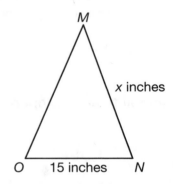

12. One furlong is equal to 220 yards. Use a proportion to determine the part of a furlong is equivalent to 132 yards. Show all your work and use a complete sentence in your answer.

Name _____ Date _____

Use the data below for Questions 13 through 15.

A local store is raising money for cancer research by selling bracelets. They will donate part of their profit on the bracelet sales to a national cancer research facility. The table at the right lists the relationship between the profit from bracelet sales and the amount of money donated to cancer research.

Profit	Donation
dollars	dollars
5	3
10	6
15	9
20	12
25	15

2

13. Make a line graph that displays the relationship between the profit from the bracelet sales and the amount of money donated to cancer research.

Variable quantity	Lower bound	Upper bound	Interval
Profit from bracelet sales	0	30	2
Money donated	0	30	2

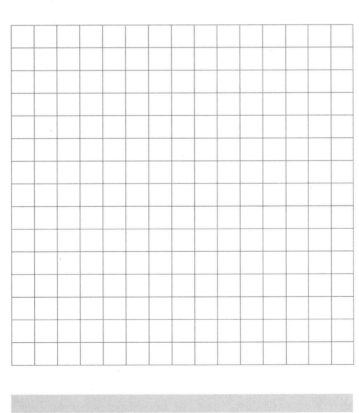

(units)

(label)

(label)   (units)

2

14. Write an equation that shows the relationship between the profit p and the amount of money donated d.

15. Use your equation to predict the amount of money donated if there is a $60 profit from bracelet sales. Show all your work and use a complete sentence in your answer.

16. Solve the equation for b.

$$\frac{a}{b} = \frac{7}{8}$$

Write each percent as a fraction and as a decimal.

17. 45%

18. 75%

Write each fraction as a decimal and as a percent.

19. $\frac{29}{100}$

20. $\frac{7}{10}$

Name _____ Date _____

21. Your bill at a restaurant is $42. You leave a 20% tip. How much do you leave for a tip? Show all your work and use a complete sentence in your answer.

Your gross pay is $375, and your net pay is $255.

22. How much do you pay in taxes? Show all your work and use a complete sentence in your answer.

23. What is the tax rate? Show all your work and use a complete sentence in your answer.

Mid-Chapter Test

© 2006 Carnegie Learning, Inc.

Name _____ Date _____

Use the table below to answer Questions 1 through 6.

The student council at your school is sponsoring a dance. Your advisor has asked you to survey a portion of the student body to determine the kind of music preferred for dancing. The results of your survey are given in the table below.

Grade	Hip-Hop	Country	Classic Rock
8	28	5	7
9	31	4	5
10	15	21	4
11	23	7	10
Total number of students	97	37	26

1. How many students were surveyed? Use a complete sentence in your answer.

2. Write the ratio of the number of students who prefer hip-hop music to the total number of students surveyed.

3. There are 960 students in your school. Use the results of the survey and a proportion to predict the number of students who prefer hip-hop music. Show all your work and use a complete sentence in your answer.

4. Write the ratio of the number of 9th grade students who prefer classic rock to the total number of 9th grade students who were surveyed.

2

5. Your advisor tells you that there 248 students in the 9th grade. Use a proportion to find the number of students in the 9th grade that prefer classic rock. Show all your work and use a complete sentence in your answer.

6. You formed the sample for your survey by asking random students in the cafeteria until you had surveyed 40 students from each grade. Explain what type of sampling method was used. Was your sample biased? Explain your answer with complete sentences.

Read the scenario below. Use the scenario to answer Questions 7 through 9.

Dwayne is in culinary school. For one of his projects, he has to make a vinaigrette dressing which uses oil, vinegar, and a variety of seasonings. Before he adds the seasonings, he wants to determine which mixture of oil and vinegar is the best. The recipes of four oil and vinegar mixtures are given below.

Recipe 1	Recipe 2	Recipe 3	Recipe 4
2 parts oil 5 parts vinegar	3 parts oil 2 parts vinegar	4 parts oil 6 parts vinegar	5 parts oil 3 parts vinegar

7. For each recipe, write a ratio that compares the number of parts of vinegar to the total number of parts in each recipe. Then simplify each ratio if possible.

Name _____ Date _____

8. Which recipe has the strongest taste of vinegar? Show all your work and use a complete sentence in your answer.

9. Dwayne decides to use Recipe 2 as the base for his vinaigrette dressing. One of his professors likes Dwayne's vinaigrette dressing so well that he decides to serve it in his restaurant. He asks Dwayne to package it in 3-cup dressing bottles. He needs 50 bottles of the dressing.

   a. How many cups of vinaigrette dressing does Dwayne need to make? Show all your work and use a complete sentence in your answer.

   b. Write a rate to find the number of cups there are in one part of the recipe. Show all your work and use a complete sentence in your answer.

   c. How many cups of oil and vinegar are needed to make enough vinaigrette dressing for the restaurant? Show all your work and use a complete sentence in your answer.

10. Triangles *QRS* and *TUV* are similar. Use proportions to find the length of *RS*. Show all your work and use a complete sentence in your answer.

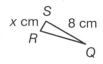

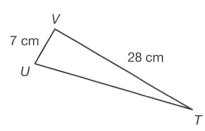

Read the scenario below. Use the scenario to answe Questions 11 through 18.

Hannah types 225 words in 5 minutes. She wants to find her average typing speed and she wants to know the number of words she types for different numbers of minutes.

11. Write a unit rate that represents Hannah's average typing speed in words per minute.

2

12. Use this rate to complete the table.

Time	Number of words
minutes	words
1	
5	
10	
15	
20	

13. Create a graph of the data from the table to show the relationship between the amount of time and the number of words Hannah types.

Variable quantity	Lower bound	Upper bound	Interval
Time	0	30	2
Number of words	0	1125	75

Name _____ Date _____

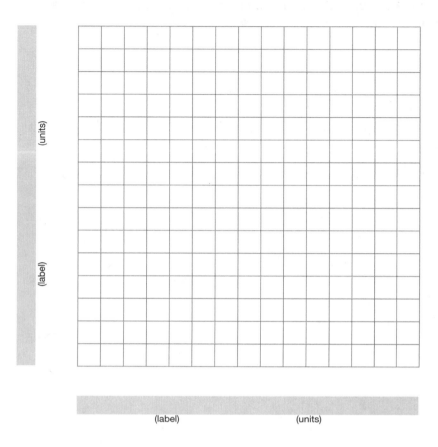

(units)

(label)

(label)   (units)

14. Use the graph to predict the number of words Hannah types in 12 minutes. Use a complete sentence in your answer.

15. Write an equation that shows the relationship between the amount of time t and the number of words w Hannah types.

16. Use the equation to predict the number of words Hannah types in 12 minutes. Show all your work and use a complete sentence in your answer.

17. Which method do you think is more accurate in making predictions, the graph or the equation? Use complete sentences to explain your reasoning.

2

18. Use a proportion to determine the number of words Hannah can type in one hour. Show all your work and use a complete sentence in your answer.

End of Chapter Test

Name _____ Date _____

Read the scenario below. Use the scenario for Questions 1 through 3.

A shoe store in the mall is surveying people to see how much they spend on shoes over the course of a year. The results of their survey are shown in the table below.

Age (years)	Less than $100	$100–$300	More than $300
Under 20	38	7	5
20–40	11	26	13
41–60	8	32	10
Over 60	22	27	1
Total number of people	79	92	29

1. How many people were surveyed? Use a complete sentence in your answer.

2. There are approximately 400,000 people that live in your city. How many of them spend more than $300 a year on shoes? Show all your work and use a complete sentence in your answer.

3. To conduct this survey, employees of the shoe store asked people who came into the store to go online and complete the survey. Explain what kind of sampling method they used and whether or not their sample was biased. Use complete sentences in your answer.

Read the scenario below. Use the scenario to answer Questions 4 and 5.

At a hot wings cook-off at the county fair, two recipes for hot wing sauce tied for first place. The recipes are shown below.

Uncle Bob's Hot Wing Sauce

6 parts hot sauce
2 parts melted butter

Jumpin' June's Hot Wing Sauce

7 parts hot sauce
5 parts melted butter

4. Which recipe has the strongest taste of hot sauce? Show all your work and use complete sentences to explain your reasoning.

5. Uncle Bob plans to package his hot wing sauce in 12-ounce bottles to sell. He is going to package 50 bottles. How many ounces of hot sauce and butter will he need? Show all your work and use a complete sentence in your answer.

Name _____ Date _____

6. Triangle *ABC* is similar to triangle *DEF*. What is the length of *BC*? Show all your work and use a complete sentence in your answer.

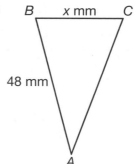
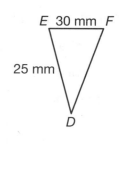

Read the scenario below. Use the scenario to answer Questions 7 through 12.

A recent survey in your area shows that 3 out of every 10 people who have food allergies are allergic to peanuts.

7. Write a ratio that compares the number of people who have a peanut allergy to the number of people who have food allergies.

8. How many people have a peanut allergy if 1000 people have food allergies? Show all your work and use a complete sentence in your answer.

9. Let *t* represent the number of people with food allergies and let *p* represent the number of people with a peanut allergy. Write an equation for *p* in terms of *t*.

10. Complete the table that represents the problem situation.

	People with food allergies	People with peanut allergy
Labels		
Units		
Expression		
	200	
	500	
	1000	
	2000	
	5000	

11. Use the grid to create a graph of the data from the table in Question 10.

Variable quantity	Lower bound	Upper bound	Interval
People with food allergies	0	6000	400
People with a peanut allergy	0	1800	230

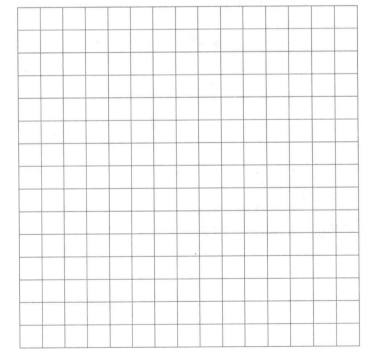

(units)

(label)

(label)   (units)

Name _____ Date _____

12. Is the relationship of the quantities represented by the variables *t* and *p* in Question 9 direct variation? Use a complete sentence to explain why or why not.

13. Write 12% as a fraction and as a decimal. Simplify the fraction, if possible.

14. Write $\frac{19}{20}$ as a decimal and as a percent.

15. Your family goes out to eat at a restaurant and the bill is $52. You leave a 15% tip. How much is the tip? Show all your work and use a complete sentence in your answer.

16. A server receives a $10.45 tip from a group who spent $47.50 on their lunches. What percent tip does the server receive? Show all your work and use a complete sentence in your answer.

2

17. A couple leaves $5.95 for a tip, which is 17% of their bill. What is the amount of their bill? Show all your work and use a complete sentence in your answer.

Jeremiah receives his first pay check in the amount of $309.40. The check stub shows that he paid $145.60 in taxes.

18. What is Jeremiah's gross pay? Show all your work and use a complete sentence in your answer.

19. What is the tax rate? Show all your work and use a complete sentence in your answer.

Anastasia's new job pays $6.25 an hour. In her first month, she works 42 hours.

20. What is her gross pay at the end of the first month? Show all your work and use a complete sentence in your answer.

Name _____ Date _____

21. Anastasia pays 28% in taxes. How much does she pay in taxes on her first pay check? Show all of your work and use a complete sentence in your answer.

Standardized Test Practice

Name _____ Date _____

Read the scenario below. Use the scenario to answer Questions 1 through 3.

A marketing firm conducted a survey for a client to gather information about how much people spend each year eating out.

Age (years)	Under $500	$500–$1000	Over $1000
Under 20	39	5	1
21–40	6	32	7
41–60	2	13	30
Over 60	14	28	3
Total number of people	61	78	41

1. How many people were surveyed?

   a. 41

   b. 61

   c. 78

   d. 180

2. There are 675,000 people living in the city where this survey was conducted. How many of these people spend more than $1000 each year eating out?

   a. 153,750

   b. 228,750

   c. 292,500

   d. 27,675,000

3. To complete this survey, the marketing firm sent representatives to the food court of the mall to interview people who were dining there. Which sampling method did they use?

   a. random sample

   b. stratified sample

   c. convenience sample

   d. systematic sample

2

4. Which of the following shows the fractions $\frac{5}{6}$, $\frac{7}{9}$, and $\frac{3}{5}$ in order from least to greatest?

   a. $\frac{5}{6}$, $\frac{7}{9}$, $\frac{3}{5}$

   b. $\frac{3}{5}$, $\frac{5}{6}$, $\frac{7}{9}$

   c. $\frac{5}{6}$, $\frac{3}{5}$, $\frac{7}{9}$

   d. $\frac{3}{5}$, $\frac{7}{9}$, $\frac{5}{6}$

5. Which is NOT an example of a rate?

   a. $\frac{75 \text{ miles}}{1 \text{ hour}}$

   b. $\frac{4 \text{ feet}}{3 \text{ feet}}$

   c. $\frac{10 \text{ cups}}{3 \text{ parts}}$

   d. $\frac{8 \text{ ounces}}{1 \text{ cup}}$

6. To make brown paint, Pierre must mix 4 parts green and 5 parts red. He needs to make 360 gallons of brown paint. How many gallons of red paint will Pierre need?

   a. 160 gallons

   b. 200 gallons

   c. 288 gallons

   d. 360 gallons

© 2006 Carnegie Learning, Inc.

Standardized Test Practice   PAGE 3

Name _____   Date _____

7. The sun is causing the flagpole and Sierra
to cast a shadow. How tall is the flagpole?

   a. 10 feet

   b. 16 feet

   c. 18 feet

   d. 20 feet

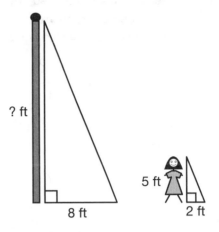

? ft

5 ft

8 ft

2 ft

8. An airplane travels at an average speed of 870 kilometers per hour. What is the airplane's
speed in meters per hour? (*Hint:* 1 kilometer = 1000 meters)

   a. 870,000 meters per hour

   b. 87,000 meters per hour

   c. 8700 meters per hour

   d. 0.87 meters per hour

9. On average a child grows 2.5 inches per year from age 2 until adolescence.
Which equation shows how to calculate the height *h* of a child given the number
of years *y* since age 2 if the child is 33 inches tall at age 2?

   a. $h = 33 - 2.5y$

   b. $h = 2.5y - 33$

   c. $h = 33 + 2.5y$

   d. $y = 2.5h + 33$

© 2006 Carnegie Learning, Inc.

2

10. A science teacher conducts a survey on color blindness. She finds that 2 out of 19 students in the 9th grade are color blind. Which equation shows the relationship between color blind students b and non-color blind students c in the 9th grade?

a. $c = \dfrac{2}{17}b$

b. $b = \dfrac{2}{17}c$

c. $c = \dfrac{2}{19}b$

d. $b = \dfrac{2}{19}c$

11. At a local high school, seven out of nine graduates obtain a college degree. Which graph shows the relationship between the number of students who graduate from high school and the number of those students who obtain a college degree?

a.
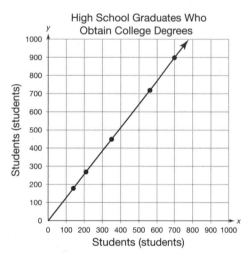

b.
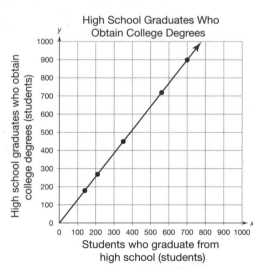

c.
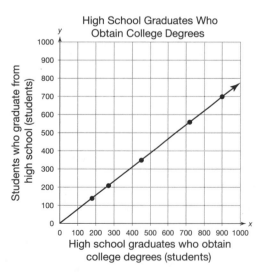

d.
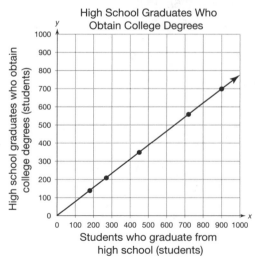

Name _____ Date _____

12. Which choice does NOT show 42% written as a fraction or a decimal?

   a. 0.42

   b. 4.2

   c. $\dfrac{42}{100}$

   d. $\dfrac{21}{50}$

13. Your aunt tips her hairdresser $6 for a $30 haircut. What percent tip does she leave her hairdresser?

   a. 0.2%

   b. 2%

   c. 5%

   d. 20%

14. Your family goes out to dinner and the bill is $115. You leave a 18% tip. How much do you leave?

   a. $2.07

   b. $6.39

   c. $20.70

   d. $27

15. A server can estimate his total food sales by using the amount he receives in tips. Over the course of the evening, the server receives $129 in tips. Customers usually tip 15%. How much was the total of the server's food sales that evening?

   a. $11.62

   b. $19.35

   c. $860

   d. $1935

2

16. David makes $7.25 an hour at work. One month he works 45 hours. He must pay 32% of what he earns in taxes. What is David's gross pay and net pay for that month?

   a. Gross pay = $221.85; Net pay = $326.25

   b. Gross pay = $326.25; Net pay = $221.85

   c. Gross pay = $326.25; Net pay = $104.40

   d. Gross pay = $104.40; Net pay = $326.85

17. Whitney pays $329.67 in taxes one month. Her tax rate is 30%. What is her gross pay and net pay for that month?

   a. Gross pay = $1098.90; Net pay = $1428.57

   b. Gross pay = $1428.57; Net pay = $1098.90

   c. Gross pay = $769.23; Net pay = $1098.90

   d. Gross pay = $1098.90; Net pay = $769.23

18. Tonya pays $268.24 in taxes one month when her gross pay is $958. What is her tax rate?

   a. 0.28%

   b. 2.8%

   c. 28%

   d. 39%

Pre-Test

© 2006 Carnegie Learning, Inc.

Name _____ Date _____

Solve each equation. Show all your work.

1. $x + 6 = 10$

2. $a - 9 = 15$

3. $3p = 27$

4. $\dfrac{t}{5} = 4$

5. $2y + 6 = 18$

6. $38 = 5s - 7$

7. $\dfrac{w}{3} + 10 = 17$

8. $28 = \dfrac{n}{2} - 4$

Read the scenario below. Use the scenario to answer Questions 9 and 10.

An online music store is selling CDs for $3 a piece and charges a flat shipping fee of $7. The cost C for buying n CDs is given by the equation $C = 3n + 7$. Below is a graph of this equation.

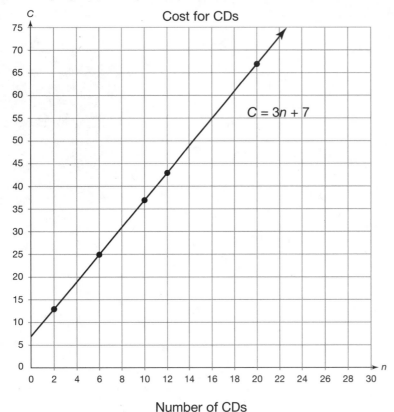

9. Explain how you would use the graph to determine whether 14 is a solution to the equation $49 = 3n + 7$. Use complete sentences in your answer.

10. Determine whether 25 is a solution of the equation $75 = 3n + 7$ algebraically. Show all your work and use a complete sentence in your answer.

Name _____ Date _____

11. In the statement below, identify *a*, *b*, and *p*. Then, write a percent equation that represents the situation.

28 is 35% of 80.

a = _____

b = _____

p = _____

Write and solve a percent equation to answer each question. Show all your work and use a complete sentence in your answer.

12. 24 is what percent of 60?

13. What is 55% of 120?

14. 24 is 12% of what number?

15. Write the integers in order from least to greatest.

6, –7, –10, 4, –6, 2

Find each sum or difference.

16. −2 + 8 = ☐

17. 9 − (−3) = ☐

18. −11 − 8 = ☐

Find each product or quotient.

19. −3(−7) = ☐

20. 2(−9) = ☐

21. $\dfrac{-24}{-3}$ = ☐

3

22. Plot and label each point in the coordinate plane.

A(−5, 6)

B(4, 7)

C(3, −4)

D(−2, −5)

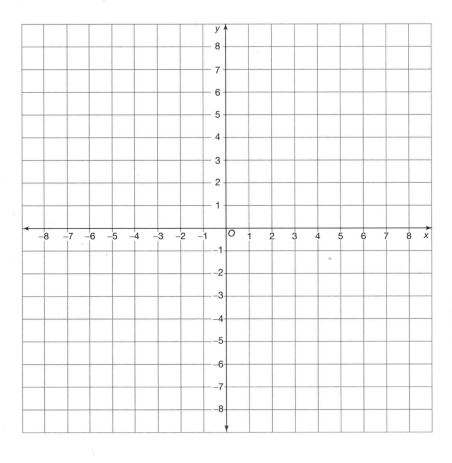

Post-Test

© 2006 Carnegie Learning, Inc.

Name _____ Date _____

Solve each equation. Show all your work.

1. $n + 5 = 19$

2. $x - 13 = 24$

3. $5r = 65$

4. $\dfrac{b}{8} = 12$

5. $4x + 8 = 52$

6. $39 = 6p - 9$

7. $\dfrac{t}{2} + 15 = 25$

8. $85 = \dfrac{y}{4} - 5$

Read the scenario below. Use the scenario to answer Questions 9 and 10.

You order tickets online to see your favorite band in concert. The tickets cost $14 each and there is a shipping fee of $5. The cost C for buying t tickets is given by the equation $C = 14t + 5$. Below is the graph of this equation.

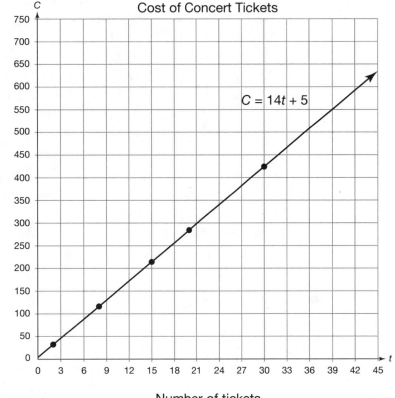

9. Explain how you would use the graph to determine whether 5 is a solution to the equation $70 = 14t + 5$. Use complete sentences in your answer.

10. Determine whether 15 is a solution of the equation $215 = 14t + 5$ algebraically. Show all your work and use a complete sentence in your answer.

Name _____ Date _____

11. In the statement below, identify a, b, and p. Then, write a percent equation that represents the situation.

63 is 42% of 150.

$a =$ _____

$b =$ _____

$p =$ _____

Write and solve a percent equation to answer each question. Show all your work and use a complete sentence in your answer.

12. 112 is what percent of 175?

13. What is 45% of 80?

14. 9 is 18% of what number?

15. Write the integers in order from least to greatest.

−13, 0, −5, 3, 18, −8

Find each sum or difference.

16. −4 + 9 = ☐

17. 18 − (−7) = ☐

18. −12 − 4 = ☐

Find each product or quotient.

19. −6(−5) = ☐

20. 8(−7) = ☐

21. $\dfrac{-36}{-9}$ = ☐

22. Plot and label each point in the coordinate plane.

A(4, −3)

B(−6, −5)

C(1, 7)

D(−3, 2)

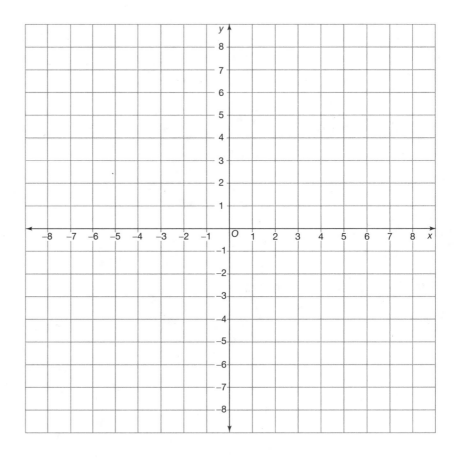

Mid-Chapter Test

Name _____ Date _____

Solve each equation. Show all your work.

1. $n + 14 = 22$

2. $x - 3 = 27$

3. $12z = 48$

4. $\dfrac{u}{8} = 10$

5. $7p + 6 = 27$

6. $4c - 9 = 47$

7. $\dfrac{t}{5} + 19 = 39$

8. $\dfrac{a}{12} - 1 = 4$

9. It takes Kelly 12 minutes to fold a load of laundry. Write an equation that shows how many minutes *m* it will take Kelly to fold *l* loads of laundry.

10. Algebraically determine whether 26 is a solution to the equation $x + 35 = 60$. Show all your work and use a complete sentence in your answer.

3

Read the scenario below. Use the scenario to answer Questions 11 through 14.

Your uncle plants a white pine that has a 15-centimeter diameter. The diameter of the trunk grows an average of 0.5 centimeter every year.

11. Write an equation that shows the diameter *d* of the tree in years *y*.

12. Use the equation you wrote in Question 11 to complete the table. Be sure to include units and expressions.

Labels	Time	Diameter
Units		
Expressions		
	10	
	20	
	40	
	80	
	100	

Name _____ Date _____

13. Use the grid below to create a graph of the data from the table in Question 12. First, choose your bounds and intervals. Be sure to label your graph clearly.

Variable quantity	Lower bound	Upper bound	Interval

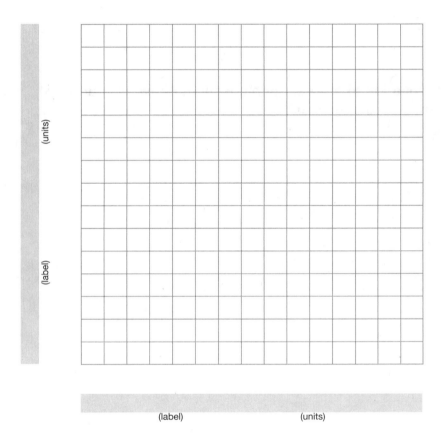

(units)

(label)

(label)   (units)

14. Use the graph to determine the diameter of the tree in 90 years. Use complete sentences to explain how you found your answer.

15. Your aunt is a So Beautiful make-up consultant. She makes a 25% commission on all of her sales. This month she sells $1420 in make-up. Use a proportion to find her commission. Show all your work and use a complete sentence in your answer.

Write and solve a percent equation to answer each question. Show all your work and use a complete sentence in your answer.

3

16. 62 is what percent of 200?

17. What is 22% of 150?

18. 91 is 65% of what number?

Mid-Chapter Test PAGE 5

Name _____ Date _____

Read the scenario below. Use the scenario to answer Questions 19 and 20.

The cost of one ticket to the art museum, history museum, or the museum of science is $8.50. You can buy a gold membership card for $85, and then pay only $6 for each ticket to any of the museums. You can by a silver membership card for $65 and then pay only $7.25 for each ticket to any of the museums.

	Non-member cost	**Gold member cost**	**Silver member cost**
Number of tickets	**Total cost**	**Total cost**	**Total cost**
tickets	dollars	dollars	dollars
t	8.5t	6t + 85	7.25t + 65
5	42.5	115	101.25
10	85	145	137.5
20	170	205	210
50	425	385	4275
100	850	685	790

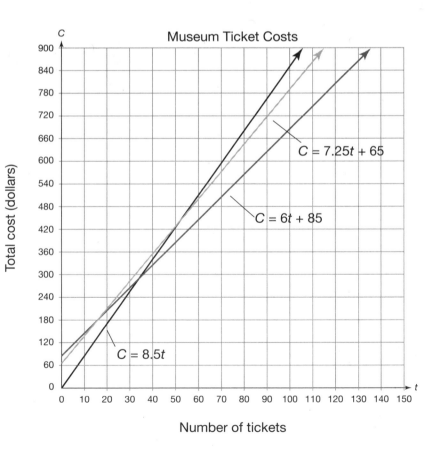

Museum Ticket Costs

$C = 7.25t + 65$

$C = 6t + 85$

$C = 8.5t$

Total cost (dollars)

Number of tickets

19. Will the cost ever be the same for the gold and silver memberships? If so, for which number of tickets? Use complete sentences to explain how you found your answer.

20. Your friend loves to visit the museums. He asks you to help him determine which option is the best deal for him. What would you recommend? Use complete sentences to explain your answer.

3

End of Chapter Test

Name _____ Date _____

Solve each equation. Show all your work.

1. $y + 12 = -4$

2. $b - 7 = -9$

3. $-8h = 72$

4. $\dfrac{r}{-5} = -13$

5. $3z + (-18) = 36$

6. $-2n - 14 = -54$

7. $\dfrac{x}{3} + 21 = 18$

8. $\dfrac{a}{-4} - 6 = 7$

9. The daily cost to visit Wild and Crazy Amusement Park is $18.75. Write an equation that shows the relationship between the cost C and the number of visits v.

10. The owners of Wild and Crazy Amusement Park are offering a special weekday pass. The weekday pass costs $75, and then the cost each time you visit the park is $15. Write an equation that shows the relationship between the cost C and the number of visits v if you purchase a weekday pass.

11. The owners of Wild and Crazy Amusement Park are also offering an anytime pass. The anytime pass costs $100, and then the cost each time you visit the park is $12.50. Write an equation that shows the relationship between the cost C and the number of visits v if you purchase an anytime pass.

12. Use the results of Questions 9 through 11 to complete the table of values that shows the relationship between the total cost and the number of visits.

	Daily	Weekday pass	Anytime pass
3			
5			
15			
20			
35			

Name _____ Date _____

13. Use the grid below to create a graph of the data from the table in Question 12. First, choose your bounds and intervals. Be sure to label your graph clearly.

Variable quantity	Lower bound	Upper bound	Interval

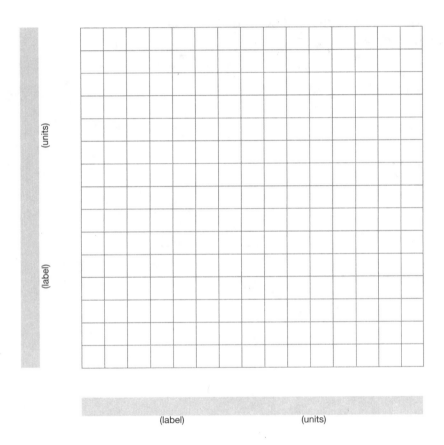

(units)

(label)

(label)   (units)

14. Will the cost ever be the same for a weekday pass and an anytime pass? If so, for which number of visits? Use complete sentences to explain your how you found your answer.

15. Compare the three options. Which one is the best deal? Use complete sentences to explain your reasoning.

Write and solve a percent equation to answer each question. Show all your work and use a complete sentence in your answer.

16. 8 is what percent of 50?

17. What is 38% of 150?

18. 2 is 5% of what number?

19. Write the integers in order from least to greatest.

2, –8, 5, –11, –3, 8

Name _____ Date _____

20. Plot and label each point in the coordinate plane.

A(3, –5)

B(2, 1)

C(–6, –7)

D(–7, 4)

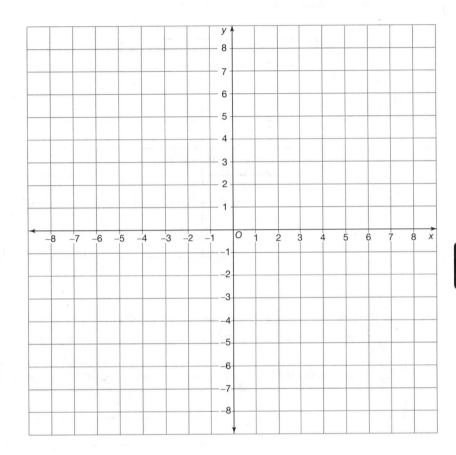

Read the scenario below. Use the scenario to answer Questions 21 through 23.

An interior decorator has asked a small linens company to make the bedspreads that she will use on the beds in a hotel she is decorating. The linens company already has 14 completed bedspreads. The interior decorator will need a total of 362 bedspreads for all of the beds in the hotel. The company can produce three and a half bedspreads each day.

21. Write an equation that represents the number of completed bedspreads b in terms of the number of days d.

22. Complete the table of values that shows the relationship between the number of days and the number of completed bedspreads.

	Time	Completed bedspreads
Labels		
Units		
Expressions		
	0	
	5	
	10	
	25	
	50	

23. Use the grid on the next page to create a graph of the data from the table in Question 22. First, choose your bounds and intervals. Be sure to label your graph clearly.

Variable quantity	Lower bound	Upper bound	Interval

Name _____   Date _____

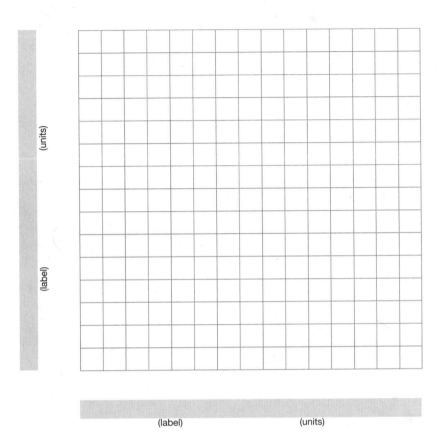

(units)

(label)

(label)   (units)

24. Use your graph to estimate when 7 bedspreads were completed. Use a complete sentence to explain how you found your answer.

Standardized Test Practice

Name _____ Date _____

1. What is the solution for this equation?

    $-2x + 9 = -17$

    a. $x = -13$

    b. $x = -4$

    c. $x = 4$

    d. $x = 13$

2. What is the solution for this equation?

    $\dfrac{x}{3} - 12 = -8$

    a. $x = -60$

    b. $x = -12$

    c. $x = 12$

    d. $x = 60$

3. Dominique charges $6 an hour when she baby sits. Which equation shows the relationship between the number of hours Dominique baby sits h and the amount of money she makes m?

    a. $m = h + 6$

    b. $m = 6h$

    c. $m = 6 - h$

    d. $\dfrac{h}{m} = 6$

4. Which problem situation matches the equation below?

$x + 3.45 = 7.04$

a. Sasha bought a pound of coffee that cost $7.04. She got $3.45 in change from the cashier. What is x, the amount of money Sasha gave the cashier?

b. Patrick did 5 pushups in 3.45 seconds. Matt did 5 pushups in 7.04 seconds. What is x, the average time it takes to do 5 pushups?

c. Katherine spent $7.04 at the store. She bought a box of cereal that cost $3.45 and a gallon of milk. What is x, the cost of the gallon of milk?

d. Tracy ran a mile in 7.04 minutes which was 3.45 minutes faster than Jordan's time. What is x, the time it took Jordan to run a mile?

3

5. The graph shows the relationship between the amount in royalties that Eric receives and the number of his books that sell. Last month, Eric received a royalty check for $360. How many of his books sold last month?

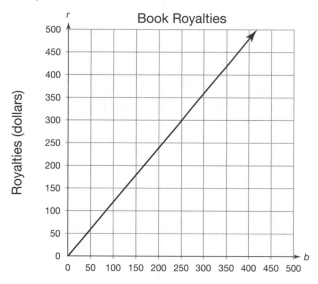

Book Royalties

Royalties (dollars)

Number of books sold

a. 200

b. 300

c. 400

d. cannot be determined

Name _____ Date _____

6. The graph shows the cost to use a local gym based on the amount of time someone spends there. There are three different rates based on the level of membership. Based on the graph, which statement below is NOT true?

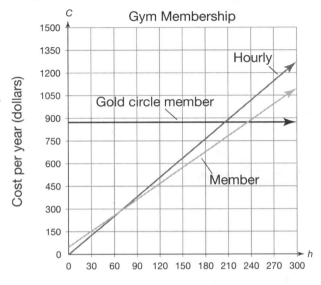

a. Being a gold circle member is a better deal if you spend more than 250 hours a year at the gym.

b. It is always a better deal to pay the hourly rate.

c. Being a member is a better deal if you spend more than 50 hours a year at the gym.

d. Paying the hourly rate is a better deal if you spend less than 50 hours a year at the gym.

7. Which percent equation shows how to find 62% of 150?

a. $62 = p(150)$

b. $a = \dfrac{62}{100}(150)$

c. $150 = \dfrac{62}{100}b$

d. $a = 62(150)$

8. Which expression is represented by the model below?

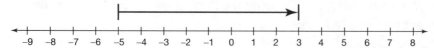

a. $-5 + 8$

b. $-5 - 8$

c. $-5 + 3$

d. $-5 - 3$

9. Which of the coordinates lie within the triangle graphed below?

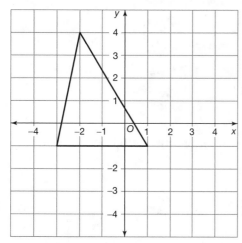

a. $(-3, 2)$

b. $(-1, 4)$

c. $(-3, -2)$

d. $(-2, 3)$

Name _____ Date _____

10. The total profit p from selling n sweatshirts is given by the equation

    $p = 15n - 30.$

    If the total profit was $720, how many sweatshirts were sold?

    a. 46

    b. 48

    c. 50

    d. 52

11. When is this statement true?

    The product of two integers is positive.

    a. This statement is never true.

    b. This statement is always true.

    c. This statement is true for the product of a positive and a negative integer.

    d. This statement is true for the product of two negative integers.

12. When Robert began working at a furniture store, he earned $7.25 per hour plus a 2% commission on each piece of furniture he sold. His boss just increased his hourly rate by $0.25 and his commission to 4%. If Robert works 20 hours a week and sells $5500 in furniture, how much will he earn?

    a. $370

    b. $480

    c. $1250

    d. $2350

3

Cumulative Test

Name _____ Date _____

For each sequence, draw the next 2 terms and describe the pattern.

1.

2. 3, –6, 12, –24, _____, _____

Use the sequence below to answer Questions 3 and 4.

Term (*n*)	1	2	3	4	5
Sequence	3	7	11	15	19

3. Write an expression showing the relationship between the term and the sequence. Let *n* represent the term.

4. Use the expression from Question 3 to find the 20th term of the sequence. Show all your work.

Perform the indicated operations. Show all your work.

5. $3^4 - (2 + 6) + 5$

6. $(10 - 6)^2 + 3(2 - 7)$

Use the table below to answer Questions 7 through 10.

Grade	Number of students with no siblings	Number of students with 1 to 3 siblings	Number of students with more than 3 siblings
8	3	21	6
9	6	19	5
10	2	25	3
11	10	11	9
Total number of students	21	76	23

7. Write a ratio of the number of students with no siblings to the total number of students surveyed.

8. There are 840 students in your school. Write and solve a proportion to determine the number of students in your school with no siblings. Show all your work and use a complete sentence in your answer.

9. To conduct the survey, your class obtained a list of the students in your school organized by grade. You randomly chose 30 students from each grade and asked them about the number of siblings they have. Which type of sampling method did you use? Use complete sentences to explain your reasoning.

Name _____ Date _____

10. Use the space below to create a bar graph of the sibling data. The bar graph should display the number of students in each grade with no siblings.

(units)

(label)

11. Triangles *LMN* and *QRS* are similar. What is the length of *QR*? Show all your work and use a complete sentence in your answer.

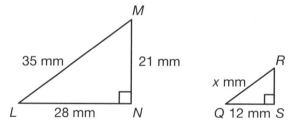

12. A couple ate dinner at a restaurant and their bill totaled $65.85. They left a 20% tip. How much did they leave for a tip? Show all your work and use a complete sentence in your answer.

13. Janelle's net pay last month was $370.60. She paid $174.40 in taxes. What was her gross pay and tax rate? Show all your work and use a complete sentence in your answer.

Solve each equation. Show all your work.

14. $-8x - 15 = -39$

15. $\dfrac{x}{5} + 23 = 30$

Name _____ Date _____

16. Algebraically determine whether 67 is a solution of the equation $3x - 45 = 156$. Show all of your work and use a complete sentence in your answer.

Read the scenario below Use the scenario to answer Questions 17 through 20.

A parking garage charges $2.25 for the first hour of parking and $1.50 for each additional hour.

17. Write an equation to represent the relationship between the time h and the cost for parking c.

18. Complete the table of values that shows the relationship between the time and the cost for parking.

Time	Cost
1	
3	
6	
10	
15	

19. Use the grid below to create a graph of the data from the table in Question 18. First, choose your bounds and intervals. Be sure to label your graph clearly.

Variable quantity	Lower bound	Upper bound	Interval
Time			
Cost			

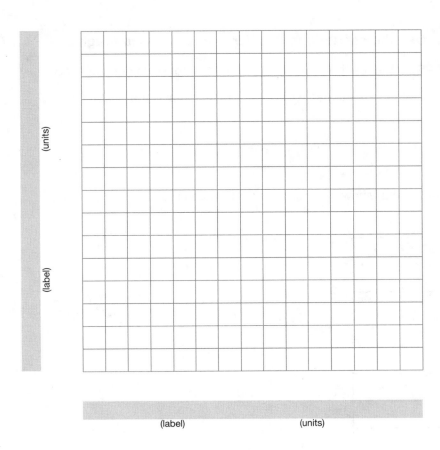

(units)

(label)

(label)   (units)

20. Use your graph to estimate how much it would cost to leave your car in the parking garage for 20 hours. Use complete sentences to explain how you found your answer.

1-3

Name _____ Date _____

Use the graph below to answer Questions 21 through 23.

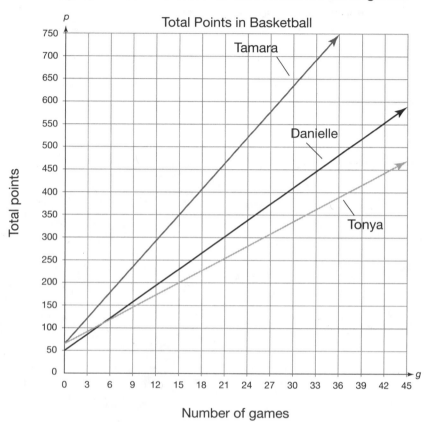

21. Danielle scored 50 points in the first two weeks of the season. On the average, she scores 12 points a game. Use the graph of Danielle's points to graphically determine whether 25 is a solution of $12g + 50 = 350$. Use complete sentences to explain your reasoning.

22. After how many games will Danielle and Tonya have the same number of points? Use complete sentences to explain how you determined your answer.

23. Use the graph to estimate when Tamara will have 600 points. Use complete sentences to explain how you determined your answer.

24. Plot and label each point in the coordinate plane.

$A(-4, 4)$

$B(-3, -2)$

$C(6, 1)$

$D(5, -6)$

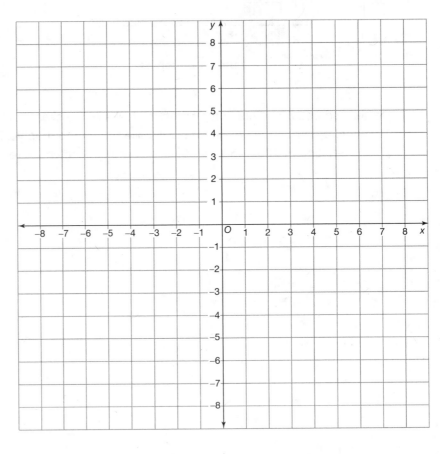

Pre-Test

Name _____ Date _____

1. An art museum offers a special admission price for children under the age of 5 and senior citizens who are 65 years or older. Everyone else must pay the full admission price to visit the museum. Write a compound inequality in compact form to show the age range for visitors paying full price for admission.

Graph each compound inequality on the number line provided.

2. $-6 \leq x < 5$

3. $x < 1$ or $x \geq 4$

Solve each inequality. Show all your work.

4. $3x + 4 > 10$

5. $-5x - 2 \leq 13$

Decide whether each relation is a function. If the relation is a function, identify the domain and range. If the relation is not a function, explain why. Use complete sentences in your answers.

6. Relation: (−1, 4), (−2, 3), (−3, 2), (−2, 1), (−4, 1)

7. Relation: (6, 4), (7, 5), (8, 6), (9, 7), (10, 8)

8. Professor Hampton has 150 exams to grade. It takes him 3 minutes to grade each exam, so it will take him 450 minutes to grade all of the exams.

   a. You can represent the number of hours Professor Hampton must spend grading using the variable y and the number of exams that have been graded using the variable x. Write an equation that represents the number of hours Professor Hampton must spend grading in terms of the number of exams that have been graded.

   b. Is this equation a function? Use complete sentences to explain your reasoning.

   c. What is the domain? Use a complete sentence in your answer.

   d. What is the range? Use a complete sentence in your answer.

Evaluate each function at the specified value. Show all your work.

9. $f(x) = 2x - 5$ at $x = 3$

10. $g(x) = 9 - 6x$ at $x = -2$

Pre-Test PAGE 3

Name _____ Date _____

Match the name of each property with its definition.

Property

____ **11.** Distributive Property of Multiplication Over Addition

____ **12.** Distributive Property of Multiplication Over Subtraction

____ **13.** Distributive Property of Division Over Addition

____ **14.** Distributive Property of Division Over Subtraction

____ **15.** Closure

____ **16.** Additive identity

____ **17.** Multiplicative identity

____ **18.** Additive inverse

____ **19.** Multiplicative inverse

____ **20.** Commutative Property of Addition

____ **21.** Commutative Property of Multiplication

____ **22.** Associative Property of Addition

____ **23.** Associative Property of Multiplication

____ **24.** Reflexive property

____ **25.** Symmetric property

____ **26.** Transitive property

Definition

a. If a, b, and c are any numbers and $c \neq 0$, then $\dfrac{a + b}{c} = \dfrac{a}{c} + \dfrac{b}{c}$.

b. A number such that when you add it to a second number, the sum is the second number.

c. A number such that when you multiply it by a second number, the product is the multiplicative identity.

d. If a, b, and c are any numbers, then $a \cdot (b - c) = a \cdot b - a \cdot c$.

e. If you are multiplying three numbers, the product is not affected by the way in which you group two of the three numbers.

f. A number such that when you add it to a second number, the sum is the additive identity.

g. For any real numbers a and b, if $a = b$, then $b = a$.

h. If a, b, and c are any numbers, then $a \cdot (b + c) = a \cdot b + a \cdot c$.

i. The order in which you multiply two or more numbers does not affect the product.

j. For any real numbers a, b, and c, if $a = b$ and $b = c$, then $a = c$.

k. A set of numbers is closed under an operation if the result of the operation on two numbers in the set is a number in the set.

l. If you are adding three numbers, the sum is not affected by the way in which you group two of the three numbers.

m. For any real number a, $a = a$.

n. The order in which you add two or more numbers does not affect the sum.

o. A number such that when you multiply it by a second number, the product is the second number.

p. If a, b, and c are any numbers and $c \neq 0$, then $\dfrac{a - b}{c} = \dfrac{a}{c} - \dfrac{b}{c}$.

Solve each equation. Show all your work.

27. $5x + 6 = 7x - 16$

28. $2(x + 3) = 3(4x - 8)$

Solve each absolute value inequality. Show all your work.

29. $|x| - 5 < 2$

30. $|2x + 1| \geq 7$

Post-Test

Name _____ Date _____

1. Your English teacher asks you to write a novella that is at least 30 pages long and no more than 60 pages long. If your novella does not fall within these page limits, you will receive a failing grade for the project. Write a compound inequality in compact form that shows the length of a novella that would receive a failing grade.

Graph each compound inequality on the number line provided.

2. $4 < x \le 9$

<-->

3. $x \le -3$ or $x > -1$

<-->

Solve each inequality. Show all your work.

4. $6x - 5 \le 37$

5. $-8x + 3 > -21$

Decide whether each relation is a function. If the relation is a function, identify the domain and range. If the relation is not a function, explain why. Use complete sentences in your answers.

6. Relation: (1, 3.2). (4, 5.5), (7, 7.8), (10, 10.1), (13, 12.4)

7. Relation: (−1, −1), (0, 2), (2, 0), (3, −1), (−1, 3)

8. A local bakery sells bagels by the dozen. Every morning, the baker makes 240 bagels.

   a. You can represent the number of bagels left using the variable y and the number of dozen bagels that have been sold using the variable x. Write an equation that represents the number of bagels left in terms of the number of dozen bagels that have been sold. (*Hint:* One dozen equals 12 bagels.)

   b. Is this equation a function? Use complete sentences to explain your reasoning.

   c. What is the domain? Use a complete sentence in your answer.

   d. What is the range? Use a complete sentence in your answer.

Evaluate each function at the specified value. Show all your work.

9. $f(x) = 4x - 1$ at $x = -3$

10. $g(x) = 15 - 2x$ at $x = 4$

Post-Test PAGE 3

Name _____ Date _____

Match the name of each property with its definition.

Property		Definition

Property

_____ 11. Distributive Property of Multiplication Over Addition

_____ 12. Distributive Property of Multiplication Over Subtraction

_____ 13. Distributive Property of Division Over Addition

_____ 14. Distributive Property of Division Over Subtraction

_____ 15. Closure

_____ 16. Additive identity

_____ 17. Multiplicative identity

_____ 18. Additive inverse

_____ 19. Multiplicative inverse

_____ 20. Commutative Property of Addition

_____ 21. Commutative Property of Multiplication

_____ 22. Associative Property of Addition

_____ 23. Associative Property of Multiplication

_____ 24. Reflexive property

_____ 25. Symmetric property

_____ 26. Transitive property

Definition

a. If a, b, and c are any numbers and $c \neq 0$, then $\dfrac{a-b}{c} = \dfrac{a}{c} - \dfrac{b}{c}$.

b. If a, b, and c are any numbers, then $a \cdot (b - c) = a \cdot b - a \cdot c$.

c. A number such that when you multiply it by a second number, the product is the multiplicative identity.

d. If a, b, and c are any numbers and $c \neq 0$, then $\dfrac{a+b}{c} = \dfrac{a}{c} + \dfrac{b}{c}$.

e. A number such that when you add it to a second number, the sum is the additive identity.

f. If you are multiplying three numbers, the product is not affected by the way in which you group two of the three numbers.

g. A number such that when you multiply it by a second number, the product is the second number.

h. The order in which you multiply two or more numbers does not affect the product.

i. A number such that when you add to a second number, the sum is the second number.

j. For any real number a, $a = a$.

k. The order in which you add two or more numbers does not affect the sum.

l. If you are adding three numbers, the sum is not affected by the way in which you group two of the three numbers.

m. For any real numbers a, b, and c, if $a = b$ and $b = c$, then $a = c$.

n. If a, b, and c are any numbers, then $a \cdot (b + c) = a \cdot b + a \cdot c$.

o. For any real numbers a and b, if $a = b$, then $b = a$.

p. A set of numbers is closed under an operation if the result of the operation on two numbers in the set is a number in the set.

Solve each equation. Show all your work.

27. $10x + 3 = 6x - 9$

28. $4(3x + 5) = 2(9x - 5)$

Solve each absolute value inequality. Show all your work.

29. $|x| + 5 > 9$

30. $|4x - 2| \leq 10$

4

Mid-Chapter Test

Name _____ Date _____

Read the scenario and table below. Use the scenario and table to answer Questions 1 and 2.

You are studying the internal structure of Earth in science class. You learn that Earth has four layers: the crust, the mantle, the outer core, and the inner core. The average depth of each layer is given in the table below.

Layer	Location
Crust	starts at Earth's surface and extends 30 kilometers below Earth's surface
Mantle	starts at the lower edge of the crust and extends 2930 below Earth's surface
Outer core	starts at the lower edge of the mantle and extends 5130 kilometers below Earth's surface
Inner core	starts at the lower edge of the outer core and extends 6380 kilometers below Earth's surface to the center

1. Let x represent the number of miles below Earth's surface. Write an inequality to represent each layer's position below Earth's surface.

   Crust: _____

   Mantle: _____

   Outer core: _____

   Inner core: _____

2. The lithosphere is the part of Earth's internal structure that begins at Earth's surface and extends 80 kilometers below Earth's surface.

   a. Does the lithosphere include the crust? Use complete sentences to explain your reasoning.

   b. Does the lithosphere include all of the mantle? Use complete sentences to explain your reasoning.

© 2006 Carnegie Learning, Inc.

Solve each inequality and graph the solution on the number line. Show all your work.

3. $-9x + 5 > 77$

4. $\dfrac{x}{2} - 6 \geq -8$

Name _____ Date _____

Read the scenario below. Use the scenario to answer Questions 5 through 9.

The state department of transportation recently filled the road salt storage building on the highway near your house with 2400 tons of road salt. A snow plow truck can hold 12 tons of road salt in one load.

5. You can represent the amount of road salt left in the storage building using the variable y and number of truckloads of road salt using the variable x. Write an equation that represents the amount of road salt left in the storage building in terms of number of truckloads.

6. Use your answer to Question 5 to find the number of truckloads of road salt that were removed if 2460 tons of road salt are left in the storage building. Does your answer make sense? Use complete sentences to explain why or why not.

7. Complete the table of values that describes the relationship between the number of truckloads of road salt that have been removed and the amount of road salt remaining in the storage building.

10	
20	
50	
100	
200	

8. How does the amount of road salt left in the storage building change as the number of truckloads increases by one? Use a complete sentence in your answer.

9. Does the relation represented by the values in the table in Question 7 represent a function? If the relation is a function, identify the domain and range. If the relation is not a function, explain why. Use complete sentences in your answer.

10. Write 5 ordered pairs that represent a relation that is not a function. Use complete sentences to explain why it is not a function.

Evaluate each function at the specified value. Show all your work.

11. $h(x) = 6x + 2$ at $x = -5$

12. $p(x) = 15 - 4x$ at $x = 7$

End of Chapter Test

Name _____   Date _____

At a carnival, there is a man who is guessing people's weights. You decide to play. If his guess is 5 pounds or less above or below your actual weight, he wins. If it is not, then you win. Your actual weight is 108 pounds.

1. Let x represent your weight. Write a compound inequality that represents the range in which the man's guess must fall for him to win.

2. Write a compound inequality that represents the range in which the man's guess must fall for you to win.

3. The man guesses 113 pounds. Who wins? Use a complete sentence to explain how you determined your answer.

Decide whether each relation is a function. If the relation is a function, identify the domain and range. If the relation is not a function, explain why. Use complete sentences in your answers.

4. Relation: (–50, 50), (–40, 40), (–30, 30), (–20, 30), (–10, 40)

5. Relation: (14, 23), (15, 25), (16, 27), (14, 29), (13, 27)

Evaluate each function at the specified value. Show all your work.

6. $f(x) = 39 - 4x$ at $x = 9$

7. $h(x) = 10x + 17$ at $x = -3$

© 2006 Carnegie Learning, Inc.

4

8. Xavier can run a mile in 7 minutes. You can represent the total amount of time Xavier runs using the variable y and the number of miles he runs using the variable x. Write an equation that represents the total amount of time Xavier runs in terms of the number of miles he runs. Does this equation represent a function? If so, identify the domain and range in terms of this real-life situation. If not, explain why. Use complete sentences in your answer.

9. Give an example of a rational number. Use complete sentences to explain how you determined your answer.

10. Give an example of an irrational number. Use complete sentences to explain how you determined your answer.

4

Write each repeating decimal as a rational number. Show all your work.

11. 0.1818...

12. 0.777...

Solve each equation. Show all your work.

13. $5x - 16 = 18x + 23$

14. $2(6x + 3) = 3(2x + 12)$

Name _____ Date _____

15. For the equation, identify the property that is used in each step.

$$2(5x + 2) = \frac{340 - 60}{20}$$ Given problem

$$10x + 4 = \frac{340 - 60}{20}$$ _____

$$10x + 4 = \frac{340}{20} - \frac{60}{20}$$ _____

$$10x + 4 = 17 - 3$$ _____

$$10x + 4 = 14$$ _____

$$10x + 4 - 4 = 14 - 4$$ _____

$$10x = 10$$ _____

$$\frac{10x}{10} = \frac{10}{10}$$ _____

$$x = 1$$ _____

Give a mathematical example of each property.

16. Multiplicative identity

17. Additive inverse

18. Commutative Property of Addition

19. Associative Property of Multiplication

Solve each inequality and graph the solution. Show all your work.

20. $2x + 7 > 19$

$\longleftarrow\hspace{8cm}\longrightarrow$

21. $-3x - 14 \geq 7$

$\longleftarrow\hspace{8cm}\longrightarrow$

4

22. $|x| + 2 \leq 11$

$\longleftarrow\hspace{8cm}\longrightarrow$

23. $|4x - 2| > 22$

$\longleftarrow\hspace{8cm}\longrightarrow$

Name _____ Date _____

Your uncle is trying to decide between a cable subscription and a satellite dish. The cable subscription has a $40 hook-up fee and costs $38 per month. The satellite dish costs $260 and the monthly fee is $16.

24. Write an expression that represents the total cost of the cable service, using x to represent the number of months that your uncle has the service.

25. Write an expression that represents the total cost of satellite service, using x to represent the number of months that you have the service.

26. Write and solve an equation to determine the number of months it takes for the total costs to be the same. Show all your work and use a complete sentence in your answer.

Standardized Test Practice

Name _____ Date _____

1. A person with a systolic blood pressure greater than 120 mmHg and less than or equal to 139 mmHg is said to have prehypertension. Which inequality represents the range of systolic blood pressure for a person with prehypertension?

   a. $120 < x < 139$

   b. $120 < x \le 139$

   c. $120 \le x < 139$

   d. $120 \le x \le 139$

2. Which inequality is represented by the graph below?

   a. $-6 \le x > 0$

   b. $-6 \le x < 0$

   c. $x < -6$ or $x \ge 0$

   d. $x \le -6$ or $x > 0$

3. What is the solution set of the inequality $|x + 3| \ge 9$?

   a. $6 \le x \le -12$

   b. $x \le 6$

   c. $x \le -12$ or $x \ge 6$

   d. $x \le -12$ and $x \ge 6$

4. Which equation is equivalent to $2(5 - 3x) + 4 = 3(9x + 7)$?

   a. $33x = 35$

   b. $33x = -7$

   c. $21x = -7$

   d. $33x = -15$

5. Solve: $2(x - 4) = \dfrac{24 - 16}{2}$

Step 1: $2x - 8 = \dfrac{24 - 16}{2}$

Step 2: $2x - 8 = \dfrac{24}{2} - \dfrac{16}{2}$

Step 3: $2x - 8 = 12 - 8$

Step 4: $2x - 8 = 4$

Step 5: $2x = 12$

Step 6: $x = 6$

Which property of real numbers was used in Step 2?

a. Distributive property of division over subtraction

b. Distributive property of multiplication over subtraction

c. Commutative property of addition

d. Multiplicative identity

6. Which relation is a function?

a. (0, 0), (1, 2), (0, 3), (2, 4)

b. (−24, 2), (−23, 2), (−24, 4), (−23, 4)

c. (−6, 1), (−6, 2), (−6, 3), (−6, 4)

d. (4, 9), (6, 13), (9, 4), (13, 6)

Name _____   Date _____

7. What is the domain of the function given in the table?

x	y
–5	15
–2	6
–1	3
3	–9
4	–12

   a. (15, 6, 3, –9, –12}

   b. (–5, 15), (–2, 6), (–1, 3), (3, –9), (4, –12)

   c. {–5, –2, –1, 3, 4}

   d. all real numbers

8. Which of the following is written in function notation?

   a. $f = 3x + 2$

   b. $y = 3x + 2$

   c. $f - x = 3x + 2$

   d. $g(x) = 3x + 2$

9. Which of the following real numbers is NOT a rational number?

   a. 4.216589...

   b. 8

   c. 1.33333...

   d. $\dfrac{5}{9}$

10. Jamal's teacher asked him to write 0.7575... as a fraction. Jamal's work is shown below.

Step 1: $10w = 7.5757...$

$-w = 0.7575...$

Step 2: $9w = 6.8182$

Step 3: $w = \dfrac{6.8182}{9}$

Which is the first *incorrect* step in Jamal's work?

a. Step 1

b. Step 2

c. Step 3

d. None of the above. Jamal did the work correctly.

11. When is this statement true?

Every function is a relation.

a. This statement is never true.

b. This statement is always true.

c. This statement is true for positive integers.

d. This statement is true for negative integers.

12. Daniel made $28,900 last year, which put him in the 15% tax bracket. The range for the 15% tax bracket is $7300 < x < $29,700. Daniel received an $800 pay raise this year. Will he still be in the 15% tax bracket? Why or why not?

a. Yes, because his new salary is $29,700, which falls within the 15% tax bracket.

b. No, because his new salary is $29,700, which does NOT fall within the 15% tax bracket.

c. Cannot be determined.

Standardized Test Practice PAGE 5

Name _____ Date _____

13. Daphne solves the inequality $5(x - 1) \geq 10$, and graphs the solution set below.

Which value is NOT part of the solution set?

a. 0

b. 3

c. 6

d. 11

14. Let $f(x) = -6x + 8$. What is $f(2)$?

a. $f(2) = -4$

b. $f(2) = 2$

c. $f(2) = 4$

d. $f(2) = 20$

15. Which equation shows an example of the Associative Property of Addition?

a. $(a \cdot b) \cdot c = a \cdot (b \cdot c)$

b. $a + b = b + a$

c. $a + (b + c) = (a + b) + c$

d. $a(b + c) = ab + ac$

16. The pep club at your school has decided to order T-shirts to sell at the school basketball games. Company A charges $5 per shirt and a one time set-up fee of $20. Company B charges $3 per shirt and a one time set-up fee of $42. Which equation would you use to determine for what number of shirts the total costs from Company A and Company B would be the same?

a. $8x = 62$

b. $5x + 20 = 3x + 42$

c. $5x - 20 = 3x - 42$

d. $5x - 3x = 20 + 42$

Pre-Test

Name _____ Date _____

1. Is $y = 2x + 7$ a linear function? Use a complete sentence to explain why or why not.

2. Is this the graph of a linear function? Use a complete sentence to explain why or why not.

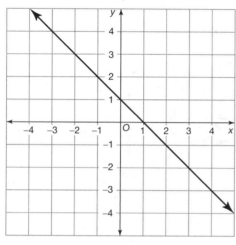

3. Write 2 sets of ordered pairs that satisfy the equation $y = 6x - 13$.

5

Use the graph to identify the intercepts of each line.

4. *x*-intercept: _____

   y-intercept: _____

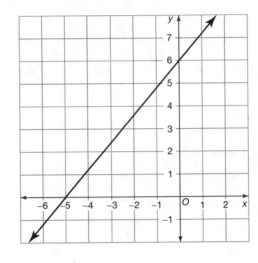

5. *x*-intercept: _____

   y-intercept: _____

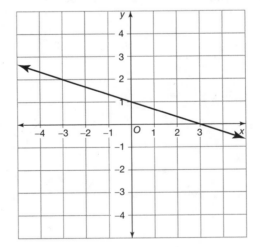

Name _____ Date _____

6. Algebraically find the intercepts of the graph of the equation $y = 2x - 6$. Show all your work.

    x-intercept: _____

    y-intercept: _____

7. Determine whether the slope of each line in the graph is positive, negative, zero, or undefined. Use complete sentences in to explain your reasoning.

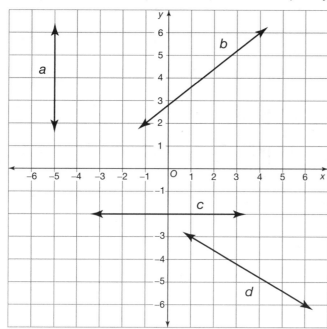

8. Use the coordinates of the points to find the slope of each line. Show all your work.

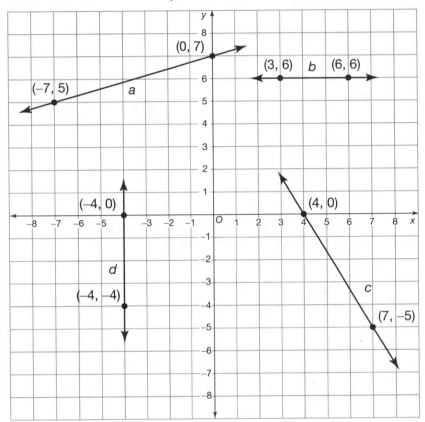

a. Slope of line *a*: _____

b. Slope of line *b*: _____

c. Slope of line *c*: _____

d. Slope of line *d*: _____

Name _____ Date _____

9. Which line has the steepest slope? Use complete sentences to explain how you found your answer.

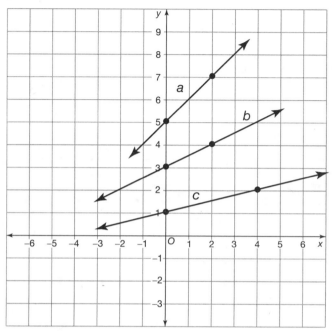

Identify the slope and y-intercept of each equation.

10. $y = \dfrac{2}{3}x + 4$

      slope: _____

      y-intercept: _____

11. $y = 3x - 5$

      slope: _____

      y-intercept: _____

12. Draw a graph of the equation by using the slope and *y*-intercept.

$$y = -\frac{3}{5}x + 4$$

13. Write the equation of the line that has a slope of 2 and passes through the point (3, 1) in slope-intercept form. Show all your work.

5

14. Write the equation of the line that passes through the points (1, 4) and (5, 12) in slope-intercept form. Show all your work.

Name _____ Date _____

15. Write the piecewise function that is represented in the graph below. Use x to represent a number from the domain of your function f.

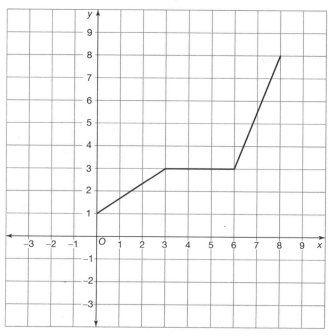

Read the scenario below. Use the scenario to answer Questions 16 and 17.

During a football game, fans can buy chili dogs and soft drinks at the concession stand. The chili dogs cost $2 each and the soft drinks cost $1.50 each. During one football game, the chili dog and soft drink sales totaled $330.

16. Write an equation that represents the total sales if x chili dogs and y soft drinks were sold.

5

17. Using the equation, write the intercepts of the equation's graph. Show all your work.

    x-intercept: _____

    y-intercept: _____

18. Write the equation in standard form. Show all your work.

    $y = -\dfrac{2}{5}x + 3$

19. Write the equation in slope-intercept form. Show all your work.

    $5x + 4y = 12$

20. Find the amount of interest earned by depositing $220 into an account that earns 4% interest for 1 year. Show all your work and use a complete sentence in your answer.

21. You can use the formula $A = \dfrac{1}{2}bh$ to find the area of a triangle, where b is the length of the base and h is the height of triangle. Solve the equation for h. Show all your work.

5

Post-Test

Name _____ Date _____

1. Is $y = -5x + 3$ a linear function? Use a complete sentence to explain why or why not.

2. Is this the graph of a linear function? Use a complete sentence to explain why or why not.

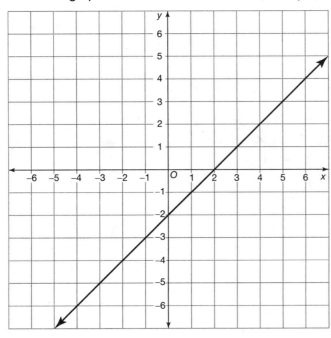

3. Write two sets of ordered pairs that satisfy the equation $y = 2x + 7$.

Use the graph to identify the intercepts of each line.

4. *x*-intercept: _____

   y-intercept: _____

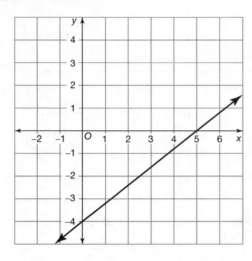

5. *x*-intercept: _____

   y-intercept: _____

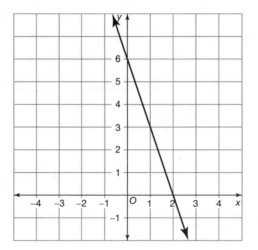

Name _____ Date _____

6. Algebraically find the intercepts of the graph of the equation $y = 2x - 6$. Show all your work.

    x-intercept: _____

    y-intercept: _____

7. Determine whether the slope of each line in the graph is positive, negative, zero, or undefined. Use complete sentences in to explain your reasoning.

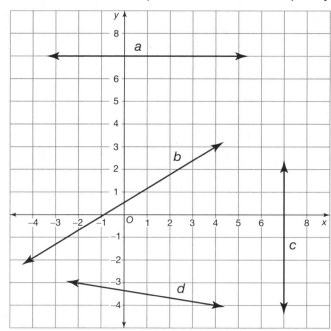

8. Use the coordinates of the points to find the slope of each line. Show all your work.

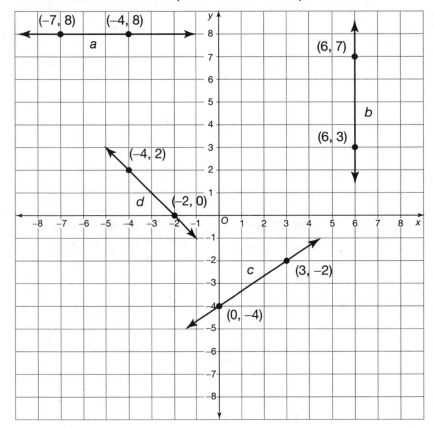

a. Slope of line *a*: _____

b. Slope of line *b*: _____

c. Slope of line *c*: _____

d. Slope of line *d*: _____

5

Post-Test PAGE 5

Name _____ Date _____

9. Which line has the steepest slope? Use a complete sentence to explain how you determined your answer.

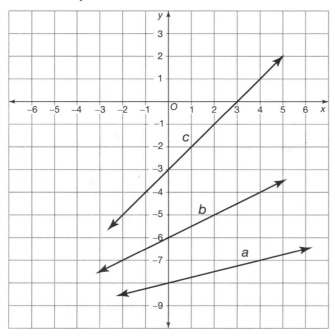

Identify the slope and *y*-intercept of each equation.

10. $y = \frac{3}{5}x + 8$

slope: _____

y-intercept: _____

11. $y = 7x - 4$

slope: _____

y-intercept: _____

12. Draw a graph of the equation by using the slope and *y*-intercept.

$$y = -\frac{1}{6}x + 2$$

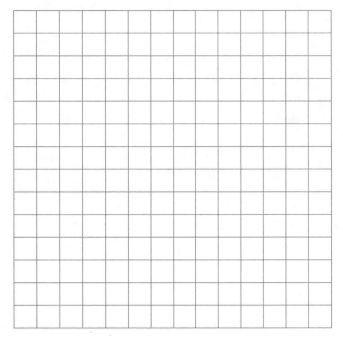

13. Write the equation of the line that has a slope of 5 and passes through the point (4, 3) in slope-intercept form. Show all your work.

14. Write the equation of the line that passes through the points (3, 1) and (7, 13) in slope-intercept form. Show all your work.

Name _____   Date _____

15. Write the piecewise function that is represented in the graph below. Use *x* to represent a number from the domain of your function *f*.

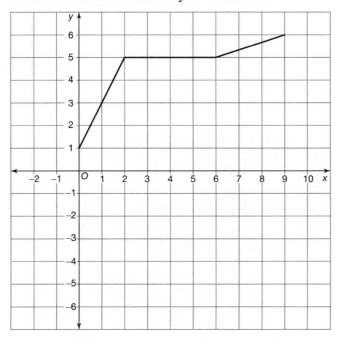

Read the scenario below. Use the scenario to answer Questions 16 and 17.

Your band is selling cheese and pepperoni pizzas to raise money for a trip to Florida. Each cheese pizza costs $8 and each pepperoni pizza costs $10. You made a total of $120 on your pizza sales.

16. Write an equation that represents the total amount you made if you sold *x* cheese pizzas and *y* pepperoni pizzas.

17. Using the equation, write the intercepts of the equation's graph. Show all your work.

      x-intercept: _____

      y-intercept: _____

18. Write the equation in standard form. Show all your work.

$$y = -\frac{3}{8}x + 1$$

19. Write the equation in slope-intercept form. Show all your work.

$$2x + 3y = 9$$

20. Find the amount of interest earned by depositing $345 into an account that earns 2% interest for 1 year. Show all your work and use a complete sentence in your answer.

21. You can use the formula $A = \frac{1}{2}ap$ to find the area of a regular polygon, where *a* is the length of the apothem and *p* is the perimeter of the polygon. Solve the equation for *a*. Show all your work.

Mid-Chapter Test

Name _____ Date _____

Read the scenario below. Use the scenario to answer Questions 1 through 3.

Your uncle Joe is running for mayor. He orders bumper stickers for his campaign. A local printer has agreed to make them for $.12 each plus a one time set-up fee of $25.

1. Write an equation that gives the total cost in terms of the number of bumper stickers. Use x to represent the number of bumper stickers and use y to represent the total cost.

2. Use your equation to find the total cost to print 500 bumper stickers. Show all your work and use a complete sentence in your answer.

3. Is the equation you wrote in Question 1 a linear function? Use complete sentences to explain your reasoning.

Read the scenario below. Use the scenario to answer Questions 4 through 8.

Janine is a marathon runner. She runs the first part of a marathon in 30 minutes. Then she runs at pace of 8 miles per hour, which means it takes her 7.5 minutes to complete each mile.

4. Write an equation that gives the total time in terms of the number of miles after the first part of the race. Use x to represent the number of miles after the first part of the race and use y to represent the total time.

5. Complete the three sets of ordered pairs so that they satisfy your equation.

   (–2, _____)

   (_____ , 30)

   (8, _____)

5

6. Use the grid to graph the ordered pairs in Question 5. Then, create a graph of your equation. Complete the table with your bounds and intervals. Be sure to label your graph clearly.

Variable quantity	Lower bound	Upper bound	Interval

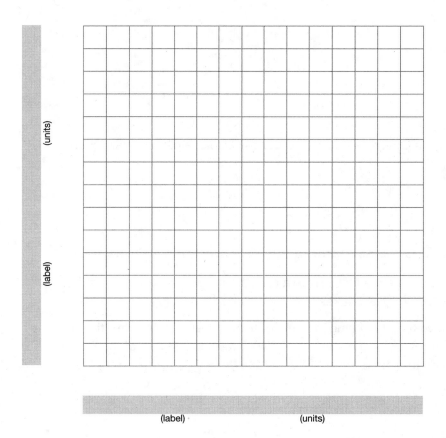

(units)

(label)

(label)   (units)

5

7. Is the graph for Question 6 the graph of a linear function? Use a complete sentence to explain your reasoning.

Name _____ Date _____

8. Use the graph to find the *x*- and *y*-intercepts of the equation. Use complete sentences to explain what these points tell you about the relationship between the number of miles and the total time.

    x-intercept: _____   *y*-intercept: _____

9. Algebraically find the intercepts of the graph of the equation $y = -2x + 6$. Show all your work.

    x-intercept: _____

    y-intercept: _____

10. Use the graph below to find the increase in interest when the principal increases by $1. Use a complete sentence in your answer. Then, write a unit rate that compares the increase in interest to the increase in the principal.

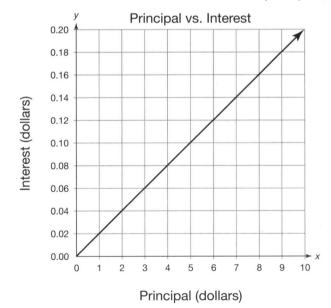

11. Use complete sentences to describe lines that have positive slope, negative slope, zero slope, or undefined slope.

12. Find the slope of the line that passes through (–2, 7) and (8, 5). Show all your work.

13.

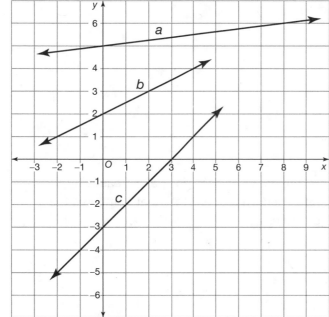

a. For each line, identify the slope and *y*-intercept.

Line *a*:   slope: _____   *y*-intercept: _____

Line *b*:   slope: _____   *y*-intercept: _____

Line *c*:   slope: _____   *y*-intercept: _____

b. How does the slope of a steep line compare to the slope of a line that is less steep? Use a complete sentence to explain.

Name _____ Date _____

14. Draw a graph of the equation by using the slope and *y*-intercept.

$$y = \frac{1}{4}x - 7$$

15. Write the equation of the line from its graph.

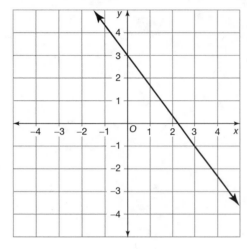

End of Chapter Test

Name _____ Date _____

1. You would like to increase the number of CDs in your collection. You currently have 25 CDs. You plan to buy 2 CDs each month. Write an equation that gives the number of CDs in terms of the number of months. Use x to represent the month and use y to represent the total number of CDs. Does the equation you wrote represent a linear function? Use a complete sentence to explain your reasoning.

Use the graph below to answer Questions 2 and 3.

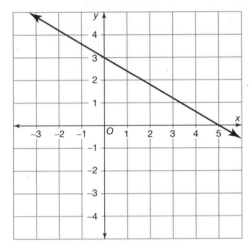

2. Is the graph above the graph of a linear function? Use a complete sentence to explain your reasoning.

3. Find the x- and y-intercepts of the graph above.

    x-intercept: _____

    y-intercept: _____

© 2006 Carnegie Learning, Inc.

5

4. Algebraically find the intercepts of the graph of the equation $y = 2x - 24$. Show all your work.

x-intercept: _____

y-intercept: _____

5. Use the graph to find the decrease in the height of a candle when the amount of time it burns increases by 30 minutes. Use a complete sentence in your answer. Then write a unit rate that compares the decrease in height to the increase in time.

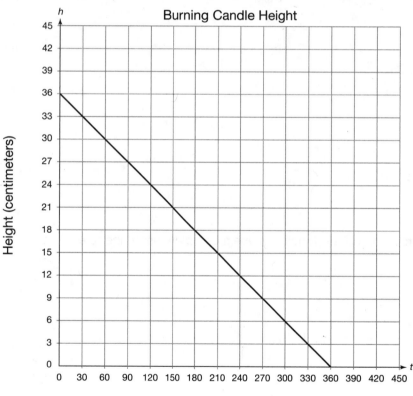

Name _____   Date _____

6. Use the coordinates of the points to find the slope of each line. Show all your work.

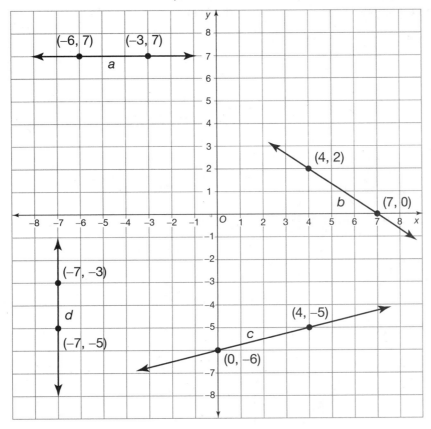

a. slope of line *a*: _____

b. slope of line *b*: _____

c. slope of line *c*: _____

d. slope of line *d*: _____

5

7. Identify the slope and *y*-intercept of the graph of each equation. Then, use the slope and *y*-intercept to graph each equation on the coordinate grid. Be sure to label each line.

a. $y = \dfrac{3}{8}x - 5$

slope: _____

y-intercept: _____

b. $y = -3x + 5$

slope: _____

y-intercept: _____

5

Name _____ Date _____

8. Write the equation of the line from its graph.

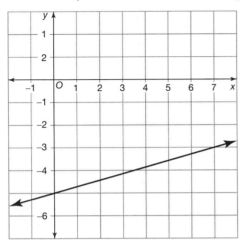

9. Write the equation of a line in slope-intercept form that has a slope of $-\dfrac{5}{9}$ and passes

    through the point (18, 7). Show all your work.

10. Write the equation of a line in slope-intercept form that passes through the points (14, 8) and (–2, 16). Show all your work.

11. Write the equation of the piecewise function given in the graph. Use x to represent a number from the domain of your function f.

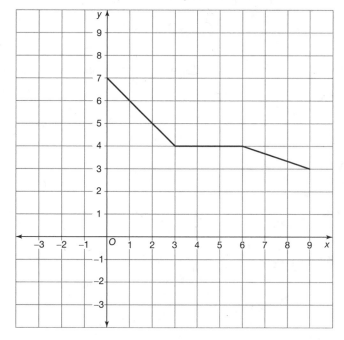

Name _____ Date _____

Read the scenario below. Use the scenario to answer Questions 12 through 15.

As the manager of the school bookstore, you want to order school hats and T-shirts to sell in the bookstore. A company says they will print hats for $5 each and T-shirts for $7 each. You have a budget of $210.

12. Write an equation that represents an order of x hats and y T-shirts whose total cost is equal to the amount of money in your budget.

13. Using the equation you wrote in Question 12, write the intercepts of the equation's graph. Show all your work.

x-intercept: _____

y-intercept: _____

14. What do the intercepts mean in terms of the problem situation? Use complete sentences in your answer.

5

15. Use the grid and the intercepts to create a graph of the equation in Question 13. First, choose your bounds and intervals. Be sure to label your graph clearly.

Variable quantity	Lower bound	Upper bound	Interval

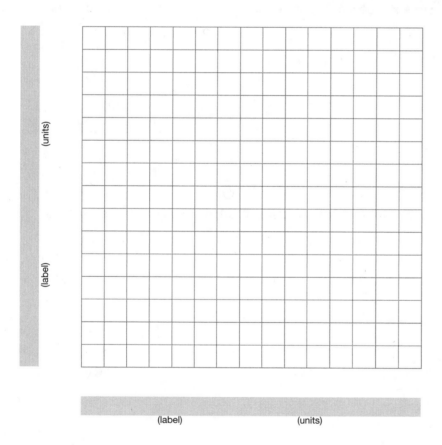

(units)

(label)

(label)   (units)

16. Write the equation $3x + 2y = 8$ in slope-intercept form. Show all your work.

5

Name _____   Date _____

17. Write the equation $y = \dfrac{4}{5}x - 2$ in standard form. Show all your work.

18. Find the amount of interest earned by depositing $5430 into an account that earns 3% interest for 1 year. Show all your work and use a complete sentence in your answer.

19. You can use the formula $I = \dfrac{746P}{V}$ to find the amperage, where I represents amperage, P represents horsepower and V represents voltage. Solve the equation for P. Show all your work.

5

Standardized Test

Name _____ Date _____

1. What is the *y*-intercept of the graph of $6x + 5y = 30$?

   a. 6

   b. 5

   c. –5

   d. –6

2. Which point lies on the line defined by $4x - 3y = 9$?

   a. $(3, 7)$

   b. $(0, 3)$

   c. $\left(2, -\dfrac{1}{3}\right)$

   d. $\left(2, \dfrac{17}{3}\right)$

3. What is the equation of the line that has a slope of –3 and passes through the point (–6, 9)?

   a. $y = -3x + 21$

   b. $y = -3x - 21$

   c. $y = -3x + 9$

   d. $y = -3x - 9$

4. The equation of line *a* is $7x + 2y = 8$, and the equation of line *b* is $2x - 7y = -28$. Which of the following statements is true?

   a. Lines *a* and *b* have the same *x*-intercept.

   b. Lines *a* and *b* have the same *y*-intercept.

   c. Lines *a* and *b* have the same slope.

   d. None of the above.

5

5. Which of the following equations shows $y = \frac{3}{7}x - 4$ written in standard form?

    a. $3x - 7y = 28$

    b. $3x + 7y = 28$

    c. $-\frac{3}{7}x + y = -4$

    d. $-\frac{3}{7}x - y = 4$

6. Find the slope of the line $3y = 2x + 6$.

    a. $-\frac{2}{3}$

    b. $\frac{2}{3}$

    c. 2

    d. -2

7. Which equation describes a line that has a y-intercept of -10 and a slope of $\frac{2}{5}$?

    a. $y = \frac{2}{5}(10) - x$

    b. $y = \frac{2}{5}(x - 10)$

    c. $y = \frac{2}{5}x + 10$

    d. $y = \frac{2}{5}x - 10$

Name _____ Date _____

8. What is the slope of the linear function shown in the graph?

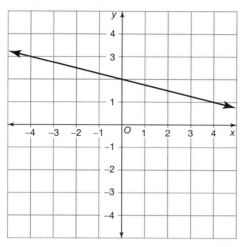

a. −4

b. $-\dfrac{1}{4}$

c. $\dfrac{1}{4}$

d. 4

9. Which of the following best describes the slope of the line?

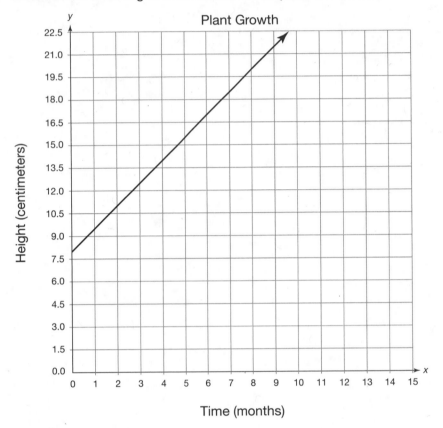

Plant Growth

Time (months)

a. The plant grows 1.5 centimeters every 2 months.

b. The plant grows 1.5 centimeters per month.

c. The plant grows 8 centimeters per month.

d. The plant grows 2 centimeters per month.

10. Which of the following statements about slope is NOT true?

a. The smaller the absolute value of the slope, the steeper the line.

b. The larger the absolute value of the slope, the steeper the line.

c. A vertical line has a slope that is undefined.

d. A horizontal line has a slope of zero.

Name _____   Date _____

11. What are the *x*- and *y*-intercepts of the function that is graphed below?

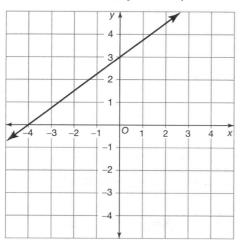

    a. (0, 4) and (–3, 0)

    b. (0, –4) and (3, 0)

    c. (4, 0) and (0, –3)

    d. (–4, 0) and (0, 3)

12. You work for a vendor selling bottles of water and lemonade at a baseball stadium. Each bottle of water sells for $2 and each bottle of lemonade sells for $2.50. Your sales for one game total $250. The equation $2x + 2.5y = 250$ represents your sales during that game if you sold *x* bottles of water and *y* bottles of lemonade. What does the *x*-intercept of the graph of the equation represent in terms of this problem situation?

    a. The number of bottles of lemonade that were sold if 0 bottles of water were sold

    b. The number of bottles of lemonade that were sold if 125 bottles of water were sold

    c. The number of bottles of water that were sold if 100 bottles of lemonade were sold

    d. The number of bottles of water that were sold if 0 bottles of lemonade were sold

5

13. Which of the following is the equation of the line that passes through (2, 6) and (–8, –14)?

   a. $y = -2x + 2$

   b. $y = 2x - 2$

   c. $y = 2x + 2$

   d. $y = -2x - 2$

14. You can use the formula $A = \frac{1}{2}d_1d_2$ to find the area of a kite, where d_1 is the length of one diagonal and d_2 is the length of the other diagonal. Solve this equation for d_1.

   a. $d_2 = \frac{2A}{d_1}$

   b. $d_1 = \frac{2A}{d_2}$

   c. $d_1 = \frac{1}{2}Ad_2$

   d. $2A = d_1d_2$

15. Which of the following shows $4x - 3y = 18$ written in slope-intercept form?

   a. $y = -\frac{4}{3}x + 6$

   b. $y = -\frac{4}{3}x + 6$

   c. $y = \frac{4}{3}x - 6$

   d. $y = \frac{4}{3}x + 6$

Pre-Test

© 2006 Carnegie Learning, Inc.

Name _____ Date _____

Use the data table below for Questions 1 through 4.

The data in the table shows the relationship between a runner's average speed and the average number of steps the runner takes each second.

Speed	Steps
feet per second	steps per second
16.00	3.00
17.00	3.10
17.50	3.20
18.50	3.25
20.00	3.40
21.00	3.50
22.00	3.60
23.00	3.75
24.00	3.80
24.50	3.90

1. Write the ordered pairs from the table that show steps as a function of speed.

2. Create a scatter plot of the ordered pairs on the grid on the next page. First, choose your bounds and intervals. Be sure to label your graph clearly.

Variable quantity	Lower bound	Upper bound	Interval
Speed			
Steps			

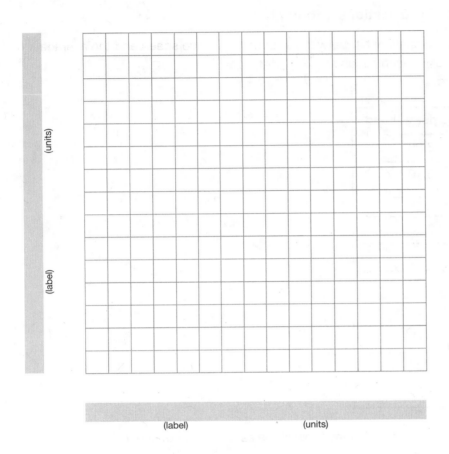

(units)

(label)

(label)   (units)

3. Use a ruler to draw the line that best fits the data in the graph. Use a complete sentence to explain how you decided where to draw the line.

4. What does the *y*-intercept of your line mean in terms of the context of the problem? Use a complete sentence in your answer.

6

Name _____ Date _____

Use the graph below to answer Questions 5 and 6.

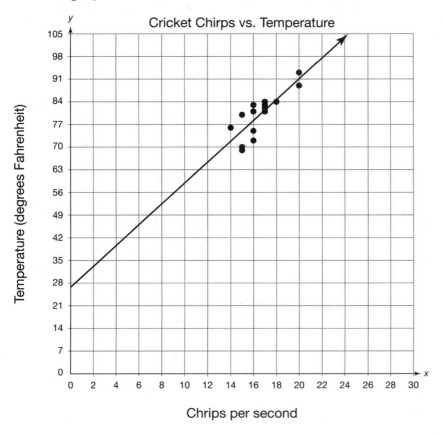

5. Write the equation of the best fit line shown in the graph above. Show all your work. Be sure to define your variables and include units. Mark and label any points on the graph that you use to find your answer.

6. What does the slope of your line mean in the context of your problem? Use a complete sentence in your answer.

6

Use the graph and best fit line given below to answer Questions 7 and 8.

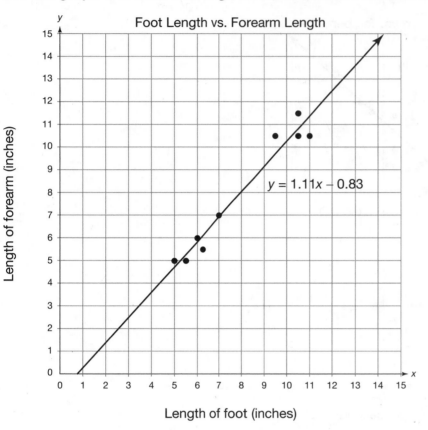

Foot Length vs. Forearm Length

$y = 1.11x - 0.83$

Length of forearm (inches)

Length of foot (inches)

7. Use the equation of the best fit line to predict the length of a person's forearm if the length of their foot is 8 inches. Is your answer reasonable in the context of the problem? Why or why not? Show all your work and use a complete sentence in your answer.

6

Name _____ Date _____

8. Use the equation of the best fit line to predict the foot length of a person with a forearm length of 12.25 inches. Show all your work and round your answer to the nearest hundredth. Use a complete sentence in your answer.

9. What is the advantage of using a graph with a break in it? Use a complete sentence in your answer.

10. What is the disadvantage of using a graph with a break in it? Use a complete sentence in your answer.

For Questions 11 through 13, determine whether the points in each scatter plot have a positive correlation, negative correlation, or no correlation. Use a complete sentence to explain your reasoning.

11.

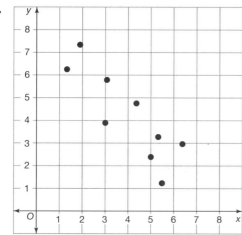

12.

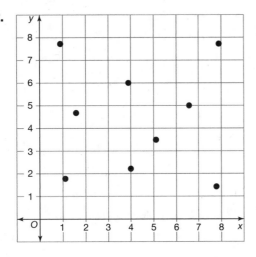

13.

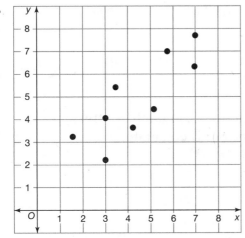

14. You use a graphing calculator to find a linear regression equation for some data. The calculator also produces a correlation coefficient of 0.9700513659. Use a complete sentence to explain what this value means.

6

Post-Test

Name _____ Date _____

Use the data table below for Questions 1 through 4.

The data in the table shows the relationship between the number of minutes a basketball player plays in a game and the number of points he scores.

Time	Points
minutes	points
2	3
5	4
8	6
12	9
18	13
22	15
25	16
30	20
32	21
35	24

1. Write the ordered pairs from the table that show points as a function of time.

2. Create a scatter plot of the ordered pairs on the grid on the next page. First, choose your bounds and intervals. Be sure to label your graph clearly.

Variable quantity	Lower bound	Upper bound	Interval

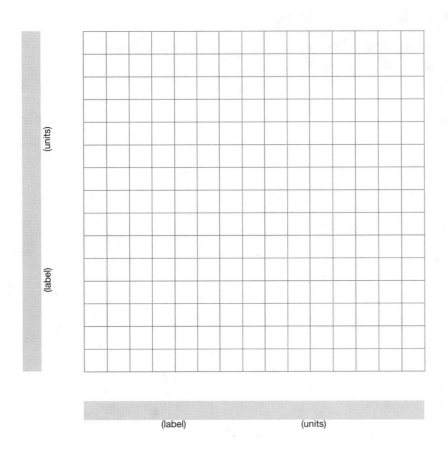

(units)

(label)

(label)   (units)

3. Use a ruler to draw the line that best fits the data in the graph. Use a complete sentence to explain how you decided where to draw the line.

4. What does the *y*-intercept of your line mean in terms of the context of the problem? Use a complete sentence in your answer.

Post-Test PAGE 3

Name _____ Date _____

Use the graph below to answer Questions 5 and 6.

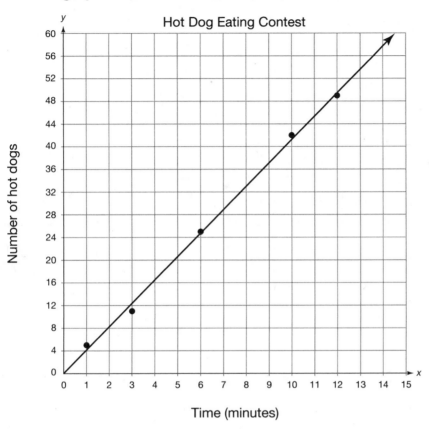

5. Write the equation of the best fit line shown in the graph above. Show all your work. Be sure to define your variables and include units. Mark and label any points on the graph that you use to find your answer.

6. What does the slope of your line mean in the context of your problem? Use a complete sentence in your answer.

Use the graph and best fit line given below to answer Questions 7 and 8.

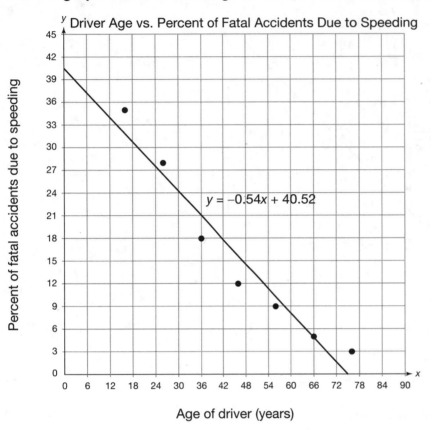

7. Use the equation of the best fit line to predict the number of fatal accidents due to speeding if the age of the driver is 84. Is your answer reasonable in the context of the problem? Why or why not? Show all your work and use a complete sentence in your answer.

© 2006 Carnegie Learning, Inc.

Name _____ Date _____

8. Use the equation of the best fit line to predict the age of the driver with 15% fatal accidents due to speeding. Show all your work and round your answer to the nearest hundredth. Use a complete sentence in your answer.

9. What is the advantage of using a graph with a break in it? Use a complete sentence in your answer.

10. What is the disadvantage of using a graph with a break in it? Use a complete sentence in your answer.

For Questions 11 through 13, determine whether the points in each scatter plot have a positive correlation, negative correlation, or no correlation. Use a complete sentence to explain your reasoning.

11.

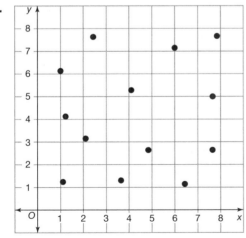

12.

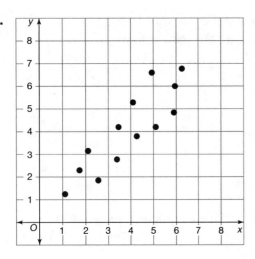

13.

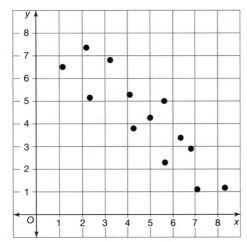

14. You use a graphing calculator to find a linear regression equation for some data. The calculator also produces a correlation coefficient of 0.9950012875. Use a complete sentence to explain what this value means.

6

Mid-Chapter Test

Name _____ Date _____

Use the data table below for Questions 1 through 5.

A scientist wonders if you can predict a person's weight at 30 years based on the person's weight at 1 year. She uses some medical files to collect the following data.

Weight at 1 year	Weight at 30 years
pounds	pounds
21	124
25	128
23	130
24	132
20	125
15	122
25	135
21	130
17	128
24	132

1. Write the ordered pairs from the table that show the weight at 30 years as a function of the weight at 1 year.

2. Create a scatter plot of the ordered pairs on the grid on the next page. First, choose your bounds and intervals. Be sure to label your graph clearly.

Variable quantity	Lower bound	Upper bound	Interval

3.

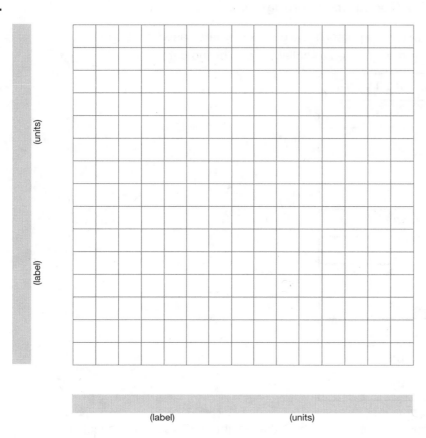

(units)

(label)

(label)   (units)

4. Use a ruler to draw the line that best fits the data in your graph.

5. What does the *y*-intercept of your line mean in terms of the context of the problem? Use a complete sentence in your answer.

Mid-Chapter Test PAGE 3

Name _____ Date _____

Read the scenario below. Use the scenario and graph to answer Questions 6 through 8.

The Fast Car dealership tracks its automobile sales based on the type of automobile.
The graph below shows the percent of sales that were SUVs for the years 1995 to 2005.

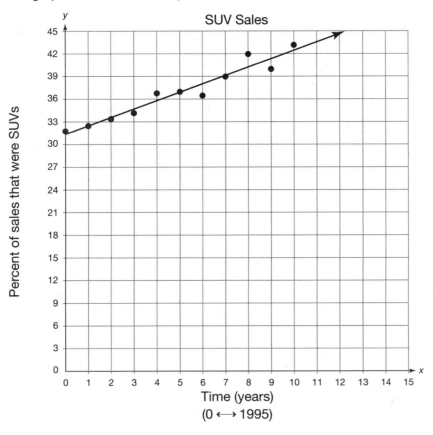

6. Explain what year is represented by 7 on the graph. Use a complete sentence in your answer.

7. Write the equation of the best fit line in the graph. Define your variables and include the units.

8. What does the slope of the line represent in this problem situation? Use a complete sentence in your answer.

Read the scenario below. Use the scenario and graph below to answer Questions 9 and 10.

The Fast Car dealership tracks its automobile sales based on the type of automobile. The graph below shows the percent of sales that were compact cars for the years 1995 to 2005.

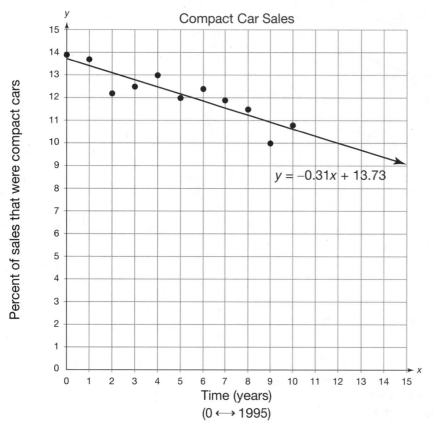

Compact Car Sales

$y = -0.31x + 13.73$

Percent of sales that were compact cars

Time (years)
(0 ⟷ 1995)

9. Use the equation provided to predict the percent of sales that were compact cars in the year 2006. Show all your work and use a complete sentence in your answer.

10. Use the equation provided to predict the year in which the percent of sales that were compact cars was 11%. Show all your work and use a complete sentence in your answer.

6

End of Chapter Test

Name _____ Date _____

Use the data table below to answer Questions 1 through 9.

You just got your ACT scores. Your composite score wasn't exactly what you had expected. You wonder if you could have predicted your composite score using your GPA. You get the following data about 10 students from the counseling office.

GPA	ACT composite score
points	points
3.2	18
3.3	21
3.1	22
3.5	25
3.4	27
3.7	29
3.8	28
3.7	28
3.9	29
4.0	29

1. Write the ordered pairs from the table that show the ACT composite score as a function of the person's GPA.

2. Create a scatter plot of the ordered pairs on the grid on the next page. Because the data points are clustered together, break the graph on the *x*-axis. Complete the bounds and intervals table provided below. Be sure to label your graph clearly.

Variable quantity	Lower bound	Upper bound	Interval
	3.1	4.5	
	0	30	

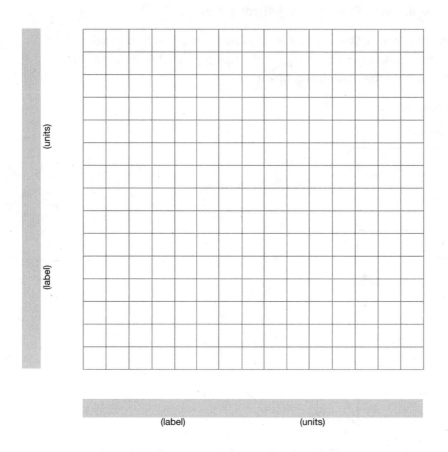

(units)

(label)

(label)   (units)

3. What is the advantage of using a graph with a break in it? Use a complete sentence in your answer.

4. What is the disadvantage of using a graph with a break in it? Use a complete sentence in your answer.

5. Use a ruler to draw the line of best fit. Then, write the equation of your line. Define your variables.

6

6. Use your equation to predict the ACT composite score of a student with a GPA of 2.9. Show all your work and use a complete sentence in your answer.

7. Use your equation to predict the GPA of a student with an ACT composite score of 20. Show all your work and use a complete sentence in your answer.

8. Describe the correlation of the data displayed in the graph in Question 2. Use complete sentences to explain your reasoning.

9. Your teacher asks you to use a graphing calculator to find the linear regression equation for this data. In addition to the linear regression equation, the calculator produces a correlation coefficient of 0.8671959024. Use a complete sentence to explain what this number tells you about the data.

10. Is a linear model the best model for the data below? Why or why not? Use a complete sentence in your answer.

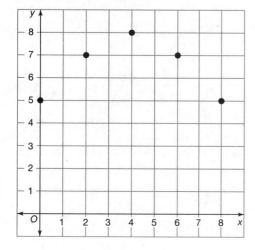

Standardized Test Practice

Name _____ Date _____

1. The data in the table show the cost of ordering DVDs from an online company, including the flat shipping fee.

Number of DVDs (n)	Cost in dollars (C)
3	11
6	17
10	25

What is the equation of the line that best fits the data if the number of DVDs n is graphed on the horizontal axis and the cost C is graphed on the vertical axis?

a. $C = 2n$

b. $C = 2n - 5$

c. $C = \frac{1}{2}n + 5$

d. $C = 2n + 5$

2. Your teacher asks you to make a scatter plot of the data below. He asks you to define time as the number of years since 1996. What number would you use for 2000?

Year	1996	1997	1998	1999	2000
Number of graduates	224	237	219	222	241

a. 2

b. 3

c. 4

d. 5

6

Read the scenario below. Use the scenario and graph to answer Questions 3 through 6.

A baseball coach would like to be able to predict the number of hits his players will get based on the number of times they are at bat. He graphs some data and finds the best fit line. The equation of the best fit line is $y = 0.32x - 20.51$, where x is the number of times at bat and y is the number of hits.

3. How many hits should he expect from a player who is at bat 175 times? Round your answer to the nearest whole number.

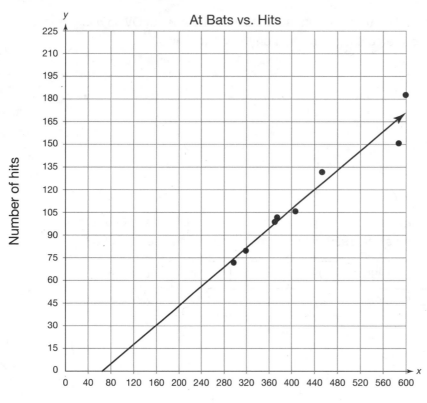

a. 35

b. 36

c. 76

d. 77

6

Name _____ Date _____

4. How many times is a player at bat if he has 200 hits? Round your answer to the nearest whole number.

   a. 560

   b. 561

   c. 689

   d. 690

5. In the best fit equation $y = 0.32x - 20.51$ from the baseball scenario, what does the slope mean?

   a. The increase in the number of hits for each time at bat

   b. The decrease in the number of hits for each time at bat

   c. The increase in the number of times at bat for each hit

   d. The decrease in the number of times at bat for each hit

6. In the best fit equation $y = 0.32x - 20.51$ from the baseball scenario, what does the y-intercept mean?

   a. The number of times at bat for zero hits

   b. The number of hits for zero times at bat

   c. The number of hits for each time at bat

   d. The number of times at bat before getting one hit

7. Which of the following is NOT an advantage of using a graph with a break in it?

   a. You can see all the data.

   b. You can see the y-intercept.

   c. You can easily draw a line of best fit.

   d. You can more easily determine the slope of the line.

6

8. Do the points in the scatter plot have a positive correlation, a negative correlation, or no correlation?

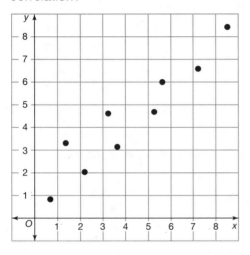

   a. positive correlation

   b. negative correlation

   c. no correlation

9. If a line of best fit models the data very well, what would you expect to see in a graph of the data and the line?

   a. The line has a positive slope.

   b. The line has a negative slope.

   c. The line is very close to all of the points.

   d. The line is close to some of the points but not very close to other points.

10. You enter data into a graphing calculator to find the linear regression equation. In addition to producing the equation, the calculator produces a correlation coefficient. Which of the following correlation coefficients would indicate that the data are NOT very close to forming a straight line?

   a. −0.897854351

   b. 0.089785435

   c. 0.897854351

   d. 0.978543518

Cumulative Test

Name _____ Date _____

Use the sequence below to answer Questions 1 and 2.

Term (*n*)	1	2	3	4	5
Sequence	−3	−1	1	3	5

1. Write an expression for the *n*th term and describe the pattern. Use a complete sentence in your answer.

2. Use the expression you wrote in Question 1 to find the 20th term of the sequence. Show all your work.

Read the scenario below. Use the scenario to answer Questions 3 through 5.

The student council at your school wants to start an intramural basketball league. During half time of a basketball game, you survey 40 students in each grade to see if they would be interested in playing in an intramural league. You found that 21 freshmen, 37 sophomores, 31 juniors, and 19 seniors said that they would be interested in playing in the intramural league.

3. Write a ratio that shows the relationship between the number of sophomores that are interested in playing in the league and the total number of sophomores that were surveyed.

4. There are 243 sophomores at your school. Use the ratio you wrote in Question 3 to determine how many of them would be interested in playing in the intramural basketball league. Show all your work and use a complete sentence in your answer.

1–6

5. Was your survey biased? Use a complete sentence to explain your reasoning.

6. Your uncle takes you and your friends out to eat to celebrate your graduation. The total bill for everyone's dinner is $214.72. Your uncle would like to leave a 20% tip because the service was so good. How much should he leave? Show all your work and use a complete sentence in your answer.

Solve each equation. Show all your work.

7. $-3x + 4 = -8$

8. $\dfrac{x}{5} - 7 = 4$

9. Evaluate $f(x) = -3x - 9$ at $x = -4$. Show all your work.

1–6

Name _____ Date _____

10. You recently joined an online book-on-CD club so that you can rent books on CD.
The membership fee is $45 and each rental is $4 which covers shipping and handling.

    a. Write an equation that gives the total cost in terms of the number of rentals.
    Use x to represent the number of rentals and y to represent the total cost.

    b. Does this equation represent a function? If so, identify the domain and range in terms
    of this real-life situation. If not, explain why. Use complete sentences in your answer.

11. Write the repeating decimal 0.2222... as a fraction. Show all your work.

12. Solve the following equation. Show all your work.

    $-2(x - 18) = 4(4x - 9)$

13. Solve the following inequality. Then, graph your solution. Show all your work.

$-5x + 8 \geq 43$

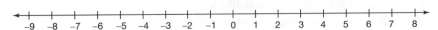

14. Solve the following inequality. Then, graph your solution. Show all your work.

$|3x - 6| < 12$

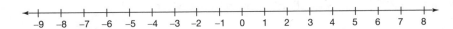

15. Find the x- and y-intercepts of the graph below.

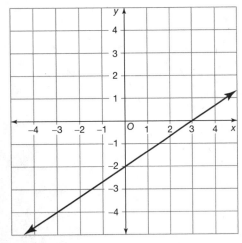

x-intercept: _____

y-intercept: _____

1–6

16. Algebraically find the *x*- and *y*-intercepts of the graph of the equation $2x + 7y = 28$. Show all your work.

x-intercept: _____

y-intercept: _____

Read the scenario below. Use the scenario to answer Questions 17 and 18.

Donna has started her own clowning business. For a fee of $12 per hour, people can hire her to come to a party to make balloon animals and do magic tricks. To get her business started, Donna borrows $20 from her parents for supplies.

17. Write an equation that gives Donna's profit in terms of the number of hours she works. Use *x* to represent the number of hours and use *y* to represent Donna's profit after she pays her parents back.

18. What does the *y*-intercept mean in terms of the problem situation? Use a complete sentence in your answer.

19. Write the equation of a line in slope-intercept form that has a slope of $-\dfrac{2}{9}$ and passes through the point (18, 5). Show all your work.

20. Write the equation of a line in slope-intercept form that passes through the points (–4, 6) and (8, 12). Show all your work.

21. Identify the slope and *y*-intercept of the equation $y = \dfrac{2}{5}x - 6$, and use them to graph the equation on the grid below.

slope: _____

y-intercept: _____

1–6

Name _____ Date _____

22. Write the equation $y = -\dfrac{3}{11}x + 6$ in standard form. Show all your work.

23. Write the equation $-7x + 9y = 54$ in slope-intercept form. Show all your work.

Read the scenario below. Use the scenario and data to answer Questions 24 through 29.

Mr. Lane is a new English teacher, and he is deciding which books he would like to have his students read over the course of the year. He wants to predict how long it will take the students to read a book based on the length of the book. Mr. Lane asks several students to read books of varying length and record the amount of time it takes them to read the book.

Number of pages	Time
pages	hours
275	3.4
324	4.5
189	2.5
202	2.75
236	3.4
357	5.5
148	2.2
218	3.2

1-6

24. Write the ordered pairs from the table that show time as a function of the number of pages.

25. Create a scatter plot of the ordered pairs on the grid below. Break the graph on the *x*-axis, so that the points will be more spread out. Complete the bounds and intervals table provided below. Be use to label your graph clearly.

Variable quantity	Lower bound	Upper bound	Interval
	95	375	
	0.0	6.0	

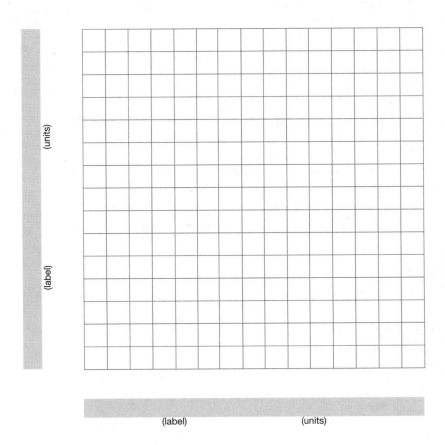

(units)

(label)

(label)   (units)

26. Use a ruler to draw a line that best fits the data in your graph. Then, write the equation of the line. Be sure to define your variables and include units.

1–6

27. What does the slope of the line mean in terms of the problem situation? Use a complete sentence in your answer.

28. Use the equation you wrote in Question 26 to predict how long it will take to read a book that is 423 pages. Show all your work and round your answer to the nearest tenth, if necessary. Use a complete sentence in your answer.

29. Use the equation you wrote in Question 26 to predict how many pages a book has if it takes 2.8 hours to read. Show all your work and round your answer to the nearest whole number, if necessary. Use a complete sentence in your answer.

Section 2
Assessments with Answers
Chapters 1–6

Pre-Test

Name _____ Date _____

Find the next two terms of each sequence.

1.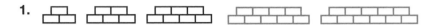

2. 2, 4, 8, 16, 32, <u> 64 </u> , <u> 128 </u>

3. Use the *n*th term to list the first five terms of the sequence. Show your work.

   $a_n = 2n + 4$

   $a_1 =$ <u>2(1) + 4 = 6</u>

   $a_2 =$ <u>2(2) + 4 = 8</u>

   $a_3 =$ <u>2(3) + 4 = 10</u>

   $a_4 =$ <u>2(4) + 4 = 12</u>

   $a_5 =$ <u>2(5) + 4 = 14</u>

Use the sequence below to answer Questions 4 through 6.

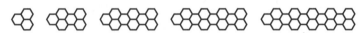

4. Complete the table by filling in the number of hexagons in each term of the sequence.

Term (*n*)	1	2	3	4	5
Number of hexagons	3	6	9	12	15

5. Write an expression showing the relationship between the term and the number of hexagons in that term. Let *n* represent the term.

   3*n*

6. Use the expression from Question 5 to find the 10th term of the sequence. Show your work.

   3(10) = 30

7. Write the power as a product.

   3^4

   3(3)(3)(3)

1

8. Write the product as a power.

   7(7)(7)(7)(7)(7)(7)(7)

   7^8

9. Perform the indicated operations. Show your work.

   $4^2 + (8 - 3)6$

   $16 + (5)6 = 16 + 30$

   $\qquad\qquad = 46$

10. You and your classmates have set up a phone chain to call each other if school is cancelled due to bad weather. You call two classmates, then each of them calls two classmates, and so on until everyone in your class has been notified. There are 31 students in your class. Draw a diagram to show how each student would be reached to be notified of school cancellations.

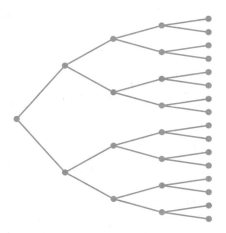

11. Find the sum of the numbers from 1 to 10. Show your work.

   $1 + 2 + 3 + 4 + 5 + 6 + 7 + 8 + 9 + 10 = 55$ OR $\dfrac{10(11)}{2} = 55$

12. Write an expression for the sum of the numbers 1 to n.

   $\dfrac{n(n + 1)}{2}$

Name _____ Date _____

Read the scenario below. Use the scenario to answer Questions 13 through 16.

The Spanish Club at your school is selling animal piñatas to raise money for a trip to Mexico City. The club earns $3 for each piñata sold. The sale runs for five weeks. The number of piñatas sold each week are 15, 22, 8, 35, and 42.

13. Make a table to show the number of piñatas sold and the profit made for each week of the sale.

Week	Number of piñatas	Profit
	piñatas	dollars
Week 1	15	45
Week 2	22	66
Week 3	8	24
Week 4	35	105
Week 5	42	126

14. Create a bar graph to display the profit for each week of the sale.

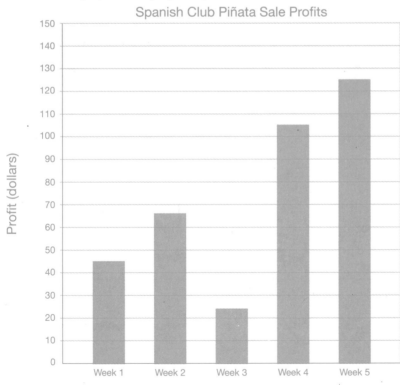

1

15. Create a graph to display the relationship between the number of piñatas sold and the profit. First, choose your bounds and intervals. Be sure to label your graph clearly.

Variable quantity	Lower bound	Upper bound	Interval
Number of piñatas	0	45	3
Profit	0	150	10

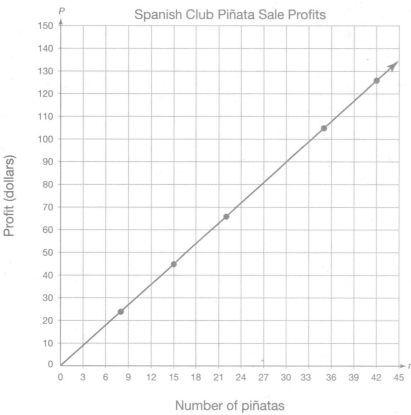

Spanish Club Piñata Sale Profits

Profit (dollars)

Number of piñatas

16. Write an algebraic equation that you could use to show the profit for any number of piñatas sold.

Sample Answer: $P = 3n$, where P is profit and n is the number of piñatas sold.

Name _____ Date _____

Read the scenario below. Use the scenario to answer Questions 17 and 18.

Two airlines offer special group rates to your school's Spanish Club for the trip to Mexico City. The Mexican Air airline offers a roundtrip airfare of $250 per person. The Fiesta airline offers a roundtrip airfare of $150 per person if the club agrees to pay a one time group rate processing fee of $1000.

17. Which airline offers the better deal if only nine students from the Spanish Club are able to fly to Mexico City? Show all your work and use complete sentences to explain your answer.

   Mexican Air: Fiesta:
   Total cost in dollars: 250(9) = 2250   150(9) + 1000 = 2350

   The total cost for nine students on Mexican Air is $2250, and the total cost for nine students on Fiesta is $2350. Therefore, Mexican Air offers a better deal if only nine students are able to fly to Mexico City.

18. Which airline offers the better deal if 20 students are able to fly to Mexico City? Show all your work and use complete sentences to explain your answer.

   Mexican Air: Fiesta:
   Total cost in dollars: 250(20) = 5000   150(20) + 1000 = 4000

   The total cost for 20 students on Mexican Air is $5000, and the total cost for 20 students on Fiesta is $4000. Therefore, Fiesta Airline offers a better deal if 20 students are able to fly to Mexico City.

Post-Test

Name _____ Date _____

Find the next two terms in each sequence.

1.

2. 4, 7, 10, 13, __16__ , __19__

3. Use the *n*th term to list the first five terms of the sequence. Show your work.

    $a_n = 3n + 5$

    $a_1 =$ __3(1) + 5 = 8__

    $a_2 =$ __3(2) + 5 = 11__

    $a_3 =$ __3(3) + 5 = 14__

    $a_4 =$ __3(4) + 5 = 17__

    $a_5 =$ __3(5) + 5 = 20__

Use the sequence below to answer Questions 4 through 6.

4. Complete the table by filling in the number of triangles in each term of the sequence.

Terms	1	2	3	4	5
Number of triangles	2	3	4	5	6

5. Write an expression showing the relationship between the term and the number of triangles in that term. Let *n* represent the term.

    n + 1

6. Use the expression from Question 5 to find the 10th term of the sequence. Show your work.

    10 + 1 = 11

7. Write the power as a product.

    5^6

    5(5)(5)(5)(5)(5)

1

8. Write the product as a power.

    3(3)(3)(3)(3)(3)(3)(3)(3)

    3^9

9. Perform the indicated operations. Show your work.

    $(2 + 1)^3 - 5(2)$

    $3^3 - 10 = 27 - 10$

    $\qquad\ \ = 17$

10. You and your classmates have set up an email chain to notify each other if school is cancelled due to bad weather. You email three classmates, then each of them emails three classmates, and so on until everyone in your class has been notified. There are 31 students in your class. Draw a diagram to show how each student would be reached to be notified of school cancellations.

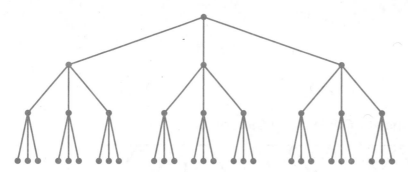

11. Find the sum of the numbers 1 to 200. Show your work.

    $\dfrac{200(201)}{2} = 20{,}100$

12. Write an expression for the sum of the numbers 1 to n.

    $\dfrac{n(n + 1)}{2}$

Post-Test PAGE 3

Name _____ Date _____

Read the scenario below. Use the scenario to answer Questions 13 through 16.

A local ballet company is selling tickets for their upcoming performances of Swan Lake. The company earns $8 on each ticket they sell. The first week that tickets are on sale, they sell 30 tickets on Monday, 27 on Tuesday, 18 on Wednesday, 6 on Thursday, and 41 tickets on Friday.

13. Make a table to show the number of tickets sold each day during the first week and the profit made on each of those days.

Day	Number of tickets	Profit
	tickets	dollars
Monday	30	240
Tuesday	27	216
Wednesday	18	144
Thursday	6	48
Friday	41	328

14. Create a bar graph to display the profit for each day of ticket sales in the first week.

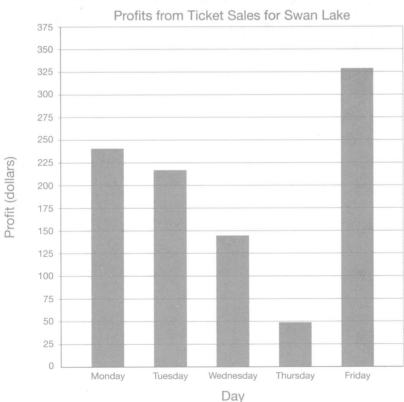

1

15. Create a graph to display the relationship between the number of tickets sold and the profit. First, choose your bounds and intervals. Be sure to label your graph clearly.

Variable quantity	Lower bound	Upper bound	Interval
Number of tickets	0	45	3
Profit (dollars)	0	375	25

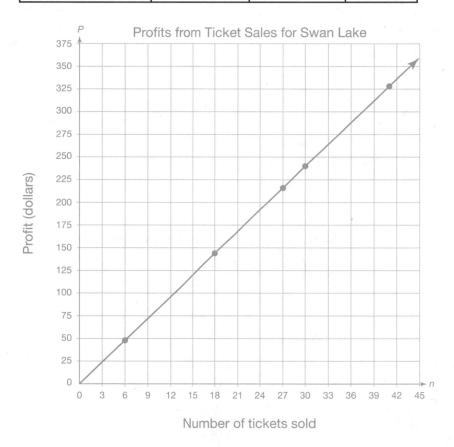

Profits from Ticket Sales for Swan Lake

16. Write an algebraic equation that you could use to show the profit for any number of tickets sold.

Sample Answer: $P = 8n$, where P is profit and n is the number of tickets sold.

Name _____ Date _____

1

Read the scenario below. Use the scenario to answer Questions 17 and 18.

The director of the local ballet company needs to print the programs for Swan Lake. Janet's Print Shop charges $.25 a program plus a $35 set-up fee. The Printing Press charges $.18 a program plus a $50 set-up fee.

17. Which printing company offers the better deal if 200 programs are printed? Show your work and use complete sentences to explain your answer.

Janet's Print Shop: The Printing Press:
Total cost in dollars: 0.25(200) + 35 = 85   0.18(200) + 50 = 86

The total cost for printing 200 programs at Janet's Print Shop is $85, and the total cost for printing 200 programs at The Printing Press is $86. Therefore, Janet's Print Shop offers a better deal if 200 programs are printed.

18. Which printing company offers the better deal if 300 programs are printed? Show your work and use complete sentences to explain your answer.

Janet's Print Shop: The Printing Press:
Total cost in dollars: 0.25(300) + 35 = 110 0.18(300) + 50 = 104

The total cost for printing 300 programs at Janet's Print Shop is $110, and the total cost for printing 300 programs at The Printing Press is $104. Therefore, The Printing Press offers a better deal if 300 programs are printed.

Mid-Chapter Test

Name _____ Date _____

Read the scenario below. Use the scenario to complete Questions 1 through 8.

A local concrete company has hired you for the summer. Your first project is to help pour a driveway. Before you can pour the driveway, you must put wood forms in place to hold the concrete until it is dry. The first form in a driveway is made by constructing a square out of four 2 × 4's that are each ten feet long. The second form is made by using one side of the first form and three other 2 × 4's to make a second square. This process is continued to the end of the driveway. The diagrams show the first two steps in completing the form.

Step 1   Step 2

1. Draw a diagram that shows steps 3, 4, and 5 in the form construction.

    Step 3

    Step 4

    Step 5

2. The completed driveway will be 80 feet long. The company would refer to this as an eight-form driveway. Draw a diagram that shows what the completed form will look like. (Hint: Draw the eighth step in the form construction.)

3. The company needs to know the number of 2 × 4's needed to complete the driveway. They will also need to know the area of the driveway in order to properly bill their clients. Complete the table to help organize this information.

Number of forms	1	2	3	4	5	6
Number of 2 × 4's	4	7	10	13	16	19
Area (square feet)	100	200	300	400	500	600

4. Write the sequence of numbers formed by the area of one form, two forms, three forms, and so on. Use a complete sentence to describe the pattern produced by the area.

   100, 200, 300, 400, 500, 600, ...

   Sample Answer: Add 100 to the previous term to get the next term.

5. Use a complete sentence to describe the relationship between the number of forms and the number of 2 × 4's required to complete the forms.

   Sample Answer: Multiply the number of forms by 3 and then add 1 to get the number of 2 × 4's needed.

6. Write an expression that gives the number of 2 × 4's needed to complete a driveway with n forms.

   Sample answer: $3n + 1$

7. Use your expression from Question 6 to determine the number of 2 × 4's needed for a 12-form driveway. Show your work.

   $3(12) + 1 = 37$

8. a. Write the sequence of numbers formed by the number of 2 × 4's.

   4, 7, 10, 13, 16, 19, ...

   b. Find the 10th term of this sequence. Show your work.

   $3(10) + 1 = 31$

   c. Use a complete sentence to explain what the 10th term represents.

   The 10th term represents the number of 2 x 4's it would take to make the forms for a 10-form driveway.

Mid-Chapter Test   PAGE 3

Name _____ Date _____

Write each power as a product.

9. 7^4

7(7)(7)(7)

10. 12^6

12(12)(12)(12)(12)(12)

Write each product as a power.

11. 15(15)(15)(15)(15)

15^5

12. 6(6)(6)(6)(6)(6)(6)(6)(6)

6^9

Perform the indicated operations. Show your work.

13. $(6 - 3)^3 + 2(1 + 4)$

$3^3 + 2(5) = 27 + 10$

$= 37$

14. $25 - (3 + 5) + 2^4$

$25 - 8 + 16 = 17 + 16$

$= 33$

Evaluate each expression for the given value of the variable. Show your work.

15. Evaluate $2r + 8$ when r is 12.

$2(12) + 8 = 24 + 8$

$= 32$

16. Evaluate $\dfrac{t}{4}$ when t is 36.

$\dfrac{36}{4} = 9$

17. Use the nth term to list the first five terms of the sequence. Show your work.

$a_n = 20 - 2n$

$a_1 =$ _20 − 2(1) = 18_

$a_2 =$ _20 − 2(2) = 16_

$a_3 =$ _20 − 2(3) = 14_

$a_4 =$ _20 − 2(4) = 12_

$a_5 =$ _20 − 2(5) = 10_

1

Read the scenario below. Use the scenario to answer Questions 18 through 20.

A local college has decided to build new sidewalks to connect the main administration building to the other buildings on campus. They can only build two new sidewalks a month. It will take 6 months to connect the administration building to all of the other buildings on campus. The diagrams show the number of sidewalks that have been built after 1, 2, and 3 months.

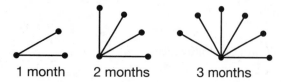

1 month   2 months   3 months

18. Draw diagrams that would represent the number of sidewalks after 4, 5, and 6 months.

    4 months   5 months   6 months

19. Complete the table to show your results.

Number of months	1	2	3	4	5	6
Number of sidewalks	2	4	6	8	10	12

20. The college wants to put in sidewalks connecting the library to the other buildings on campus. There is already a sidewalk connecting the library to the main administration building. How many more sidewalks will need to be built in order to connect the library to the remaining buildings on campus?

11

21. Write an algebraic expression to find the sum of the numbers from 1 to n.

$$\frac{n(n + 1)}{2}$$

22. Use your answer to Question 21 to find the sum of the numbers from 1 to 85.
Show your work.

$$\frac{85(85 + 1)}{1} = \frac{85(86)}{2}$$

$$= \frac{7310}{2}$$

$$= 3655$$

End of Chapter Test

Name _____ Date _____

For each sequence, find the next two terms and describe the pattern.

1. 3, 8, 13, 18, 23, __28__ , __33__

    Add 5 to the previous term to find the next term.

2. 3, 9, 27, 81, __243__ , __−729__

    Multiply the previous term by 3 to find the next term.

3.

    Start with the previous term. Draw a concentric circle around the other circles to find the next term.

4.

    Start with the previous term. Add of row a triangles below the figure to find the next term.

For each sequence, find the expression for the *n*th term and describe the pattern.

5.

Term (*n*)	1	2	3	4	5
Sequence	5	15	25	35	45

    The expression is $10n - 5$, so multiply the term number (*n*) by 10 and then subtract 5.

6.

Term (*n*)	1	2	3	4	5
Sequence	5	25	125	625	3125

    The expression is $5n$, so raise 5 to the power of the term number (*n*).

End of Chapter Test PAGE 2

7. Write the power as a product.

5^4

5(5)(5)(5)

8. Write the product as a power.

8(8)(8)

8^3

Use the nth term to list the first five terms of each sequence. Show your work.

9. $a_n = \dfrac{3(n+1)}{2}$

$a_1 = \dfrac{3(1+1)}{2} = 3$

$a_2 = \dfrac{3(2+1)}{2} = \dfrac{9}{2}$

$a_3 = \dfrac{3(3+1)}{2} = 6$

$a_4 = \dfrac{3(4+1)}{2} = \dfrac{15}{2}$

$a_5 = \dfrac{3(5+1)}{2} = 9$

10. $a_n = (n-1)^2 + 3$

$a_1 = (1-1)^2 + 3 = 3$

$a_2 = (2-1)^2 + 3 = 4$

$a_3 = (3-1)^2 + 3 = 7$

$a_4 = (4-1)^2 + 3 = 12$

$a_5 = (5-1)^2 + 3 = 19$

Read the scenario below. Use the scenario to answer Questions 11 through 23.

You are a volunteer for the school store. One of the most popular items is strawberry-banana-orange juice. There are two local vendors that will deliver the juice to the school store at the beginning of every month. Healthy Drinks, Inc. charges $.39 per bottle with a delivery fee of $25. The Squeeze charges $.18 per bottle with a delivery fee of $65.

11. You want to stock the store with juice at the beginning of the school year. How much will it cost to purchase 300 bottles of strawberry-banana-orange juice from Healthy Drinks, Inc.? Show your work and use a complete sentence in your answer.

Cost for 300 bottles of strawberry-banana-orange juice: 0.39(300) + 25 = 142

It will cost $142 to purchase 300 bottles of strawberry-banana-orange juice from Healthy Drinks, Inc.

12. How much will it cost to purchase 300 bottles of strawberry-banana-orange juice from The Squeeze? Show your work and use a complete sentence in your answer.

Cost for 300 bottles of strawberry-banana-orange juice: 0.18(300) + 65 = 119

It will cost $119 to purchase 300 bottles of strawberry-banana-orange juice from The Squeeze.

Name _____ Date _____

1

13. Complete the table summarizing the cost of purchasing strawberry-banana-orange juice from each vendor based on last year's actual monthly sales. Remember to label units.

Month	Number of bottles of juice purchased	Cost of purchasing from Healthy Drinks, Inc.	Cost of purchasing from The Squeeze
	bottles	dollars	dollars
September	187	97.93	98.66
October	229	114.31	106.22
November	162	88.18	94.16
December	137	78.43	89.66
January	171	91.69	95.78
February	201	103.39	101.18
March	192	99.88	99.56
April	258	125.62	111.44
May	214	108.46	103.52
June	79	55.81	79.22

14. Let C represent the cost of purchasing bottles of juice from Healthy Drinks, Inc. and b represent the number of bottles. Write an equation that relates C and b for this problem situation.

$C = 0.39b + 25$

15. Let C represent the cost of purchasing bottles of juice from The Squeeze and b represent the number of bottles. Write an equation that relates C and b for this problem situation.

$C = 0.18b + 65$

16. What was the average number of bottles of juice sold in a month last year? Show your work and use a complete sentence in your answer.

Average number of bottles of juice sold in a month: $1830 \div 10 = 183$

The average number of bottles of juice sold in a month was 183 bottles.

1

17. Create a bar graph to display the costs of purchasing strawberry-banana-orange juice from Healthy Drinks, Inc. each month.

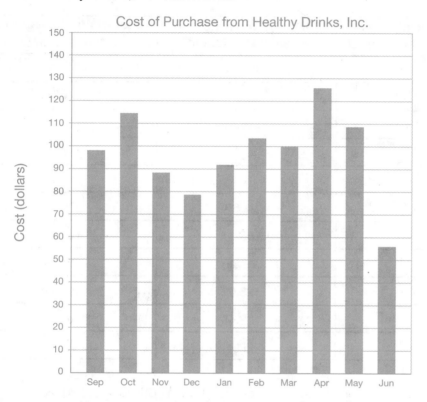

18. Create a graph displaying the cost of purchasing strawberry-banana-orange juice from both Healthy Drinks, Inc. and The Squeeze. First, choose your bounds and intervals. Be sure to label your graph clearly.

Variable quantity	Lower bound	Upper bound	Interval
Juice	0	300	20
Cost	0	150	10

© 2006 Carnegie Learning, Inc.

Name _____   Date _____

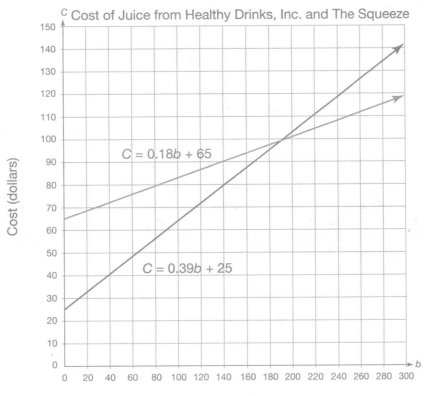

19. Estimate the number of bottles of juice for which the total costs for each company are the same and explain how you found your answer. Use complete sentences in your answer.

Sample Answer: The total costs are about the same when about 190 bottles of juice are purchased. The total costs are the same where the lines intersect each other on the graph. To find this number, start at the point of intersection and move straight down to the horizontal axis to read the number of bottles of juice for this total cost.

20. For how many bottles of juice is Healthy Drinks, Inc. more expensive to order from? Use a complete sentence in your answer.

Healthy Drinks, Inc. is more expensive to order from when you order more than 190 bottles of juice.

1

21. For how many bottles of juice is The Squeeze more expensive to order from? Use a complete sentence in your answer.

    The Squeeze is more expensive to order from when you order 190 or fewer bottles of juice.

22. The faculty sponsor who is responsible for the school store has asked you to write a report that compares the costs of ordering from each vendor. She would also like you to make a recommendation about which vendor you would choose if you had to order from the same vendor for the entire school year. Use complete sentences in your answer.

    Sample Answer: The total cost is the same when approximately 190 bottles of juice are purchased. If you purchase 190 or less bottles, Healthy Drinks, Inc. is cheaper. If you purchase more than 190 bottles, The Squeeze is cheaper. Because the average number of bottles sold each month last year is 183, I would recommend Healthy Drinks, Inc. as the vendor for the entire school year.

23. If you were able to choose a different vendor each month, would you? Explain your answer using complete sentences.

    Answers will vary.

Standardized Test Practice

Name _____ Date _____

1. Which choice shows the next two terms in the sequence?

   1, 101, 2, 102, 3, 103, …

   a. 4 and 140

   b. 4 and 401

   c. 4 and 104

   d. 4 and 114

2. Which choice shows the next two terms in the sequence?

   a. ☺ ☺ ◁ ☺ ☺ ♡

   b. ☺ ☺ ♡ ☺ ☺ ◁

   c. ☺ ☺ ◁ ☺ ☺ ▷

   d. ☺ ☺ ♡ ☺ ☺ ▷

3. Which statement describes the pattern?

   −1, 10, −100, 1000, …

   a. Start with the previous term, and multiply by 10 to get the next term.

   b. Start with the previous term, and add a zero to get the next term.

   c. Start with the previous term, and multiply by 100 to get the next term.

   d. Start with the previous term, and multiply by −10 to get the next term.

4. Simplify $5^2 - (3 + 6) + \dfrac{14}{7}$.

   a. −1

   b. 3

   c. 14

   d. 18

1

5. Which expression is equivalent to 4^6?

    a. 4(6)

    b. 4(4)(4)(4)(4)(4)

    c. 6(6)(6)(6)

    d. 46

6. How many cups of flour are needed for 10 loaves of bread?

Loaves of bread	1	2	3	4	5
Cups of flour	2	4	6	8	10

    a. 12

    b. 16

    c. 20

    d. 24

7. Evaluate $3p + 5$ when $p = 6$.

    a. 14

    b. 18

    c. 23

    d. 41

8. Which expression represents the nth term of the sequence?

Term (n)	1	2	3	4	5
Sequence	6	13	20	27	34

    a. $7n - 1$

    b. $7n$

    c. $6n$

    d. $n + 7$

Name _____ Date _____

1

9. Which number represents a_4?

 $a_n = 2n + 4$

 a. 6

 b. 8

 c. 10

 (d.) 12

10. A family of 8 has just signed a contract for a new cellular phone service so that they can call each other for free. To try it out, each person in the family calls every other person once unless that person has already called them. How many calls does the family make?

 a. 10

 b. 15

 c. 21

 (d.) 28

11. What is the sum of the numbers 1 to 300?

 a. 301

 b. 4515

 (c.) 45,150

 d. 300,001

12. The average speed of an airplane is 325 miles per hour. Which expression shows the distance in miles an airplane could travel in n hours?

 a. $\dfrac{325}{n}$

 (b.) $325n$

 c. $325 + n$

 d. $\dfrac{n}{325}$

1

13. James earns $6.25 an hour at work. The table shows his hours and earnings for each week in one month. Which graph correctly displays the relationship between hours worked and earnings?

Week	Time worked	Earnings
	hours	dollars
Week 1	15	93.75
Week 2	18	112.50
Week 3	12	75
Week 4	13	81.25

a.

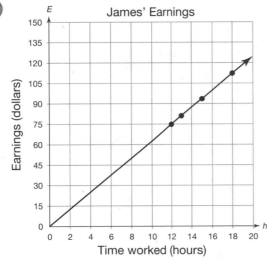

b.

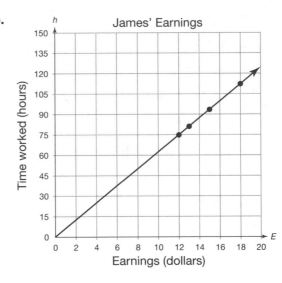

c.

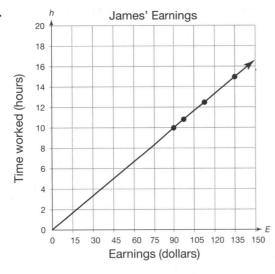

d.

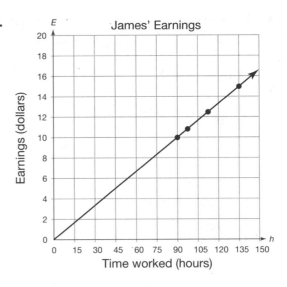

Name _____ Date _____

14. James earns $6.25 an hour at work. The table in Question 13 shows his hours and earnings for each week in one month. Which bar graph correctly displays the relationship between the week and the time worked?

a.
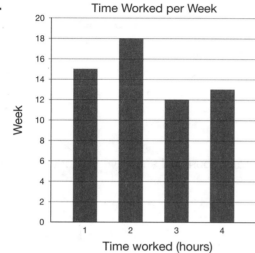

b.
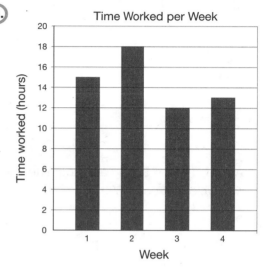

c.
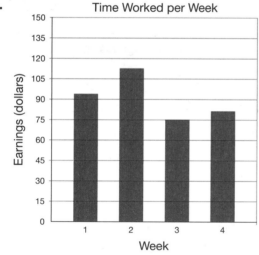

d.
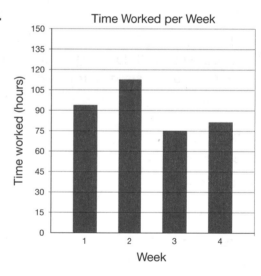

1

15. James earns $6.25 an hour at work. Which algebraic equation shows the amount of money E that James earns in n hours?

   a. $E = 6.25 + n$

   b. $E = \dfrac{6.25}{n}$

   c. $n = 6.25E$

   d. $E = 6.25n$

16. Angelica earns $7.50 each hour she works. How many hours will she have to work to buy a bicycle that costs $90?

   a. 6

   b. 9

   c. 12

   d. 15

17. Angelica earns $7.50 each hour she works. How much money will Angelica earn if she works for 6 hours and 12 minutes?

   a. $45

   b. $46.50

   c. $46.75

   d. $135

18. T-Shirts & More Print Shop will print any image on a Frisbee for a cost of $2 per Frisbee and a one-time charge of $12 to set up the Frisbee design. The total cost of an order was $562. How many Frisbees were printed?

   a. 47

   b. 275

   c. 281

   d. 550

Name _____ Date _____

1

19. T-Shirts & More Print Shop will print any image on a Frisbee for a cost of $2 per Frisbee and a one-time charge of $12 to set up the Frisbee design. Which algebraic equation shows the cost C of printing f Frisbees?

    a. $C = 2f$

    b. $C = 12f + 2$

    c. $f = 2C + 12$

    d. $C = 2f + 12$

20. T-Shirts & More Print Shop will print any image on a Frisbee for a cost of $2 per Frisbee and a one-time charge of $12 to set up the Frisbee design. You Say It, We Print It will print any image on a Frisbee for a cost of $5 per Frisbee and no set-up fee. Which statement is true?

    a. You Say It, We Print It is a better buy if you purchase more than four Frisbees.

    b. T-Shirts & More Print Shop is always the better buy.

    c. You Say It, We Print It is always the better buy.

    d. T-Shirts & More Print Shop is the better buy if you purchase more than four Frisbees.

Pre-Test

Name _____ Date _____

Use the table below to answer Questions 1 through 3.

Grade	Blue eyes	Brown eyes	Other
8	13	14	3
9	5	18	7
10	9	8	13
11	2	25	3
Total number of students	29	65	26

1. How many students were surveyed? Use a complete sentence in your answer.

   One hundred twenty students were surveyed.

2. Write the ratio of the number of blue-eyed students to the number of students surveyed. Write the ratio two different ways.

   $\dfrac{29 \text{ students}}{120 \text{ students}}$; 29 students : 120 students

3. Write the ratio of the number of brown-eyed students in the 9th grade to the total number of brown-eyed students. Write the ratio two different ways.

   $\dfrac{18 \text{ students}}{65 \text{ students}}$; 18 students : 65 students

Complete each proportion.

4. $\dfrac{4}{9} = \dfrac{\boxed{24}}{54}$

5. $\dfrac{16}{52} = \dfrac{4}{\boxed{13}}$

Solve each proportion using the products of the means and the extremes. Show all your work.

6. $\dfrac{2}{7} = \dfrac{x}{4221}$

   $7x = 2(4221)$

   $7x = 8442$

   $x = 1206$

7. $\dfrac{40}{576} = \dfrac{5}{x}$

   $576(5) = 40x$

   $2880 = 40x$

   $72 = x$

8. To make the color orange using food coloring, you must mix 2 drops of red and 3 drops of yellow. Write a ratio that compares the number of drops of red to the total number of drops. Then simplify the ratio, if possible.

$$\frac{2 \text{ drops of red}}{5 \text{ total drops}}$$

9. Write the given fractions in order from least to greatest. Show all your work and use a complete sentence in your answer.

$$\frac{3}{4}, \frac{5}{9}, \frac{1}{3}$$

$$\frac{3}{4} = \frac{27}{36}; \quad \frac{5}{9} = \frac{20}{36}; \quad \frac{1}{3} = \frac{12}{36}$$

The fractions in order from least to greatest are $\frac{1}{3}$, $\frac{5}{9}$, and $\frac{3}{4}$.

10. Bethany can run 1600 meters in 10 minutes. Write a rate to determine the number of meters Bethany can run in one minute.

$$\frac{1600 \text{ meters}}{10 \text{ minutes}} = \frac{160 \text{ meters}}{1 \text{ minute}}$$

11. Triangle ABC is similar to triangle DEF. What is the length of EF? Show all your work and use a complete sentence in your answer.

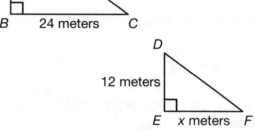

$$\frac{18 \text{ meters}}{24 \text{ meters}} = \frac{12 \text{ meters}}{x}$$

$$24(12) = 18x$$

$$288 = 18x$$

$$16 = x$$

The length of EF is 16 meters.

12. One mile is equal to 5280 feet. Use a proportion to determine the part of a mile is equivalent to 3960 feet. Show all your work and use a complete sentence in your answer.

$$\frac{1 \text{ mile}}{5280 \text{ feet}} = \frac{x}{3960 \text{ feet}}$$

$$5280x = 3960$$

$$x = 0.75$$

3960 feet is equivalent to 0.75 mile.

Name _____ Date _____

Use the data below for Questions 13 through 15.

Your school band has decided to sell pizza kits for a fundraiser.
The table at the right lists the relationship between the selling price
and the profit your band will make on those sales.

Selling price	Profit
dollars	dollars
6	4
9	6
12	8
15	10
18	12

13. Make a line graph that displays the relationship between the selling price of pizza kits and the profit.

Variable quantity	Lower bound	Upper bound	Interval
Selling price of pizza kits	0	30	2
Profit	0	15	1

Selling Price vs. Profit

$p = \frac{2}{3}s$

Profit (dollars)

Selling price (dollars)

2

14. Write an equation that shows the relationship between the selling price s and the profit p.

$$p = \frac{2}{3}s$$

15. Use your equation to predict the profit for a pizza kit that has a selling price of $24 dollars. Show all your work and use a complete sentence in your answer.

$$p = \frac{2}{3}s$$

$$p = \frac{2}{3}(24)$$

$$p = 16$$

A pizza kit that has a selling price of $24 will yield a profit of $16.

16. Solve the equation for a.

$$\frac{a}{b} = \frac{4}{9}$$

$$9a = 4b$$

$$a = \frac{4}{9}b$$

Write each percent as a fraction and as a decimal.

17. 30%

$$\frac{30}{100} = \frac{3}{10}; \, 0.3$$

18. 78%

$$\frac{78}{100} = \frac{39}{50}; \, 0.78$$

Write each fraction as a decimal and as a percent.

19. $\dfrac{29}{100}$

0.29; 29%

20. $\dfrac{37}{50}$

0.74; 74%

Name _____ Date _____

21. Your bill at a restaurant is $36. You leave a 15% tip. How much do you leave for a tip? Show all your work and use a complete sentence in your answer.

$$\frac{x}{36} = \frac{15}{100}$$

$36(15) = 100x$

$540 = 100x$

$5.4 = x$

You leave $5.40 for a tip.

Your gross pay is $450, and your net pay is $315.

22. How much do you pay in taxes? Show all your work and use a complete sentence in your answer.

$450 = 315 + t$

$135 = t$

You pay $135 in taxes.

23. What is the tax rate? Show all your work and use a complete sentence in your answer.

$$\frac{135}{450} = \frac{x}{100}$$

$450x = 13{,}500$

$x = 30$

The tax rate is 30%.

Post-Test

Name _____ Date _____

Use the table below to answer Questions 1 through 3.

Grade	Brunette	Blonde	Other
8	27	8	15
9	15	21	14
10	33	11	6
11	20	23	7
Total number of students	95	63	42

1. How many students were surveyed? Use a complete sentence in your answer.

   Two hundred students were surveyed.

2. Write the ratio of the number of blonde students to the number of students surveyed. Write the ratio two different ways.

   $\dfrac{63 \text{ students}}{200 \text{ students}}$; 63 students : 200 students

3. Write the ratio of the number of brunette students in the 10th grade to the total number of brunette students. Write the ratio two different ways.

   $\dfrac{33 \text{ students}}{95 \text{ students}}$; 33 students : 95 students

Complete each proportion.

4. $\dfrac{27}{63} = \dfrac{3}{\boxed{7}}$

5. $\dfrac{3}{5} = \dfrac{\boxed{12}}{20}$

Solve each proportion using the products of the means and the extremes. Show all your work.

6. $\dfrac{297}{x} = \dfrac{3}{11}$

   $3x = 11(297)$

   $3x = 3267$

   $x = 1089$

7. $\dfrac{35}{90} = \dfrac{x}{18}$

   $90x = 18(35)$

   $90x = 630$

   $x = 7$

8. To make pink paint, Tamika mixes 2 parts white paint and 5 parts red paint. Write a ratio that compares the number of parts of red paint to the total number of parts of paint. Then simplify the ratio, if possible.

$$\frac{5 \text{ parts red}}{7 \text{ total parts}}$$

9. Write the given fractions in order from least to greatest. Show all your work and use a complete sentence in your answer.

$$\frac{4}{9}, \frac{2}{5}, \frac{3}{7}$$

$$\frac{4}{9} = \frac{140}{315}; \quad \frac{2}{5} = \frac{126}{315}; \quad \frac{3}{7} = \frac{135}{315}$$

The fractions in order from least to greatest are $\frac{2}{5}$, $\frac{3}{7}$, and $\frac{4}{9}$.

10. Donald can ride his bicycle 63 miles in 3 hours. Write a rate to determine the number of miles Donald can ride in one hour.

$$\frac{63 \text{ miles}}{3 \text{ hours}} = \frac{21 \text{ miles}}{1 \text{ hour}}$$

11. Triangle *JKL* is similar to triangle *MNO*. What is the length of *MN*? Show all your work and use a complete sentence in your answer.

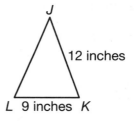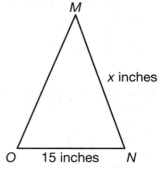

$$\frac{12 \text{ inches}}{9 \text{ inches}} = \frac{x}{15 \text{ inches}}$$

$$9x = 12(15)$$

$$9x = 180$$

$$x = 20$$

The length of *MN* is 20 inches.

12. One furlong is equal to 220 yards. Use a proportion to determine the part of a furlong is equivalent to 132 yards. Show all your work and use a complete sentence in your answer.

$$\frac{1 \text{ furlong}}{220 \text{ yards}} = \frac{x}{132 \text{ yards}}$$

$$220x = 132$$

$$x = 0.6$$

132 yards is equivalent to 0.6 furlong.

Post-Test PAGE 3

Name _____ Date _____

Use the data below for Questions 13 through 15.

A local store is raising money for cancer research by selling bracelets. They will donate part of their profit on the bracelet sales to a national cancer research facility. The table at the right lists the relationship between the profit from bracelet sales and the amount of money donated to cancer research.

Profit	Donation
dollars	dollars
5	3
10	6
15	9
20	12
25	15

13. Make a line graph that displays the relationship between the profit from the bracelet sales and the amount of money donated to cancer research.

Variable quantity	Lower bound	Upper bound	Interval
Profit from bracelet sales	0	30	2
Money donated	0	30	2

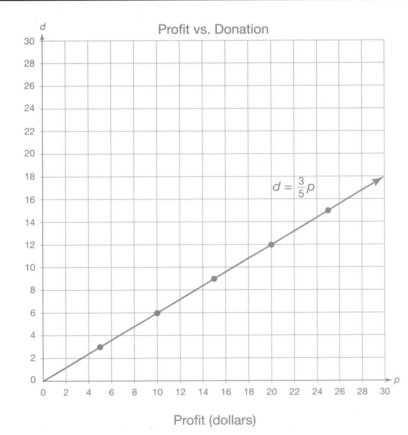

© 2006 Carnegie Learning, Inc.

14. Write an equation that shows the relationship between the profit *p* and the amount of money donated *d*.

$$d = \frac{3}{5}p$$

15. Use your equation to predict the amount of money donated if there is a $60 profit from bracelet sales. Show all your work and use a complete sentence in your answer.

$$d = \frac{3}{5}p$$

$$d = \frac{3}{5}(60)$$

$$d = 36$$

If there is a $60 profit from bracelet sales, $36 will be donated to cancer research.

16. Solve the equation for *b*.

$$\frac{a}{b} = \frac{7}{8}$$

$$8a = 7b$$

$$\frac{8}{7}a = b$$

Write each percent as a fraction and as a decimal.

17. 45%

$$\frac{45}{100} = \frac{9}{20}; 0.45$$

18. 75%

$$\frac{75}{100} = \frac{3}{4}; 0.75$$

Write each fraction as a decimal and as a percent.

19. $\frac{29}{100}$

0.29; 29%

20. $\frac{7}{10}$

0.7; 70%

Name _____ Date _____

21. Your bill at a restaurant is $42. You leave a 20% tip. How much do you leave for a tip? Show all your work and use a complete sentence in your answer.

$$\frac{x}{42} = \frac{20}{100}$$

$$42(20) = 100x$$

$$840 = 100x$$

$$8.4 = x$$

You leave $8.40 for a tip.

Your gross pay is $375, and your net pay is $255.

22. How much do you pay in taxes? Show all your work and use a complete sentence in your answer.

$$375 = 255 + t$$

$$120 = t$$

You pay $120 in taxes.

23. What is the tax rate? Show all your work and use a complete sentence in your answer.

$$\frac{120}{375} = \frac{x}{100}$$

$$375x = 12{,}000$$

$$x = 32$$

The tax rate is 32%.

Mid-Chapter Test

Name _____ Date _____

Use the table below to answer Questions 1 through 6.

The student council at your school is sponsoring a dance. Your advisor has asked you to survey a portion of the student body to determine the kind of music preferred for dancing. The results of your survey are given in the table below.

Grade	Hip-Hop	Country	Classic Rock
8	28	5	7
9	31	4	5
10	15	21	4
11	23	7	10
Total number of students	97	37	26

1. How many students were surveyed? Use a complete sentence in your answer.

   One hundred sixty students were surveyed.

2. Write the ratio of the number of students who prefer hip-hop music to the total number of students surveyed.

   $$\frac{97 \text{ students who prefer hip--hop}}{160 \text{ students surveyed}}$$

3. There are 960 students in your school. Use the results of the survey and a proportion to predict the number of students who prefer hip-hop music. Show all your work and use a complete sentence in your answer.

   $$\frac{97 \text{ students who prefer hip--hop}}{160 \text{ students surveyed}} = \frac{x \text{ students who prefer hip--hop}}{960 \text{ students}}$$

   $$160x = 97(960)$$
   $$160x = 93{,}120$$
   $$x = 582$$

   There are 582 students in your school who prefer hip-hop music.

4. Write the ratio of the number of 9th grade students who prefer classic rock to the total number of 9th grade students who were surveyed.

   $$\frac{5 \text{ students in 9th grade who prefer classic rock}}{40 \text{ 9th grade students surveyed}}$$

5. Your advisor tells you that there 248 students in the 9th grade. Use a proportion to find the number of students in the 9th grade that prefer classic rock. Show all your work and use a complete sentence in your answer.

$$\frac{5 \text{ 9th grade students who prefer classic rock}}{40 \text{ 9th grade students surveyed}} = \frac{x \text{ 9th grade students who prefer classic rock}}{248 \text{ 9th grade students surveyed}}$$

$$40x = 5(248)$$
$$40x = 1240$$
$$x = 31$$

There are 31 students in the 9th grade who prefer classic rock.

6. You formed the sample for your survey by asking random students in the cafeteria until you had surveyed 40 students from each grade. Explain what type of sampling method was used. Was your sample biased? Explain your answer with complete sentences.

Sample Answer: You used a convenience sampling method by selecting people who were easily accessible to you in the cafeteria at your lunch time. This sample is biased as it does not represent the population accurately. Students who have lunch at a different time than you or do not eat their lunch in the cafeteria were unable to be a part of the sample.

Read the scenario below. Use the scenario to answer Questions 7 through 9.

Dwayne is in culinary school. For one of his projects, he has to make a vinaigrette dressing which uses oil, vinegar, and a variety of seasonings. Before he adds the seasonings, he wants to determine which mixture of oil and vinegar is the best. The recipes of four oil and vinegar mixtures are given below.

Recipe 1	Recipe 2	Recipe 3	Recipe 4
2 parts oil	3 parts oil	4 parts oil	5 parts oil
5 parts vinegar	2 parts vinegar	6 parts vinegar	3 parts vinegar

7. For each recipe, write a ratio that compares the number of parts of vinegar to the total number of parts in each recipe. Then simplify each ratio if possible.

Recipe 1: $\dfrac{5 \text{ parts vinegar}}{7 \text{ total parts}}$

Recipe 2: $\dfrac{2 \text{ parts vinegar}}{5 \text{ total parts}}$

Recipe 3: $\dfrac{6 \text{ parts vinegar}}{10 \text{ total parts}} = \dfrac{3 \text{ parts vinegar}}{5 \text{ total parts}}$

Recipe 4: $\dfrac{3 \text{ parts vinegar}}{8 \text{ total parts}}$

Name _____ Date _____

8. Which recipe has the strongest taste of vinegar? Show all your work and use a complete sentence in your answer.

$$\frac{5}{7} = \frac{200}{280}; \quad \frac{2}{5} = \frac{112}{280}; \quad \frac{3}{5} = \frac{168}{280}; \quad \frac{3}{8} = \frac{105}{280}$$

Because $\frac{5}{7}$ is greater than $\frac{2}{5}$, $\frac{3}{5}$, and $\frac{3}{8}$, Recipe 1 has the strongest taste of vinegar.

9. Dwayne decides to use Recipe 2 as the base for his vinaigrette dressing. One of his professors likes Dwayne's vinaigrette dressing so well that he decides to serve it in his restaurant. He asks Dwayne to package it in 3-cup dressing bottles. He needs 50 bottles of the dressing.

   a. How many cups of vinaigrette dressing does Dwayne need to make? Show all your work and use a complete sentence in your answer.

   $3(50) = 150$

   Dwayne needs to make 150 cups of vinaigrette dressing.

   b. Write a rate to find the number of cups there are in one part of the recipe. Show all your work and use a complete sentence in your answer.

   $$\frac{150 \text{ cups}}{5 \text{ parts}} = \frac{30 \text{ cups}}{1 \text{ part}}$$

   There are 30 cups in one part of the recipe.

   c. How many cups of oil and vinegar are needed to make enough vinaigrette dressing for the restaurant? Show all your work and use a complete sentence in your answer.

   Number of cups of oil

   $$\frac{30 \text{ cups}}{1 \text{ part}} = \frac{x \text{ cups}}{3 \text{ parts}}$$

   $x = 90$

   Number of cups of vinegar

   $$\frac{30 \text{ cups}}{1 \text{ part}} = \frac{x \text{ cups}}{2 \text{ parts}}$$

   $x = 60 \text{ cups}$

   Dwayne needs 90 cups of oil and 60 cups of vinegar to make enough vinaigrette dressing for the restaurant.

10. Triangles *QRS* and *TUV* are similar. Use proportions to find the length of *RS*. Show all your work and use a complete sentence in your answer.

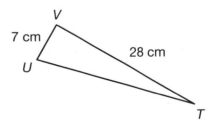

$$\frac{x \text{ centimeters}}{8 \text{ centimeters}} = \frac{7 \text{ centimeters}}{28 \text{ centimeters}}$$

$$8(7) = 28x$$

$$56 = 28x$$

$$2 = x$$

The length of *RS* is 2 centimeters.

2

Read the scenario below. Use the scenario to answe Questions 11 through 18.

Hannah types 225 words in 5 minutes. She wants to find her average typing speed and she wants to know the number of words she types for different numbers of minutes.

11. Write a unit rate that represents Hannah's average typing speed in words per minute.

$$\frac{225 \text{ words}}{5 \text{ minutes}} = \frac{45 \text{ words}}{1 \text{ minute}}$$

12. Use this rate to complete the table.

Time	Number of words
minutes	words
1	45
5	225
10	450
15	675
20	900

13. Create a graph of the data from the table to show the relationship between the amount of time and the number of words Hannah types.

Variable quantity	Lower bound	Upper bound	Interval
Time	0	30	2
Number of words	0	1125	75

Name _____ Date _____

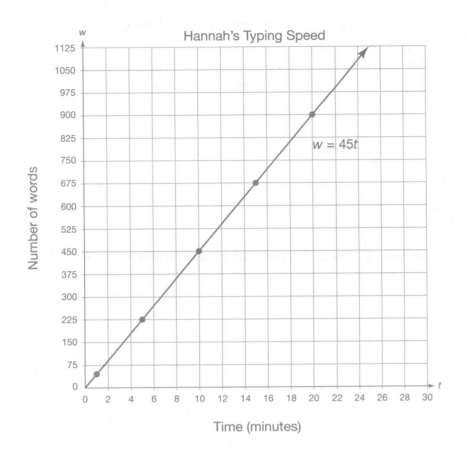

14. Use the graph to predict the number of words Hannah types in 12 minutes. Use a complete sentence in your answer.

Answers will vary, but should be about 540 words per minute.

15. Write an equation that shows the relationship between the amount of time t and the number of words w Hannah types.

$w = 45t$

16. Use the equation to predict the number of words Hannah types in 12 minutes. Show all your work and use a complete sentence in your answer.

$w = 45(12)$

$w = 540$

Hannah can type 540 words in 12 minutes.

17. Which method do you think is more accurate in making predictions, the graph or the equation? Use complete sentences to explain your reasoning.

Sample Answer: The equation should be more accurate because you are actually calculating the number of words based on the time. It is difficult to read from the graph how many words are typed in 12 minutes.

2

18. Use a proportion to determine the number of words Hannah can type in one hour. Show all your work and use a complete sentence in your answer.

$$\frac{45 \text{ words}}{1 \text{ minute}} = \frac{x \text{ words}}{60 \text{ minutes}}$$

$$x = 2700$$

Because there are 60 minutes in 1 hour, Hannah can type 2700 words in 1 hour.

End of Chapter Test

Name _____ Date _____

Read the scenario below. Use the scenario for Questions 1 through 3.

A shoe store in the mall is surveying people to see how much they spend on shoes over the course of a year. The results of their survey are shown in the table below.

Age (years)	Less than $100	$100–$300	More than $300
Under 20	38	7	5
20–40	11	26	13
41–60	8	32	10
Over 60	22	27	1
Total number of people	79	92	29

1. How many people were surveyed? Use a complete sentence in your answer.

   Two hundred people were surveyed.

2. There are approximately 400,000 people that live in your city. How many of them spend more than $300 a year on shoes? Show all your work and use a complete sentence in your answer.

   $$\frac{29 \text{ people spend more than } \$300}{200 \text{ people surveyed}} = \frac{x \text{ people spend more than } \$300}{400{,}000 \text{ people}}$$

   $$200x = 29(400{,}000)$$

   $$200x = 11{,}600{,}000$$

   $$x = 58{,}000$$

   In your city, 58,000 people spend more than $300 a year on shoes.

3. To conduct this survey, employees of the shoe store asked people who came into the store to go online and complete the survey. Explain what kind of sampling method they used and whether or not their sample was biased. Use complete sentences in your answer.

   Sample Answer: The employees of the shoe store used self-selected sampling. Those who wanted to participate went online to complete the survey. This sample was biased, because participants were volunteers.

Read the scenario below. Use the scenario to answer Questions 4 and 5.

At a hot wings cook-off at the county fair, two recipes for hot wing sauce tied for first place. The recipes are shown below.

Uncle Bob's Hot Wing Sauce	**Jumpin' June's Hot Wing Sauce**
6 parts hot sauce 2 parts melted butter	7 parts hot sauce 5 parts melted butter

4. Which recipe has the strongest taste of hot sauce? Show all your work and use complete sentences to explain your reasoning.

Uncle Bob's Hot Wing Sauce: $\dfrac{6 \text{ parts hot sauce}}{8 \text{ total parts}} = \dfrac{3 \text{ parts hot sauce}}{4 \text{ total parts}}$

Jumpin' June's Hot Wing Sauce: $\dfrac{7 \text{ parts hot sauce}}{12 \text{ total parts}}$

$\dfrac{3}{4} = \dfrac{9}{12}$

Because $\frac{3}{4}$ is greater than $\frac{7}{12}$, Uncle Bob's recipe has the strongest taste of hot sauce.

5. Uncle Bob plans to package his hot wing sauce in 12-ounce bottles to sell. He is going to package 50 bottles. How many ounces of hot sauce and butter will he need? Show all your work and use a complete sentence in your answer.

Number of ounces: 50(12) = 600

Number of ounces per part: $\dfrac{600 \text{ ounces}}{8 \text{ total parts}} = \dfrac{75 \text{ ounces}}{1 \text{ part}}$

Hot sauce needed:

$\dfrac{75 \text{ ounces}}{1 \text{ part}} = \dfrac{x \text{ ounces}}{6 \text{ parts}}$

$x = 450$

Melted butter needed:

$\dfrac{75 \text{ ounces}}{1 \text{ part}} = \dfrac{x \text{ ounces}}{2 \text{ parts}}$

$x = 150$

Uncle Bob will need 450 ounces of hot sauce and 150 ounces of melted butter.

Name _____   Date _____

6. Triangle *ABC* is similar to triangle *DEF*. What is the length of *BC*? Show all your work and use a complete sentence in your answer.

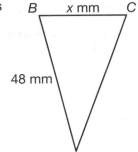
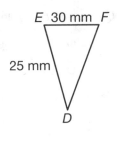

$$\frac{48 \text{ millimeters}}{x \text{ millimeters}} = \frac{30 \text{ millimeters}}{25 \text{ millimeters}}$$

$$30x = 1200$$

$$x = 40$$

The length of *BC* is 40 millimeters.

Read the scenario below. Use the scenario to answer Questions 7 through 12.

A recent survey in your area shows that 3 out of every 10 people who have food allergies are allergic to peanuts.

7. Write a ratio that compares the number of people who have a peanut allergy to the number of people who have food allergies.

$$\frac{3 \text{ people with peanut allergy}}{10 \text{ people with food allergies}}$$

8. How many people have a peanut allergy if 1000 people have food allergies? Show all your work and use a complete sentence in your answer.

$$\frac{3 \text{ people with peanut allergy}}{10 \text{ people with food allergies}} = \frac{100 \ (3 \text{ people with peanut allergy})}{100 \ (10 \text{ people with food allergies})}$$

$$= \frac{300 \text{ people with peanut allergy}}{1000 \text{ people with food allergies}}$$

If 1000 people have food allergies, 300 of them have a peanut allergy.

9. Let *t* represent the number of people with food allergies and let *p* represent the number of people with a peanut allergy. Write an equation for *p* in terms of *t*.

$$p = \frac{3}{10}t$$

10. Complete the table that represents the problem situation.

	People with food allergies	People with peanut allergy
Labels		
Units	people	people
Expression	t	$\frac{3}{10}t$
	200	60
	500	150
	1000	300
	2000	600
	5000	1500

11. Use the grid to create a graph of the data from the table in Question 10.

Variable quantity	Lower bound	Upper bound	Interval
People with food allergies	0	6000	400
People with a peanut allergy	0	1800	230

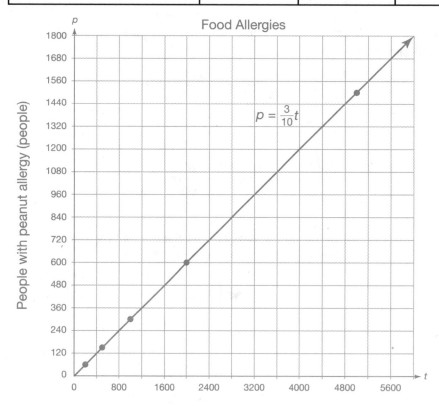

Food Allergies

$p = \frac{3}{10}t$

People with peanut allergy (people)

People with food allergies (people)

End of Chapter PAGE 5

Name _____ Date _____

12. Is the relationship of the quantities represented by the variables t and p in Question 9 direct variation? Use a complete sentence to explain why or why not.

Sample Answer: Yes, because there is the constant ratio $\dfrac{3}{10}$ in the

equation $p = \dfrac{3}{10}t$.

13. Write 12% as a fraction and as a decimal. Simplify the fraction, if possible.

$\dfrac{12}{100} = \dfrac{3}{25}$; 0.12

14. Write $\dfrac{19}{20}$ as a decimal and as a percent.

0.95; 95%

15. Your family goes out to eat at a restaurant and the bill is $52. You leave a 15% tip. How much is the tip? Show all your work and use a complete sentence in your answer.

$\dfrac{15}{100} = \dfrac{x}{52}$

$100x = 15(52)$

$100x = 780$

$x = 7.8$

The tip is $7.80.

16. A server receives a $10.45 tip from a group who spent $47.50 on their lunches. What percent tip does the server receive? Show all your work and use a complete sentence in your answer.

$\dfrac{10.45}{47.50} = \dfrac{x}{100}$

$47.5x = 10.45(100)$

$47.5x = 1045$

$x = 22$

The server receives a 22% tip.

17. A couple leaves $5.95 for a tip, which is 17% of their bill. What is the amount of their bill? Show all your work and use a complete sentence in your answer.

$$\frac{17}{100} = \frac{5.95}{x}$$

$$100(5.95) = 17x$$

$$595 = 17x$$

$$35 = x$$

The amount of the bill is $35.

Jeremiah receives his first pay check in the amount of $309.40. The check stub shows that he paid $145.60 in taxes.

18. What is Jeremiah's gross pay? Show all your work and use a complete sentence in your answer.

Jeremiah's gross pay: 309.40 + 145.60 = 455

Jeremiah's gross pay is $455.

19. What is the tax rate? Show all your work and use a complete sentence in your answer.

$$\frac{145.60}{455} = \frac{x}{100}$$

$$455x = 145.60(100)$$

$$455x = 14,560$$

$$x = 32$$

The tax rate is 32%.

Anastasia's new job pays $6.25 an hour. In her first month, she works 42 hours.

20. What is her gross pay at the end of the first month? Show all your work and use a complete sentence in your answer.

Anastasia's gross pay: 42(6.25) = 262.5

Anastasia's gross pay at the end of the first month is $262.50.

Name _____ Date _____

21. Anastasia pays 28% in taxes. How much does she pay in taxes on her first pay check? Show all of your work and use a complete sentence in your answer.

$$\frac{28}{100} = \frac{x}{262.5}$$

$$100x = 7350$$

$$x = 73.5$$

Anastasia pays $73.50 in taxes on her first paycheck.

Standardized Test Practice

Name _____ Date _____

Read the scenario below. Use the scenario to answer Questions 1 through 3.

A marketing firm conducted a survey for a client to gather information about how much people spend each year eating out.

Age (years)	Under $500	$500–$1000	Over $1000
Under 20	39	5	1
21–40	6	32	7
41–60	2	13	30
Over 60	14	28	3
Total number of people	61	78	41

1. How many people were surveyed?

   a. 41

   b. 61

   c. 78

   d. 180

2. There are 675,000 people living in the city where this survey was conducted. How many of these people spend more than $1000 each year eating out?

   a. 153,750

   b. 228,750

   c. 292,500

   d. 27,675,000

3. To complete this survey, the marketing firm sent representatives to the food court of the mall to interview people who were dining there. Which sampling method did they use?

   a. random sample

   b. stratified sample

   c. convenience sample

   d. systematic sample

4. Which of the following shows the fractions $\frac{5}{6}$, $\frac{7}{9}$, and $\frac{3}{5}$ in order from least to greatest?

   a. $\frac{5}{6}, \frac{7}{9}, \frac{3}{5}$

   b. $\frac{3}{5}, \frac{5}{6}, \frac{7}{9}$

   c. $\frac{5}{6}, \frac{3}{5}, \frac{7}{9}$

   d. $\frac{3}{5}, \frac{7}{9}, \frac{5}{6}$

5. Which is NOT an example of a rate?

   a. $\frac{75 \text{ miles}}{1 \text{ hour}}$

   b. $\frac{4 \text{ feet}}{3 \text{ feet}}$

   c. $\frac{10 \text{ cups}}{3 \text{ parts}}$

   d. $\frac{8 \text{ ounces}}{1 \text{ cup}}$

6. To make brown paint, Pierre must mix 4 parts green and 5 parts red. He needs to make 360 gallons of brown paint. How many gallons of red paint will Pierre need?

   a. 160 gallons

   b. 200 gallons

   c. 288 gallons

   d. 360 gallons

Name _____   Date _____

7. The sun is causing the flagpole and Sierra to cast a shadow. How tall is the flagpole?

   a. 10 feet

   b. 16 feet

   c. 18 feet

   d. 20 feet

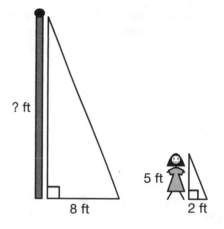

8. An airplane travels at an average speed of 870 kilometers per hour. What is the airplane's speed in meters per hour? (*Hint:* 1 kilometer = 1000 meters)

   a. 870,000 meters per hour

   b. 87,000 meters per hour

   c. 8700 meters per hour

   d. 0.87 meters per hour

9. On average a child grows 2.5 inches per year from age 2 until adolescence. Which equation shows how to calculate the height *h* of a child given the number of years *y* since age 2 if the child is 33 inches tall at age 2?

   a. $h = 33 - 2.5y$

   b. $h = 2.5y - 33$

   c. $h = 33 + 2.5y$

   d. $y = 2.5h + 33$

10. A science teacher conducts a survey on color blindness. She finds that 2 out of 19 students in the 9th grade are color blind. Which equation shows the relationship between color blind students b and non-color blind students c in the 9th grade?

a. $c = \dfrac{2}{17}b$

b. $b = \dfrac{2}{17}c$

c. $c = \dfrac{2}{19}b$

d. $b = \dfrac{2}{19}c$

11. At a local high school, seven out of nine graduates obtain a college degree. Which graph shows the relationship between the number of students who graduate from high school and the number of those students who obtain a college degree?

a.

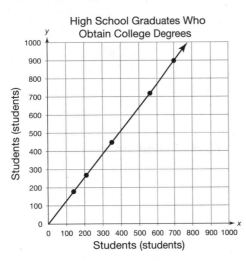

High School Graduates Who Obtain College Degrees

b.

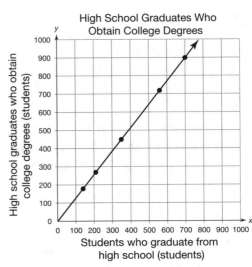

High School Graduates Who Obtain College Degrees

c.

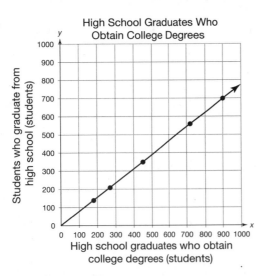

High School Graduates Who Obtain College Degrees

d.

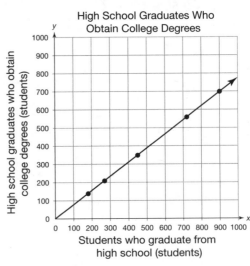

High School Graduates Who Obtain College Degrees

Name _____ Date _____

12. Which choice does NOT show 42% written as a fraction or a decimal?

    a. 0.42

    (b.) 4.2

    c. $\dfrac{42}{100}$

    d. $\dfrac{21}{50}$

13. Your aunt tips her hairdresser $6 for a $30 haircut. What percent tip does she leave her hairdresser?

    a. 0.2%

    b. 2%

    c. 5%

    (d.) 20%

14. Your family goes out to dinner and the bill is $115. You leave a 18% tip. How much do you leave?

    a. $2.07

    b. $6.39

    (c.) $20.70

    d. $27

15. A server can estimate his total food sales by using the amount he receives in tips. Over the course of the evening, the server receives $129 in tips. Customers usually tip 15%. How much was the total of the server's food sales that evening?

    a. $11.62

    b. $19.35

    (c.) $860

    d. $1935

2

16. David makes $7.25 an hour at work. One month he works 45 hours. He must pay 32% of what he earns in taxes. What is David's gross pay and net pay for that month?

   a. Gross pay = $221.85; Net pay = $326.25

   b. Gross pay = $326.25; Net pay = $221.85

   c. Gross pay = $326.25; Net pay = $104.40

   d. Gross pay = $104.40; Net pay = $326.85

17. Whitney pays $329.67 in taxes one month. Her tax rate is 30%. What is her gross pay and net pay for that month?

   a. Gross pay = $1098.90; Net pay = $1428.57

   b. Gross pay = $1428.57; Net pay = $1098.90

   c. Gross pay = $769.23; Net pay = $1098.90

   d. Gross pay = $1098.90; Net pay = $769.23

18. Tonya pays $268.24 in taxes one month when her gross pay is $958. What is her tax rate?

   a. 0.28%

   b. 2.8%

   c. 28%

   d. 39%

Pre-Test

© 2006 Carnegie Learning, Inc.

Name _____ Date _____

Solve each equation. Show all your work.

1. $x + 6 = 10$

$x + 6 - 6 = 10 - 6$

$x = 4$

2. $a - 9 = 15$

$a - 9 + 9 = 15 + 9$

$a = 24$

3. $3p = 27$

$\dfrac{3p}{3} = \dfrac{27}{3}$

$p = 9$

4. $\dfrac{t}{5} = 4$

$\dfrac{t}{5} \cdot 5 = 4 \cdot 5$

$t = 20$

5. $2y + 6 = 18$

$2y + 6 - 6 = 18 - 6$

$2y = 12$

$\dfrac{2y}{2} = \dfrac{12}{2}$

$y = 6$

6. $38 = 5s - 7$

$38 + 7 = 5s - 7 + 7$

$45 = 5s$

$\dfrac{45}{5} = \dfrac{5s}{5}$

$s = 9$

7. $\dfrac{w}{3} + 10 = 17$

$\dfrac{w}{3} + 10 - 10 = 17 - 10$

$\dfrac{w}{3} = 7$

$\dfrac{w}{3} \cdot 3 = 7 \cdot 3$

$w = 21$

8. $28 = \dfrac{n}{2} - 4$

$28 + 4 = \dfrac{n}{2} - 4 + 4$

$32 = \dfrac{n}{2}$

$32 \cdot 2 = \dfrac{n}{2} \cdot 2$

$n = 64$

Read the scenario below. Use the scenario to answer Questions 9 and 10.

An online music store is selling CDs for $3 a piece and charges a flat shipping fee of $7. The cost C for buying n CDs is given by the equation $C = 3n + 7$. Below is a graph of this equation.

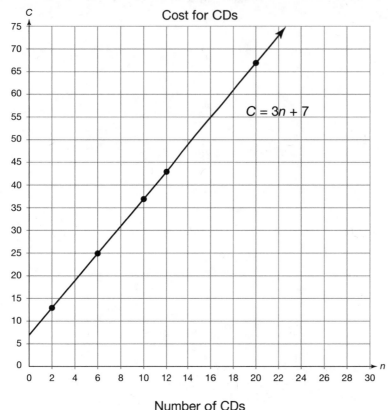

Cost for CDs

9. Explain how you would use the graph to determine whether 14 is a solution to the equation $49 = 3n + 7$. Use complete sentences in your answer.

    Sample Answer: I located 14 CDs on the horizontal axis. I followed the vertical gridline up to the graph of the equation. From that point, I followed along a horizontal line until I reached the vertical axis. I read the cost at this point on the horizontal axis, which was $49. Therefore, I know that 14 is a solution to the equation $49 = 3n + 7$.

10. Determine whether 25 is a solution of the equation $75 = 3n + 7$ algebraically. Show all your work and use a complete sentence in your answer.

    $75 \overset{?}{=} 3(25) + 7$

    $75 \overset{?}{=} 75 + 7$

    $75 \neq 82$

    The number 25 is not a solution of the equation $75 = 3n + 7$.

© 2006 Carnegie Learning, Inc.

Name _____ Date _____

11. In the statement below, identify *a*, *b*, and *p*. Then, write a percent equation that represents the situation.

   28 is 35% of 80.

   $a = \underline{\quad 28 \quad}$

   $b = \underline{\quad 80 \quad}$

   $p = \underline{\quad 35 \quad}$

   $28 = \dfrac{35}{100}(80)$

Write and solve a percent equation to answer each question. Show all your work and use a complete sentence in your answer.

12. 24 is what percent of 60?

   $24 = p(60)$

   $p = 0.4$

   The number 24 is 40% of 60.

13. What is 55% of 120?

   $a = \dfrac{55}{100}(120)$

   $a = 66$

   The number 66 is 55% of 120.

14. 24 is 12% of what number?

   $24 = \dfrac{12}{100}b$

   $b = 200$

   The number 24 is 12% of 200.

15. Write the integers in order from least to greatest.

6, –7, –10, 4, –6, 2

–10, –7, –6, 2, 4, 6

Find each sum or difference.

16. −2 + 8 = 6

17. 9 − (−3) = 12

18. −11 − 8 = -19

Find each product or quotient.

19. −3(−7) = 21

20. 2(−9) = -18

21. $\dfrac{-24}{-3}$ = 8

3

22. Plot and label each point in the coordinate plane.

A(−5, 6)

B(4, 7)

C(3, −4)

D(−2, −5)

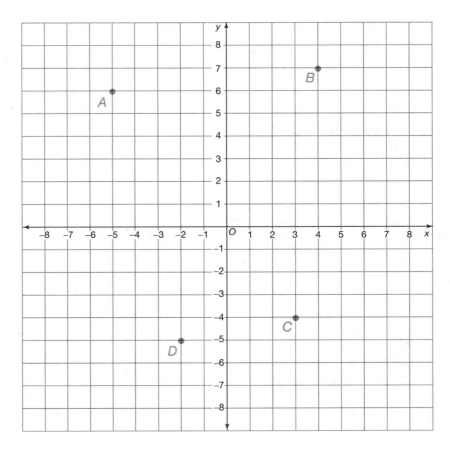

Post-Test

© 2006 Carnegie Learning, Inc.

Name _____ Date _____

Solve each equation. Show all your work.

1. $n + 5 = 19$

$n + 5 - 5 = 19 - 5$

$n = 14$

2. $x - 13 = 24$

$x - 13 + 13 = 24 + 13$

$x = 37$

3. $5r = 65$

$\dfrac{5r}{5} = \dfrac{65}{5}$

$r = 13$

4. $\dfrac{b}{8} = 12$

$\dfrac{b}{8} \cdot 8 = 12 \cdot 8$

$b = 96$

5. $4x + 8 = 52$

$4x + 8 - 8 = 52 - 8$

$4x = 44$

$\dfrac{4x}{4} = \dfrac{44}{4}$

$x = 11$

6. $39 = 6p - 9$

$39 + 9 = 6p - 9 + 9$

$48 = 6p$

$\dfrac{48}{6} = \dfrac{6p}{6}$

$p = 8$

7. $\dfrac{t}{2} + 15 = 25$

$\dfrac{t}{2} + 15 - 15 = 25 - 15$

$\dfrac{t}{2} = 10$

$\dfrac{t}{2} \cdot 2 = 10 \cdot 2$

$t = 20$

8. $85 = \dfrac{y}{4} - 5$

$85 + 5 = \dfrac{y}{4} - 5 + 5$

$90 = \dfrac{y}{4}$

$90 \cdot 4 = \dfrac{y}{4} \cdot 4$

$360 = y$

Read the scenario below. Use the scenario to answer Questions 9 and 10.

You order tickets online to see your favorite band in concert. The tickets cost $14 each and there is a shipping fee of $5. The cost C for buying t tickets is given by the equation $C = 14t + 5$. Below is the graph of this equation.

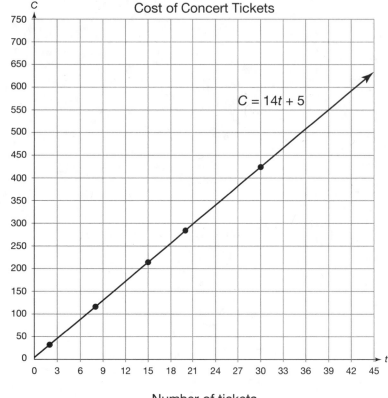

Cost of Concert Tickets

$C = 14t + 5$

Cost (dollars)

Number of tickets

9. Explain how you would use the graph to determine whether 5 is a solution to the equation $70 = 14t + 5$. Use complete sentences in your answer.

   Sample Answer: I located 5 on the horizontal axis. I followed the vertical gridline up to the graph of the equation. From that point, I followed along a horizontal line until I reached the vertical axis. I read the cost at this point on the horizontal axis, which was $75. Therefore, I know that 5 is not a solution to the equation $70 = 14t + 5$.

10. Determine whether 15 is a solution of the equation $215 = 14t + 5$ algebraically. Show all your work and use a complete sentence in your answer.

   $215 \stackrel{?}{=} 14(15) + 5$

   $215 \stackrel{?}{=} 210 + 5$

   $215 = 215$

   The number 15 is a solution of $215 = 14t + 5$.

Name _____ Date _____

11. In the statement below, identify a, b, and p. Then, write a percent equation that represents the situation.

63 is 42% of 150.

$a = $ ___63___

$b = $ ___150___

$p = $ ___42___

$63 = \dfrac{42}{100}(150)$

Write and solve a percent equation to answer each question. Show all your work and use a complete sentence in your answer.

12. 112 is what percent of 175?

$112 = p(175)$

$p = 0.64$

The number 112 is 64% of 175.

13. What is 45% of 80?

$a = \dfrac{45}{100}(80)$

$a = 36$

The number 36 is 45% of 80.

14. 9 is 18% of what number?

$9 = \dfrac{18}{100}b$

$b = 50$

The number 9 is 18% of 50.

15. Write the integers in order from least to greatest.

−13, 0, −5, 3, 18, −8

−13, −8, −5, 0, 3, 18

Find each sum or difference.

16. −4 + 9 = [5]

17. 18 − (−7) = [25]

18. −12 − 4 = [−16]

Find each product or quotient.

19. −6(−5) = [30]

20. 8(−7) = [−56]

21. $\dfrac{-36}{-9}$ = [4]

22. Plot and label each point in the coordinate plane.

A(4, −3)

B(−6, −5)

C(1, 7)

D(−3, 2)

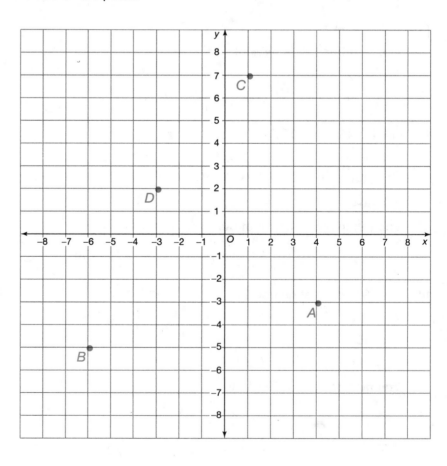

Mid-Chapter Test

Name _____ Date _____

Solve each equation. Show all your work.

1. $n + 14 = 22$

$n + 14 - 14 = 22 - 14$

$n = 8$

2. $x - 3 = 27$

$x - 3 + 3 = 27 + 3$

$x = 30$

3. $12z = 48$

$\dfrac{12z}{12} = \dfrac{48}{12}$

$z = 4$

4. $\dfrac{u}{8} = 10$

$\dfrac{u}{8} \cdot 8 = 10 \cdot 8$

$u = 80$

5. $7p + 6 = 27$

$7p + 6 - 6 = 27 - 6$

$7p = 21$

$\dfrac{7p}{7} = \dfrac{21}{7}$

$p = 3$

6. $4c - 9 = 47$

$4c - 9 + 9 = 47 + 9$

$4c = 56$

$\dfrac{4c}{4} = \dfrac{56}{4}$

$c = 14$

7. $\dfrac{t}{5} + 19 = 39$

$\dfrac{t}{5} + 19 - 19 = 39 - 19$

$\dfrac{t}{5} = 20$

$\dfrac{t}{5} \cdot 5 = 20 \cdot 5$

$t = 100$

8. $\dfrac{a}{12} - 1 = 4$

$\dfrac{a}{12} - 1 + 1 = 4 + 1$

$\dfrac{a}{12} = 5$

$\dfrac{a}{12} \cdot 12 = 5 \cdot 12$

$a = 60$

9. It takes Kelly 12 minutes to fold a load of laundry. Write an equation that shows how many minutes *m* it will take Kelly to fold *l* loads of laundry.

    m = 12*l*

10. Algebraically determine whether 26 is a solution to the equation *x* + 35 = 60. Show all your work and use a complete sentence in your answer.

    26 + 35 $\overset{?}{=}$ 60

    61 ≠ 60

    The number 26 is not a solution to the equation *x* + 35 = 60.

3

Read the scenario below. Use the scenario to answer Questions 11 through 14.

Your uncle plants a white pine that has a 15-centimeter diameter. The diameter of the trunk grows an average of 0.5 centimeter every year.

11. Write an equation that shows the diameter *d* of the tree in years *y*.

    d = 0.5*y* + 15

12. Use the equation you wrote in Question 11 to complete the table. Be sure to include units and expressions.

Labels	Time	Diameter
Units	years	centimeters
Expressions	*y*	0.5*y* + 15
	10	20
	20	25
	40	35
	80	55
	100	65

Name _____ Date _____

13. Use the grid below to create a graph of the data from the table in Question 12. First, choose your bounds and intervals. Be sure to label your graph clearly.

Variable quantity	Lower bound	Upper bound	Interval
Time	0	150	10
Diameter	0	75	5

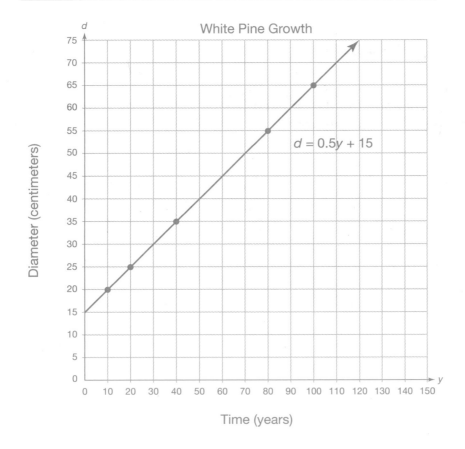

14. Use the graph to determine the diameter of the tree in 90 years. Use complete sentences to explain how you found your answer.

Sample Answer: The tree would have a 60-centimeter diameter in 90 years. To find my answer, I found 90 years on the x-axis. I followed the vertical line up to the graph of the equation. From that point, I followed a horizontal line to the y-axis. Finally, I read the number at that place on the y-axis, which was 60 centimeters.

15. Your aunt is a So Beautiful make-up consultant. She makes a 25% commission on all of her sales. This month she sells $1420 in make-up. Use a proportion to find her commission. Show all your work and use a complete sentence in your answer.

$$\frac{x}{1420} = \frac{25}{100}$$

$$1420(25) = 100x$$

$$35{,}500 = 100x$$

$$355 = x$$

Your aunt earns $355 in commission this month.

Write and solve a percent equation to answer each question. Show all your work and use a complete sentence in your answer.

16. 62 is what percent of 200?

$$62 = p(200)$$

$$p = 0.31$$

The number 62 is 31% of 200.

17. What is 22% of 150?

$$a = \frac{22}{100}(150)$$

$$a = 33$$

The number 33 is 22% of 150.

18. 91 is 65% of what number?

$$91 = \frac{65}{100}b$$

$$b = 140$$

The number 91 is 65% of 140.

Name _____ Date _____

Read the scenario below. Use the scenario to answer Questions 19 and 20.

The cost of one ticket to the art museum, history museum, or the museum of science is $8.50. You can buy a gold membership card for $85, and then pay only $6 for each ticket to any of the museums. You can by a silver membership card for $65 and then pay only $7.25 for each ticket to any of the museums.

Number of tickets	Non-member cost	Gold member cost	Silver member cost
	Total cost	Total cost	Total cost
tickets	dollars	dollars	dollars
t	8.5t	6t + 85	7.25t + 65
5	42.5	115	101.25
10	85	145	137.5
20	170	205	210
50	425	385	4275
100	850	685	790

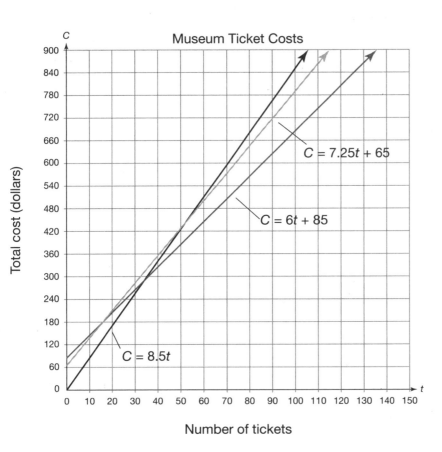

Number of tickets

19. Will the cost ever be the same for the gold and silver memberships? If so, for which number of tickets? Use complete sentences to explain how you found your answer.

Sample Answer: The cost will be the same for gold and silver memberships if a person purchases 16 tickets. I found my answer by finding the point where the lines for the gold and silver memberships intersect on the graph.

20. Your friend loves to visit the museums. He asks you to help him determine which option is the best deal for him. What would you recommend? Use complete sentences to explain your answer.

Sample Answer: If your friend visits the museums less than 34 times a year, it is better for him to pay the non-member ticket price of $8.50. If your friend visits the museum 34 or more times a year, it is better for him to buy a gold membership card.

3

End of Chapter Test

Name _____ Date _____

Solve each equation. Show all your work.

1. $y + 12 = -4$

$y + 12 - 12 = -4 - 12$

$y = -16$

2. $b - 7 = -9$

$b - 7 + 7 = -9 + 7$

$b = -2$

3. $-8h = 72$

$\dfrac{-8h}{-8} = \dfrac{72}{-8}$

$h = -9$

4. $\dfrac{r}{-5} = -13$

$\dfrac{r}{-5} \cdot -5 = -13 \cdot -5$

$r = 65$

5. $3z + (-18) = 36$

$3z + (-18) - (-18) = 36 - (-18)$

$3z = 54$

$\dfrac{3z}{3} = \dfrac{54}{3}$

$z = 18$

6. $-2n - 14 = -54$

$-2n - 14 + 14 = -54 + 14$

$-2n = -40$

$\dfrac{-2n}{-2} = \dfrac{-40}{-2}$

$n = 20$

7. $\dfrac{x}{3} + 21 = 18$

$\dfrac{x}{3} + 21 - 21 = 18 - 21$

$\dfrac{x}{3} = -3$

$\dfrac{x}{3} \cdot 3 = -3 \cdot 3$

$x = -9$

8. $\dfrac{a}{-4} - 6 = 7$

$\dfrac{a}{-4} - 6 + 6 = 7 + 6$

$\dfrac{a}{-4} = 13$

$\dfrac{a}{-4} \cdot 4 = 13 \cdot -4$

$a = -52$

9. The daily cost to visit Wild and Crazy Amusement Park is $18.75. Write an equation that shows the relationship between the cost C and the number of visits v.

   $C = 18.75v$

10. The owners of Wild and Crazy Amusement Park are offering a special weekday pass. The weekday pass costs $75, and then the cost each time you visit the park is $15. Write an equation that shows the relationship between the cost C and the number of visits v if you purchase a weekday pass.

   $C = 15v + 75$

11. The owners of Wild and Crazy Amusement Park are also offering an anytime pass. The anytime pass costs $100, and then the cost each time you visit the park is $12.50. Write an equation that shows the relationship between the cost C and the number of visits v if you purchase an anytime pass.

   $C = 12.5v + 100$

12. Use the results of Questions 9 through 11 to complete the table of values that shows the relationship between the total cost and the number of visits.

Number of visits	Daily Total cost	Weekday pass Total cost	Anytime pass Total cost
visits	dollars	dollars	dollars
v	$18.75v$	$15v + 75$	$12.5v + 100$
3	56.25	120	137.5
5	93.75	150	162.5
15	281.25	300	287.5
20	375	375	350
35	656.25	600	537.5

© 2006 Carnegie Learning, Inc.

End of Chapter Test PAGE 3

Name _____ Date _____

13. Use the grid below to create a graph of the data from the table in Question 12. First, choose your bounds and intervals. Be sure to label your graph clearly.

Variable quantity	Lower bound	Upper bound	Interval
Number of visits	0	45	3
Total cost	0	750	50

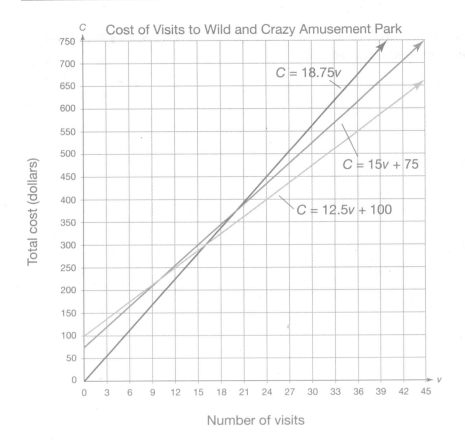

14. Will the cost ever be the same for a weekday pass and an anytime pass? If so, for which number of visits? Use complete sentences to explain your how you found your answer.

Sample Answer: Yes, the cost will be the same for the weekday pass and anytime pass at 10 visits. To find this answer, I found the point on the graph where the line for the weekday pass cost intersects the line for the anytime pass cost.

15. Compare the three options. Which one is the best deal? Use complete sentences to explain your reasoning.

Sample Answer: If you look at the graph, you can see that the line for the cost at the daily rate is lower than the other lines until it intersects the line for the cost of the anytime pass at 16. Therefore, the daily rate is the better deal if you visit the amusement park fewer than 16 times, and the anytime pass is the better deal if you visit the amusement park more than 16 times.

Write and solve a percent equation to answer each question. Show all your work and use a complete sentence in your answer.

16. 8 is what percent of 50?

$8 = p(50)$

$p = 0.16$

The number 8 is 16% of 50.

17. What is 38% of 150?

$a = \dfrac{38}{100}(150)$

$a = 57$

The number 57 is 38% of 150.

18. 2 is 5% of what number?

$2 = \dfrac{5}{100}b$

$b = 40$

The number 2 is 5% of 40.

19. Write the integers in order from least to greatest.

2, –8, 5, –11, –3, 8

–11, –8, –3, 2, 5, 8

Name _____   Date _____

20. Plot and label each point in the coordinate plane.

A(3, –5)

B(2, 1)

C(–6, –7)

D(–7, 4)

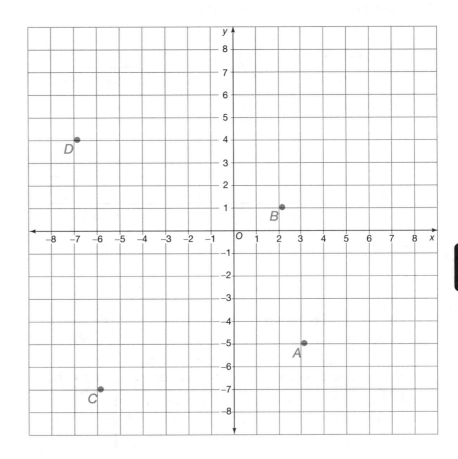

3

Read the scenario below. Use the scenario to answer Questions 21 through 23.

An interior decorator has asked a small linens company to make the bedspreads that she will use on the beds in a hotel she is decorating. The linens company already has 14 completed bedspreads. The interior decorator will need a total of 362 bedspreads for all of the beds in the hotel. The company can produce three and a half bedspreads each day.

21. Write an equation that represents the number of completed bedspreads *b* in terms of the number of days *d*.

$b = 3.5d + 14$

22. Complete the table of values that shows the relationship between the number of days and the number of completed bedspreads.

	Time	Completed bedspreads
Labels		
Units	days	bedspreads
Expressions	d	$3.5d + 14$
	0	14
	5	31.5
	10	49
	25	101.5
	50	189

3

23. Use the grid on the next page to create a graph of the data from the table in Question 22. First, choose your bounds and intervals. Be sure to label your graph clearly.

Variable quantity	Lower bound	Upper bound	Interval
Time	−15	60	5
Completed bedspreads	0	210	14

Name _____ Date _____

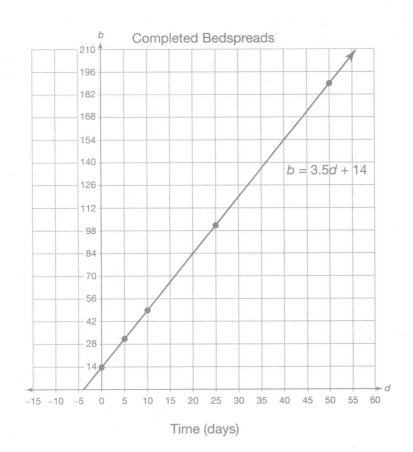

24. Use your graph to estimate when 7 bedspreads were completed. Use a complete sentence to explain how you found your answer.

Sample Answer: I found 7 bedspreads on the vertical axis. Then, I moved on a horizontal line to the left until I intersected the graph of the equation. From that point, I moved on a vertical line down to the horizontal axis. This vertical line intersected the horizontal axis at −2, which indicates that 7 bedspreads were completed 2 days before the hotel project started.

Standardized Test Practice

Name _____ Date _____

1. What is the solution for this equation?

   $-2x + 9 = -17$

   a. $x = -13$

   b. $x = -4$

   c. $x = 4$

   d. $x = 13$

2. What is the solution for this equation?

   $\dfrac{x}{3} - 12 = -8$

   a. $x = -60$

   b. $x = -12$

   c. $x = 12$

   d. $x = 60$

3. Dominique charges $6 an hour when she baby sits. Which equation shows the relationship between the number of hours Dominique baby sits h and the amount of money she makes m?

   a. $m = h + 6$

   b. $m = 6h$

   c. $m = 6 - h$

   d. $\dfrac{h}{m} = 6$

4. Which problem situation matches the equation below?

   $x + 3.45 = 7.04$

   a. Sasha bought a pound of coffee that cost $7.04. She got $3.45 in change from the cashier. What is x, the amount of money Sasha gave the cashier?

   b. Patrick did 5 pushups in 3.45 seconds. Matt did 5 pushups in 7.04 seconds. What is x, the average time it takes to do 5 pushups?

   c. Katherine spent $7.04 at the store. She bought a box of cereal that cost $3.45 and a gallon of milk. What is x, the cost of the gallon of milk?

   d. Tracy ran a mile in 7.04 minutes which was 3.45 minutes faster than Jordan's time. What is x, the time it took Jordan to run a mile?

5. The graph shows the relationship between the amount in royalties that Eric receives and the number of his books that sell. Last month, Eric received a royalty check for $360. How many of his books sold last month?

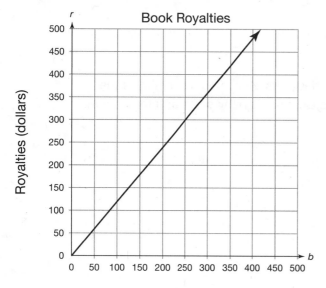

Book Royalties

   a. 200
   b. 300
   c. 400
   d. cannot be determined

Name _____ Date _____

6. The graph shows the cost to use a local gym based on the amount of time someone spends there. There are three different rates based on the level of membership. Based on the graph, which statement below is NOT true?

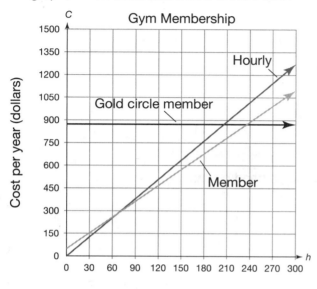

a. Being a gold circle member is a better deal if you spend more than 250 hours a year at the gym.

b. It is always a better deal to pay the hourly rate.

c. Being a member is a better deal if you spend more than 50 hours a year at the gym.

d. Paying the hourly rate is a better deal if you spend less than 50 hours a year at the gym.

7. Which percent equation shows how to find 62% of 150?

a. $62 = p(150)$

b. $a = \dfrac{62}{100}(150)$

c. $150 = \dfrac{62}{100}b$

d. $a = 62(150)$

8. Which expression is represented by the model below?

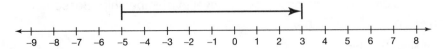

a. −5 + 8

b. −5 − 8

c. −5 + 3

d. −5 − 3

9. Which of the coordinates lie within the triangle graphed below?

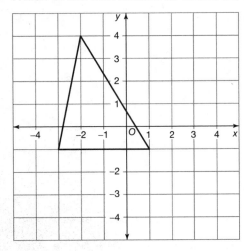

a. (−3, 2)

b. (−1, 4)

c. (−3, −2)

d. (−2, 3)

Name _____ Date _____

10. The total profit p from selling n sweatshirts is given by the equation

   $p = 15n - 30.$

   If the total profit was $720, how many sweatshirts were sold?

   a. 46

   b. 48

   c. 50

   d. 52

11. When is this statement true?

   The product of two integers is positive.

   a. This statement is never true.

   b. This statement is always true.

   c. This statement is true for the product of a positive and a negative integer.

   d. This statement is true for the product of two negative integers.

12. When Robert began working at a furniture store, he earned $7.25 per hour plus a 2% commission on each piece of furniture he sold. His boss just increased his hourly rate by $0.25 and his commission to 4%. If Robert works 20 hours a week and sells $5500 in furniture, how much will he earn?

   a. $370

   b. $480

   c. $1250

   d. $2350

Cumulative Test

Name _____ Date _____

For each sequence, draw the next 2 terms and describe the pattern.

1.

  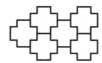  

Start with the previous term and alternately add 1 and 2 shapes.

2. 3, –6, 12, –24, __48__ , __–96__

Start with the previous term and multiply by –2.

Use the sequence below to answer Questions 3 and 4.

Term (n)	1	2	3	4	5
Sequence	3	7	11	15	19

3. Write an expression showing the relationship between the term and the sequence. Let n represent the term.

4n – 1

4. Use the expression from Question 3 to find the 20th term of the sequence. Show all your work.

$4(20) - 1 = 80 - 1$
$= 79$

Perform the indicated operations. Show all your work.

5. $3^4 - (2 + 6) + 5$

$81 - 8 + 5 = 73 + 5$
$= 78$

6. $(10 - 6)^2 + 3(2 - 7)$

$(4)^2 + 3(-5) = 16 + (-15)$
$= 1$

1–3

Cumulative Test PAGE 2

Use the table below to answer Questions 7 through 10.

Grade	Number of students with no siblings	Number of students with 1 to 3 siblings	Number of students with more than 3 siblings
8	3	21	6
9	6	19	5
10	2	25	3
11	10	11	9
Total number of students	21	76	23

7. Write a ratio of the number of students with no siblings to the total number of students surveyed.

   21 students with no siblings
   ─────────────────────────────
      120 students surveyed

8. There are 840 students in your school. Write and solve a proportion to determine the number of students in your school with no siblings. Show all your work and use a complete sentence in your answer.

   $$\frac{21 \text{ students with no siblings}}{120 \text{ students surveyed}} = \frac{x \text{ students with no siblings}}{840 \text{ students}}$$

   $$120x = 21(840)$$
   $$120x = 17{,}640$$
   $$x = 147$$

   There are 147 students in your school with no siblings.

9. To conduct the survey, your class obtained a list of the students in your school organized by grade. You randomly chose 30 students from each grade and asked them about the number of siblings they have. Which type of sampling method did you use? Use complete sentences to explain your reasoning.

   Sample Answer: I used a stratified random sample. First the students were divided by grade and then 30 students were randomly selected from each grade.

92   Chapter 3 ■ Assessments

Name _____ Date _____

10. Use the space below to create a bar graph of the sibling data. The bar graph should display the number of students in each grade with no siblings.

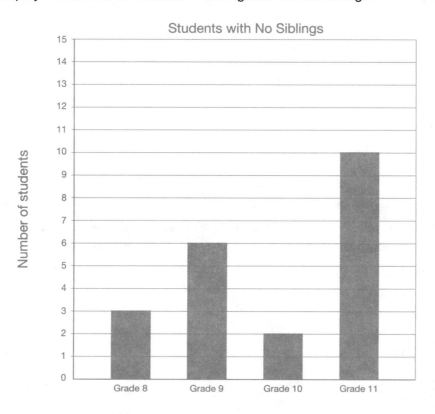

11. Triangles *LMN* and *QRS* are similar. What is the length of *QR*? Show all your work and use a complete sentence in your answer.

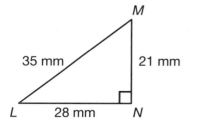

$$\frac{35 \text{ mm}}{28 \text{ mm}} = \frac{x \text{ mm}}{12 \text{ mm}}$$

$$28x = 35(12)$$

$$28x = 420$$

$$x = 15$$

The length of *QR* is 15 millimeters.

© 2006 Carnegie Learning, Inc.

12. A couple ate dinner at a restaurant and their bill totaled $65.85. They left a 20% tip. How much did they leave for a tip? Show all your work and use a complete sentence in your answer.

$$\frac{x}{65.85} = \frac{20}{100}$$

$$65.85(20) = 100x$$

$$1317 = 100x$$

$$13.17 = x$$

They left a tip of $13.17.

13. Janelle's net pay last month was $370.60. She paid $174.40 in taxes. What was her gross pay and tax rate? Show all your work and use a complete sentence in your answer.

Gross pay: net pay + taxes = 370.60 + 174.40 = 545

$$\frac{174.4}{545} = \frac{x}{100}$$

$$545x = 174.4(100)$$

$$545x = 17,440$$

$$x = 32$$

Janelle's gross pay was $545 and her tax rate was 32%.

Solve each equation. Show all your work.

14. $-8x - 15 = -39$

$$-8x - 15 + 15 = -39 + 15$$

$$-8x = -24$$

$$\frac{-8x}{-8} = \frac{-24}{-8}$$

$$x = 3$$

15. $\frac{x}{5} + 23 = 30$

$$\frac{x}{5} + 23 - 23 = 30 - 23$$

$$\frac{x}{5} = 7$$

$$\frac{x}{5} \cdot 5 = 7 \cdot 5$$

$$x = 35$$

1-3

Name _____ Date _____

16. Algebraically determine whether 67 is a solution of the equation $3x - 45 = 156$. Show all of your work and use a complete sentence in your answer.

$$3(67) - 45 \overset{?}{=} 156$$

$$201 - 45 \overset{?}{=} 156$$

$$156 = 156$$

The number 67 is a solution of the equation $3x - 45 = 156$.

Read the scenario below Use the scenario to answer Questions 17 through 20.

A parking garage charges $2.25 for the first hour of parking and $1.50 for each additional hour.

17. Write an equation to represent the relationship between the time h and the cost for parking c.

$$c = 1.5(h - 1) + 2.25$$

18. Complete the table of values that shows the relationship between the time and the cost for parking.

Time	Cost
hours	dollars
h	$1.5(h - 1) + 2.25$
1	2.25
3	5.25
6	9.75
10	15.75
15	23.25

19. Use the grid below to create a graph of the data from the table in Question 18. First, choose your bounds and intervals. Be sure to label your graph clearly.

Variable quantity	Lower bound	Upper bound	Interval
Time	0	30	2
Cost	0	60	4

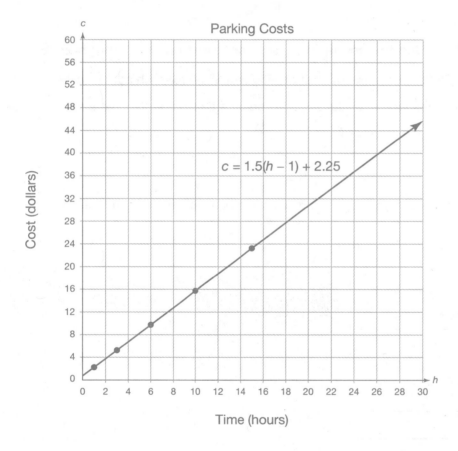

$$c = 1.5(h - 1) + 2.25$$

Parking Costs

Cost (dollars)

Time (hours)

20. Use your graph to estimate how much it would cost to leave your car in the parking garage for 20 hours. Use complete sentences to explain how you found your answer.

Sample answer: I located 20 hours on the horizontal axis. I followed a vertical line from there to the graph of the equation. From that point, I followed a horizontal line to the vertical axis. It intersected the axis at $30.75. Therefore, it would cost $30.75 to leave my car in the parking garage for 20 hours.

Cumulative Test PAGE 7

Name _____ Date _____

Use the graph below to answer Questions 21 through 23.

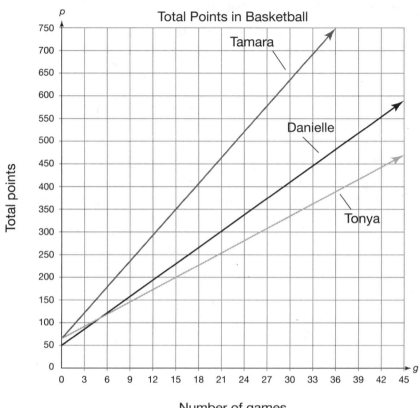

21. Danielle scored 50 points in the first two weeks of the season. On the average, she scores 12 points a game. Use the graph of Danielle's points to graphically determine whether 25 is a solution of $12g + 50 = 350$. Use complete sentences to explain your reasoning.

Sample answer: The number 25 is a solution of the equation $12g + 50 = 350$. I found 25 games on the horizontal axis. I followed a vertical line up to the graph of Danielle's points. From that point I followed a horizontal line to the vertical axis. It intersected the vertical axis at 350. Therefore, I know 25 is a solution of the equation $12g + 50 = 350$.

© 2006 Carnegie Learning, Inc.

22. After how many games will Danielle and Tonya have the same number of points? Use complete sentences to explain how you determined your answer.

Sample Answer: Danielle and Tonya will both have 110 points after 5 games. I looked for the intersections of the graphs of their points to determine when they had the same number of points.

23. Use the graph to estimate when Tamara will have 600 points. Use complete sentences to explain how you determined your answer.

Sample Answer: I found 600 points on the vertical axis. I followed a horizontal line to the graph of Tamara's points. From that point, I followed a vertical line down to the horizontal axis. Tamara will have 600 points after the 28th game.

24. Plot and label each point in the coordinate plane.

A(–4, 4)

B(–3, –2)

C(6, 1)

D(5, –6)

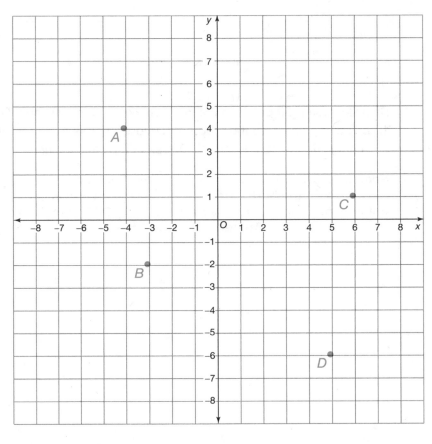

Pre-Test

Name _____ Date _____

1. An art museum offers a special admission price for children under the age of 5 and senior citizens who are 65 years or older. Everyone else must pay the full admission price to visit the museum. Write a compound inequality in compact form to show the age range for visitors paying full price for admission.

   $5 \leq x < 65$

Graph each compound inequality on the number line provided.

2. $-6 \leq x < 5$

3. $x < 1$ or $x \geq 4$

Solve each inequality. Show all your work.

4. $3x + 4 > 10$

   $3x + 4 - 4 > 10 - 4$

   $3x > 6$

   $\dfrac{3x}{3} > \dfrac{6}{3}$

   $x > 2$

5. $-5x - 2 \leq 13$

   $-5x - 2 + 2 \leq 13 + 2$

   $-5x \leq 15$

   $\dfrac{-5x}{-5} \geq \dfrac{15}{-5}$

   $x \geq -3$

Decide whether each relation is a function. If the relation is a function, identify the domain and range. If the relation is not a function, explain why. Use complete sentences in your answers.

6. Relation: (–1, 4), (–2, 3), (–3, 2), (–2, 1), (–4, 1)

    The relation is not a function because the input –2 has two outputs, 1 and 3.

7. Relation: (6, 4), (7, 5), (8, 6), (9, 7), (10, 8)

    The relation is a function. The domain is {6, 7, 8, 9, 10}. The range is {4, 5, 6, 7, 8}.

8. Professor Hampton has 150 exams to grade. It takes him 3 minutes to grade each exam, so it will take him 450 minutes to grade all of the exams.

    a. You can represent the number of hours Professor Hampton must spend grading using the variable y and the number of exams that have been graded using the variable x. Write an equation that represents the number of hours Professor Hampton must spend grading in terms of the number of exams that have been graded.

    $y = 450 - 3x$

    b. Is this equation a function? Use complete sentences to explain your reasoning.

    Sample Answer: The equation is a function. For each number of exams that have been graded, there is only one amount of time that must be spent grading.

    c. What is the domain? Use a complete sentence in your answer.

    The domain is {0, 1, 2, 3, ..., 150}.

    d. What is the range? Use a complete sentence in your answer.

    The range is {0, 1, 2, 3, ..., 450}.

Evaluate each function at the specified value. Show all your work.

9. $f(x) = 2x - 5$ at $x = 3$

    $f(3) = 2(3) - 5$
    $ = 6 - 5$
    $ = 1$

10. $g(x) = 9 - 6x$ at $x = -2$

    $g(-2) = 9 - 6(-2)$
    $ = 9 - (-12)$
    $ = 21$

Name _____ Date _____

Match the name of each property with its definition.

Property	Definition

<u>h</u> **11.** Distributive Property of Multiplication Over Addition

<u>d</u> **12.** Distributive Property of Multiplication Over Subtraction

<u>a</u> **13.** Distributive Property of Division Over Addition

<u>p</u> **14.** Distributive Property of Division Over Subtraction

<u>k</u> **15.** Closure

<u>b</u> **16.** Additive identity

<u>o</u> **17.** Multiplicative identity

<u>f</u> **18.** Additive inverse

<u>c</u> **19.** Multiplicative inverse

<u>n</u> **20.** Commutative Property of Addition

<u>i</u> **21.** Commutative Property of Multiplication

<u>l</u> **22.** Associative Property of Addition

<u>e</u> **23.** Associative Property of Multiplication

<u>m</u> **24.** Reflexive property

<u>g</u> **25.** Symmetric property

<u>j</u> **26.** Transitive property

a. If a, b, and c are any numbers and $c \neq 0$, then $\dfrac{a + b}{c} = \dfrac{a}{c} + \dfrac{b}{c}$.

b. A number such that when you add it to a second number, the sum is the second number.

c. A number such that when you multiply it by a second number, the product is the multiplicative identity.

d. If a, b, and c are any numbers, then $a \cdot (b - c) = a \cdot b - a \cdot c$.

e. If you are multiplying three numbers, the product is not affected by the way in which you group two of the three numbers.

f. A number such that when you add it to a second number, the sum is the additive identity.

g. For any real numbers a and b, if $a = b$, then $b = a$.

h. If a, b, and c are any numbers, then $a \cdot (b + c) = a \cdot b + a \cdot c$.

i. The order in which you multiply two or more numbers does not affect the product.

j. For any real numbers a, b, and c, if $a = b$ and $b = c$, then $a = c$.

k. A set of numbers is closed under an operation if the result of the operation on two numbers in the set is a number in the set.

l. If you are adding three numbers, the sum is not affected by the way in which you group two of the three numbers.

m. For any real number a, $a = a$.

n. The order in which you add two or more numbers does not affect the sum.

o. A number such that when you multiply it by a second number, the product is the second number.

p. If a, b, and c are any numbers and $c \neq 0$, then $\dfrac{a - b}{c} = \dfrac{a}{c} - \dfrac{b}{c}$.

Solve each equation. Show all your work.

27. $5x + 6 = 7x - 16$

$6 = 2x - 16$

$22 = 2x$

$11 = x$

28. $2(x + 3) = 3(4x - 8)$

$2x + 6 = 12x - 24$

$6 = 10x - 24$

$30 = 10x$

$3 = x$

Solve each absolute value inequality. Show all your work.

29. $|x| - 5 < 2$

$|x| - 5 < 2$

$|x| < 7$

$-7 < x < 7$

30. $|2x + 1| \geq 7$

$2x + 1 \geq 7$

$2x \geq 6$

$x \geq 3$

$2x + 1 \leq -7$

$2x \leq -8$

$x \leq -4$

4

Post-Test

Name _____ Date _____

1. Your English teacher asks you to write a novella that is at least 30 pages long and no more than 60 pages long. If your novella does not fall within these page limits, you will receive a failing grade for the project. Write a compound inequality in compact form that shows the length of a novella that would receive a failing grade.

   $0 \le x < 30$ or $x > 60$

Graph each compound inequality on the number line provided.

2. $4 < x \le 9$

3. $x \le -3$ or $x > -1$

Solve each inequality. Show all your work.

4. $6x - 5 \le 37$

   $6x - 5 + 5 \le 37 + 5$

   $6x \le 42$

   $\dfrac{6x}{6} \le \dfrac{42}{6}$

   $x \le 7$

5. $-8x + 3 > -21$

   $-8x + 3 - 3 > -21 - 3$

   $-8x > -24$

   $\dfrac{-8x}{-8} < \dfrac{-24}{-8}$

   $x < 3$

Decide whether each relation is a function. If the relation is a function, identify the domain and range. If the relation is not a function, explain why. Use complete sentences in your answers.

6. Relation: (1, 3.2). (4, 5.5), (7, 7.8), (10, 10.1), (13, 12.4)

   The relation is a function. The domain is {1, 4, 7, 10, 13}.

   The range is {3.2, 5.5, 7.8, 10.1, 12.4}.

7. Relation: (−1, −1), (0, 2), (2, 0), (3, −1), (−1, 3)

   The relation is not a function, because the input −1 has two outputs, −1 and 3.

8. A local bakery sells bagels by the dozen. Every morning, the baker makes 240 bagels.

   a. You can represent the number of bagels left using the variable y and the number of dozen bagels that have been sold using the variable x. Write an equation that represents the number of bagels left in terms of the number of dozen bagels that have been sold. (*Hint:* One dozen equals 12 bagels.)

   $y = 240 - 12x$

   b. Is this equation a function? Use complete sentences to explain your reasoning.

   Sample Answer: The equation is a function. For each number of dozen bagels that have been sold, there is only one amount of bagels left.

   c. What is the domain? Use a complete sentence in your answer.

   The domain is {0, 1, 2, 3, ..., 20}.

   d. What is the range? Use a complete sentence in your answer.

   The range is {0, 1, 2, 3, ..., 240}.

Evaluate each function at the specified value. Show all your work.

9. $f(x) = 4x - 1$ at $x = -3$

   $f(-3) = 4(-3) - 1$

   $= -12 - 1$

   $= -13$

10. $g(x) = 15 - 2x$ at $x = 4$

    $g(4) = 15 - 2(4)$

    $= 15 - 8$

    $= 7$

Post-Test PAGE 3

Name _____ Date _____

Match the name of each property with its definition.

Property

_n_ 11. Distributive Property of Multiplication Over Addition

_b_ 12. Distributive Property of Multiplication Over Subtraction

_d_ 13. Distributive Property of Division Over Addition

_a_ 14. Distributive Property of Division Over Subtraction

_p_ 15. Closure

_i_ 16. Additive identity

_g_ 17. Multiplicative identity

_e_ 18. Additive inverse

_c_ 19. Multiplicative inverse

_k_ 20. Commutative Property of Addition

_h_ 21. Commutative Property of Multiplication

_l_ 22. Associative Property of Addition

_f_ 23. Associative Property of Multiplication

_j_ 24. Reflexive property

_o_ 25. Symmetric property

_m_ 26. Transitive property

Definition

a. If a, b, and c are any numbers and $c \neq 0$, then
$$\frac{a - b}{c} = \frac{a}{c} - \frac{b}{c}.$$

b. If a, b, and c are any numbers, then
$a \cdot (b - c) = a \cdot b - a \cdot c.$

c. A number such that when you multiply it by a second number, the product is the multiplicative identity.

d. If a, b, and c are any numbers and $c \neq 0$, then
$$\frac{a + b}{c} = \frac{a}{c} + \frac{b}{c}.$$

e. A number such that when you add it to a second number, the sum is the additive identity.

f. If you are multiplying three numbers, the product is not affected by the way in which you group two of the three numbers.

g. A number such that when you multiply it by a second number, the product is the second number.

h. The order in which you multiply two or more numbers does not affect the product.

i. A number such that when you add to a second number, the sum is the second number.

j. For any real number a, $a = a$.

k. The order in which you add two or more numbers does not affect the sum.

l. If you are adding three numbers, the sum is not affected by the way in which you group two of the three numbers.

m. For any real numbers a, b, and c, if $a = b$ and $b = c$, then $a = c$.

n. If a, b, and c are any numbers, then
$a \cdot (b + c) = a \cdot b + a \cdot c.$

o. For any real numbers a and b, if $a = b$, then $b = a$.

p. A set of numbers is closed under an operation if the result of the operation on two numbers in the set is a number in the set.

Post-Test PAGE 4

Solve each equation. Show all your work.

27. $10x + 3 = 6x - 9$

$4x + 3 = -9$

$4x = -12$

$x = -3$

28. $4(3x + 5) = 2(9x - 5)$

$12x + 20 = 18x - 10$

$20 = 6x - 10$

$30 = 6x$

$5 = x$

Solve each absolute value inequality. Show all your work.

29. $|x| + 5 > 9$

$|x| > 4$

$x > 4$ or $x < -4$

30. $|4x - 2| \leq 10$

$4x - 2 \leq 10$ $4x - 2 \geq -10$

$4x \leq 12$ $4x \geq -8$

$x \leq 3$ $x \geq -2$

4

Mid-Chapter Test

Name _____ Date _____

Read the scenario and table below. Use the scenario and table to answer Questions 1 and 2.

You are studying the internal structure of Earth in science class. You learn that Earth has four layers: the crust, the mantle, the outer core, and the inner core. The average depth of each layer is given in the table below.

Layer	Location
Crust	starts at Earth's surface and extends 30 kilometers below Earth's surface
Mantle	starts at the lower edge of the crust and extends 2930 below Earth's surface
Outer core	starts at the lower edge of the mantle and extends 5130 kilometers below Earth's surface
Inner core	starts at the lower edge of the outer core and extends 6380 kilometers below Earth's surface to the center

1. Let x represent the number of miles below Earth's surface. Write an inequality to represent each layer's position below Earth's surface.

   Crust: _____ $0 \le x \le 30$ _____

   Mantle: _____ $30 < x \le 2930$ _____

   Outer core: _____ $2930 < x \le 5130$ _____

   Inner core: _____ $5130 < x \le 6380$ _____

2. The lithosphere is the part of Earth's internal structure that begins at Earth's surface and extends 80 kilometers below Earth's surface.

   a. Does the lithosphere include the crust? Use complete sentences to explain your reasoning.

   Sample Answer: The lithosphere includes the crust, because the crust only extends to 30 kilometers below Earth's surface and the lithosphere extends to 80 kilometers below Earth's surface.

   b. Does the lithosphere include all of the mantle? Use complete sentences to explain your reasoning.

   Sample Answer: The lithosphere does not contain all of the mantle, because the mantle starts at the lower edge of the crust and extends 2930 kilometers below Earth's surface. The lithosphere begins at the crust and extends 80 kilometers below Earth's surface, so it will only include about 50 kilometers of the mantle.

Mid-Chapter Test PAGE 2

Solve each inequality and graph the solution on the number line. Show all your work.

3. $-9x + 5 > 77$

$$-9x + 5 - 5 > 77 - 5$$

$$-9x > 72$$

$$\frac{-9x}{-9} < \frac{72}{-9}$$

$$x < -8$$

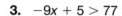

4. $\dfrac{x}{2} - 6 \geq -8$

$$\frac{x}{2} - 6 + 6 \geq -8 + 6$$

$$\frac{x}{2} \geq -2$$

$$\frac{x}{2} \cdot 2 \geq -2 \cdot 2$$

$$x \geq -4$$

Name _____ Date _____

Read the scenario below. Use the scenario to answer Questions 5 through 9.

The state department of transportation recently filled the road salt storage building on the highway near your house with 2400 tons of road salt. A snow plow truck can hold 12 tons of road salt in one load.

5. You can represent the amount of road salt left in the storage building using the variable y and number of truckloads of road salt using the variable x. Write an equation that represents the amount of road salt left in the storage building in terms of number of truckloads.

   $y = 2400 - 12x$

6. Use your answer to Question 5 to find the number of truckloads of road salt that were removed if 2460 tons of road salt are left in the storage building. Does your answer make sense? Use complete sentences to explain why or why not.

   $2460 = 2400 - 12x$

   $60 = -12x$

   $x = -5$

   Sample Answer: Two thousand four hundred sixty tons of road salt cannot be left in the building because there were only 2400 tons of road salt in the building. Also, you cannot have a negative number of truckloads.

7. Complete the table of values that describes the relationship between the number of truckloads of road salt that have been removed and the amount of road salt remaining in the storage building.

Salt removed	Salt remaining
truck loads	tons
x	$2400 - 12x$
10	2280
20	2160
50	1800
100	1200
200	0

8. How does the amount of road salt left in the storage building change as the number of truckloads increases by one? Use a complete sentence in your answer.

   Sample Answer: The amount of road salt left in the storage building decreases by 12 tons because one truckload contains 12 tons of road salt.

9. Does the relation represented by the values in the table in Question 7 represent a function? If the relation is a function, identify the domain and range. If the relation is not a function, explain why. Use complete sentences in your answer.

   Yes, the relation represents a function. The domain is {10, 20, 50, 100, 200}, and the range is {2280, 2160, 1800, 1200, 0}.

10. Write 5 ordered pairs that represent a relation that is not a function. Use complete sentences to explain why it is not a function.

    Answers may vary. In their explanations, students should include the fact that one input has more than one output.

Evaluate each function at the specified value. Show all your work.

11. $h(x) = 6x + 2$ at $x = -5$

    $h(-5) = 6(-5) + 2$

    $\qquad = -30 + 2$

    $\qquad = -28$

12. $p(x) = 15 - 4x$ at $x = 7$

    $p(7) = 15 - 4(7)$

    $\qquad = 15 - 28$

    $\qquad = -13$

End of Chapter Test

Name _____ Date _____

At a carnival, there is a man who is guessing people's weights. You decide to play. If his guess is 5 pounds or less above or below your actual weight, he wins. If it is not, then you win. Your actual weight is 108 pounds.

1. Let x represent your weight. Write a compound inequality that represents the range in which the man's guess must fall for him to win.

   $103 \leq x \leq 113$

2. Write a compound inequality that represents the range in which the man's guess must fall for you to win.

   $x < 103$ or $x > 113$

3. The man guesses 113 pounds. Who wins? Use a complete sentence to explain how you determined your answer.

   Sample Answer: He wins because he guessed 5 pounds more than my actual weight.

Decide whether each relation is a function. If the relation is a function, identify the domain and range. If the relation is not a function, explain why. Use complete sentences in your answers.

4. Relation: (–50, 50), (–40, 40), (–30, 30), (–20, 30), (–10, 40)

   The relation is a function. The domain is {–50, –40, –30, –20, –10} and the range is {50, 40, 30, 30, 40}.

5. Relation: (14, 23), (15, 25), (16, 27), (14, 29), (13, 27)

   The relation is not a function. The input 14 has two outputs, 23 and 29.

Evaluate each function at the specified value. Show all your work.

6. $f(x) = 39 - 4x$ at $x = 9$

   $f(9) = 39 - 4(9)$

   $= 39 - 36$

   $= 3$

7. $h(x) = 10x + 17$ at $x = -3$

   $h(-3) = 10(-3) + 17$

   $= -30 + 17$

   $= -13$

8. Xavier can run a mile in 7 minutes. You can represent the total amount of time Xavier runs using the variable y and the number of miles he runs using the variable x. Write an equation that represents the total amount of time Xavier runs in terms of the number of miles he runs. Does this equation represent a function? If so, identify the domain and range in terms of this real-life situation. If not, explain why. Use complete sentences in your answer.

$y = 7x$

Sample answer: The equation represents a function, because for each number of miles there is one time. The answers given for domain and range may vary, however students should comment about the fact that Xavier will not be able to run forever. So, the domain and range cannot be all real numbers.

9. Give an example of a rational number. Use complete sentences to explain how you determined your answer.

Answers will vary. In their explanations, students should include the fact that a rational number is a number that can be written as the quotient of two integers with the denominator not equal to zero.

10. Give an example of an irrational number. Use complete sentences to explain how you determined your answer.

Answers will vary. In their explanations, students should include the fact that an irrational number is a number that cannot be written as the quotient of two integers.

4

Write each repeating decimal as a rational number. Show all your work.

11. 0.1818...

$100w = 18.1818...$

$- \ w = 0.1818...$
_____
$99w = 18$

$w = \dfrac{18}{99}$ or $\dfrac{6}{33}$

12. 0.777...

$10w = 7.777...$

$- \ w = 0.777...$
_____
$9w = 7$

$w = \dfrac{7}{9}$

Solve each equation. Show all your work.

13. $5x - 16 = 18x + 23$

$-16 = 13x + 23$

$-39 = 13x$

$-3 = x$

14. $2(6x + 3) = 3(2x + 12)$

$12x + 6 = 6x + 36$

$6x = 30$

$x = 5$

Name _____   Date _____

15. For the equation, identify the property that is used in each step.

$$2(5x + 2) = \frac{340 - 60}{20}$$ Given problem

$$10x + 4 = \frac{340 - 60}{20}$$ __Distributive Property of Multiplication Over Addition__

$$10x + 4 = \frac{340}{20} - \frac{60}{20}$$ __Distributive Property of Division Over Subtraction__

$$10x + 4 = 17 - 3$$ __Divide.__

$$10x + 4 = 14$$ __Subtract.__

$$10x + 4 - 4 = 14 - 4$$ __Subtract 4 from each side.__

$$10x = 10$$ __Subtract.__

$$\frac{10x}{10} = \frac{10}{10}$$ __Divide each side by 10.__

$$x = 1$$ __Reflexive Property of Equality__

Give a mathematical example of each property.

16. Multiplicative identity

Answers will vary.

17. Additive inverse

Answers will vary.

18. Commutative Property of Addition

Answers will vary.

19. Associative Property of Multiplication

Answers will vary.

Solve each inequality and graph the solution. Show all your work.

20. $2x + 7 > 19$

$2x > 12$

$x > 6$

21. $-3x - 14 \geq 7$

$-3x \geq 21$

$x \leq -7$

4

22. $|x| + 2 \leq 11$

$|x| \leq 9$

$-9 \leq x \leq 9$

23. $|4x - 2| > 22$

$4x - 2 > 22$ $4x - 2 < -22$

$4x > 24$ $4x < -20$

$x > 6$ $x < -5$

Name _____ Date _____

Your uncle is trying to decide between a cable subscription and a satellite dish. The cable subscription has a $40 hook-up fee and costs $38 per month. The satellite dish costs $260 and the monthly fee is $16.

24. Write an expression that represents the total cost of the cable service, using x to represent the number of months that your uncle has the service.

$38x + 40$

25. Write an expression that represents the total cost of satellite service, using x to represent the number of months that you have the service.

$16x + 260$

26. Write and solve an equation to determine the number of months it takes for the total costs to be the same. Show all your work and use a complete sentence in your answer.

$$38x + 40 = 16x + 260$$
$$22x = 220$$
$$x = 10$$

It will take 10 months for the total costs to be the same.

4

Standardized Test Practice

Name _____ Date _____

1. A person with a systolic blood pressure greater than 120 mmHg and less than or equal to 139 mmHg is said to have prehypertension. Which inequality represents the range of systolic blood pressure for a person with prehypertension?

    a. $120 < x < 139$

    (b.) $120 < x \leq 139$

    c. $120 \leq x < 139$

    d. $120 \leq x \leq 139$

2. Which inequality is represented by the graph below?

    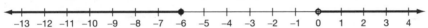

    a. $-6 \leq x > 0$

    b. $-6 \leq x < 0$

    c. $x < -6$ or $x \geq 0$

    (d.) $x \leq -6$ or $x > 0$

3. What is the solution set of the inequality $|x + 3| \geq 9$?

    a. $6 \leq x \leq -12$

    b. $x \leq 6$

    (c.) $x \leq -12$ or $x \geq 6$

    d. $x \leq -12$ and $x \geq 6$

4. Which equation is equivalent to $2(5 - 3x) + 4 = 3(9x + 7)$?

    a. $33x = 35$

    (b.) $33x = -7$

    c. $21x = -7$

    d. $33x = -15$

5. Solve: $2(x - 4) = \dfrac{24 - 16}{2}$

Step 1: $2x - 8 = \dfrac{24 - 16}{2}$

Step 2: $2x - 8 = \dfrac{24}{2} - \dfrac{16}{2}$

Step 3: $2x - 8 = 12 - 8$

Step 4: $2x - 8 = 4$

Step 5: $2x = 12$

Step 6: $x = 6$

Which property of real numbers was used in Step 2?

a. Distributive property of division over subtraction

b. Distributive property of multiplication over subtraction

c. Commutative property of addition

d. Multiplicative identity

6. Which relation is a function?

a. (0, 0), (1, 2), (0, 3), (2, 4)

b. (–24, 2), (–23, 2), (–24, 4), (–23, 4)

c. (–6, 1), (–6, 2), (–6, 3), (–6, 4)

d. (4, 9), (6, 13), (9, 4), (13, 6)

Name _____ Date _____

7. What is the domain of the function given in the table?

x	y
−5	15
−2	6
−1	3
3	−9
4	−12

    a. (15, 6, 3, −9, −12}

    b. (−5, 15), (−2, 6), (−1, 3), (3, −9), (4, −12)

    c. {−5, −2, −1, 3, 4}

    d. all real numbers

8. Which of the following is written in function notation?

    a. $f = 3x + 2$

    b. $y = 3x + 2$

    c. $f - x = 3x + 2$

    d. $g(x) = 3x + 2$

9. Which of the following real numbers is NOT a rational number?

    a. 4.216589...

    b. 8

    c. 1.33333...

    d. $\dfrac{5}{9}$

4

10. Jamal's teacher asked him to write 0.7575... as a fraction. Jamal's work is shown below.

Step 1: $10w = 7.5757...$

                  $- w = 0.7575...$

Step 2: $9w = 6.8182$

Step 3: $w = \dfrac{6.8182}{9}$

Which is the first *incorrect* step in Jamal's work?

a. Step 1

b. Step 2

c. Step 3

d. None of the above. Jamal did the work correctly.

11. When is this statement true?

Every function is a relation.

a. This statement is never true.

b. This statement is always true.

c. This statement is true for positive integers.

d. This statement is true for negative integers.

12. Daniel made $28,900 last year, which put him in the 15% tax bracket. The range for the 15% tax bracket is $7300 < x < $29,700. Daniel received an $800 pay raise this year. Will he still be in the 15% tax bracket? Why or why not?

a. Yes, because his new salary is $29,700, which falls within the 15% tax bracket.

b. No, because his new salary is $29,700, which does NOT fall within the 15% tax bracket.

c. Cannot be determined.

4

Standardized Test Practice PAGE 5

Name _____ Date _____

13. Daphne solves the inequality $5(x - 1) \geq 10$, and graphs the solution set below.

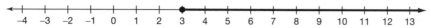

Which value is NOT part of the solution set?

(a.) 0

b. 3

c. 6

d. 11

14. Let $f(x) = -6x + 8$. What is $f(2)$?

(a.) $f(2) = -4$

b. $f(2) = 2$

c. $f(2) = 4$

d. $f(2) = 20$

15. Which equation shows an example of the Associative Property of Addition?

a. $(a \cdot b) \cdot c = a \cdot (b \cdot c)$

b. $a + b = b + a$

(c.) $a + (b + c) = (a + b) + c$

d. $a(b + c) = ab + ac$

16. The pep club at your school has decided to order T-shirts to sell at the school basketball games. Company A charges $5 per shirt and a one time set-up fee of $20. Company B charges $3 per shirt and a one time set-up fee of $42. Which equation would you use to determine for what number of shirts the total costs from Company A and Company B would be the same?

a. $8x = 62$

(b.) $5x + 20 = 3x + 42$

c. $5x - 20 = 3x - 42$

d. $5x - 3x = 20 + 42$

Pre-Test

Name _____ Date _____

1. Is $y = 2x + 7$ a linear function? Use a complete sentence to explain why or why not.

   Sample Answer: Yes, because each variable is raised to the first power and each variable only appears once.

2. Is this the graph of a linear function? Use a complete sentence to explain why or why not.

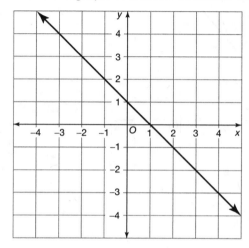

   Yes, because the graph is a straight, non-vertical line.

3. Write 2 sets of ordered pairs that satisfy the equation $y = 6x - 13$.

   Answers will vary.

Use the graph to identify the intercepts of each line.

4. *x*-intercept: __−5__

   y-intercept: __6__

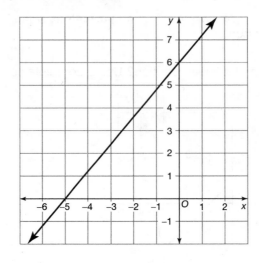

5. *x*-intercept: __3__

   y-intercept: __1__

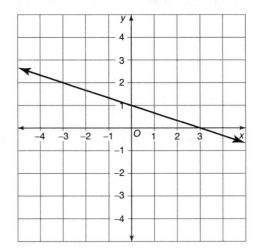

Name _____ Date _____

6. Algebraically find the intercepts of the graph of the equation $y = 2x - 6$. Show all your work.

   x-intercept: ___3___

   y-intercept: ___-6___

$0 = 2x - 6$	$y = 2(0) - 6$
$6 = 2x$	$y = 0 - 6$
$3 = x$	$y = -6$

7. Determine whether the slope of each line in the graph is positive, negative, zero, or undefined. Use complete sentences in to explain your reasoning.

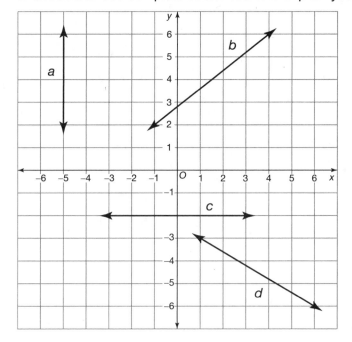

Line *a* is a vertical line, so its slope is undefined. Line *b* rises from left to right, so it has a positive slope. Line *c* is a horizontal line, so its slope is zero. Line *d* falls from left to right, so it has a negative slope.

5

8. Use the coordinates of the points to find the slope of each line. Show all your work.

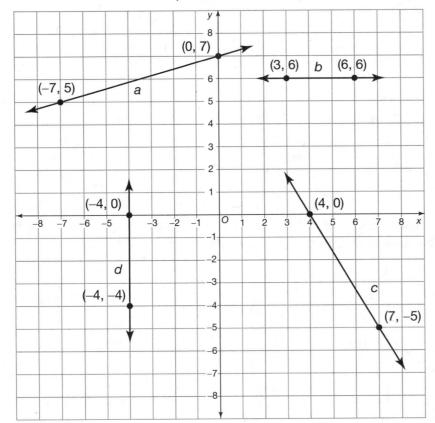

a. Slope of line *a*: ___$\dfrac{2}{7}$___

$$m = \frac{7 - 5}{0 - (-7)}$$

$$m = \frac{2}{7}$$

b. Slope of line *b*: ___0___

$$m = \frac{6 - 6}{6 - 3}$$

$$m = \frac{0}{3}$$

$$m = 0$$

c. Slope of line *c*: ___$-\dfrac{5}{3}$___

$$m = \frac{0 - (-5)}{4 - 7}$$

$$m = \frac{5}{-3}$$

d. Slope of line *d*: ___undefined___

$$m = \frac{-4 - 0}{-4 - (-4)}$$

$$m = \frac{-4}{0}$$

The slope is undefined.

Name _____ Date _____

9. Which line has the steepest slope? Use complete sentences to explain how you found your answer.

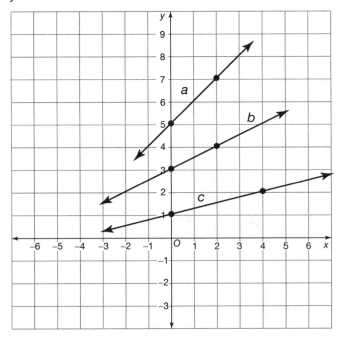

Line *a* has a slope of 1, line *b* has a slope of $\frac{1}{2}$, and line *c* has a slope of $\frac{1}{4}$. Line *a* has the steepest slope because it has the largest slope.

Identify the slope and *y*-intercept of each equation.

10. $y = \frac{2}{3}x + 4$

slope: $\frac{2}{3}$

y-intercept: 4

11. $y = 3x - 5$

slope: 3

y-intercept: −5

© 2006 Carnegie Learning, Inc.

5

12. Draw a graph of the equation by using the slope and *y*-intercept.

$$y = -\frac{3}{5}x + 4$$

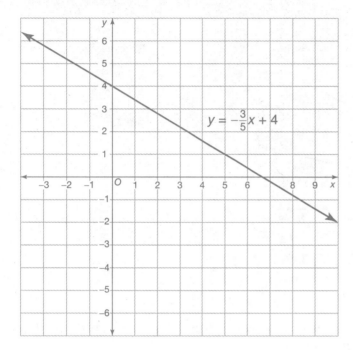

13. Write the equation of the line that has a slope of 2 and passes through the point (3, 1) in slope-intercept form. Show all your work.

$$y - 1 = 2(x - 3)$$
$$y - 1 = 2x - 6$$
$$y = 2x - 5$$

14. Write the equation of the line that passes through the points (1, 4) and (5, 12) in slope-intercept form. Show all your work.

$$m = \frac{12 - 4}{5 - 1} = \frac{8}{4} = 2$$
$$y - 4 = 2(x - 1)$$
$$y - 4 = 2x - 2$$
$$y = 2x + 2$$

Name _____ Date _____

15. Write the piecewise function that is represented in the graph below. Use x to represent a number from the domain of your function f.

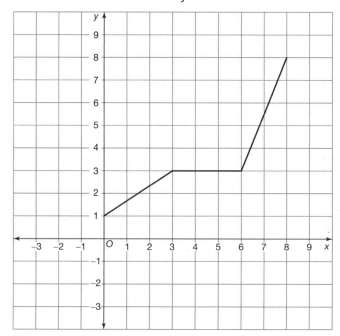

$$f(x) = \begin{cases} \dfrac{2}{3}x + 1, & 0 \le x \le 3 \\ 3, & 3 < x \le 6 \\ \dfrac{5}{2}x - 12, & 6 < x \le 8 \end{cases}$$

Read the scenario below. Use the scenario to answer Questions 16 and 17.

During a football game, fans can buy chili dogs and soft drinks at the concession stand. The chili dogs cost $2 each and the soft drinks cost $1.50 each. During one football game, the chili dog and soft drink sales totaled $330.

16. Write an equation that represents the total sales if x chili dogs and y soft drinks were sold.

$2x + 1.5y = 330$

17. Using the equation, write the intercepts of the equation's graph. Show all your work.

    x-intercept: <u> 165 </u>

    y-intercept: <u> 220 </u>

$2x + 1.5(0) = 330$	$2(0) + 1.5y = 330$
$2x = 330$	$1.5y = 330$
$x = 165$	$y = 220$

18. Write the equation in standard form. Show all your work.

$$y = -\frac{2}{5}x + 3$$

$$\frac{2}{5}x + y = 3$$

$$2x + 5y = 15$$

19. Write the equation in slope-intercept form. Show all your work.

$$5x + 4y = 12$$

$$4y = -5x + 12$$

$$y = -\frac{5}{4}x + 3$$

20. Find the amount of interest earned by depositing $220 into an account that earns 4% interest for 1 year. Show all your work and use a complete sentence in your answer.

$$I = 220(0.04)(1)$$

$$I = 8.8$$

The amount of interest earned is $8.80.

21. You can use the formula $A = \frac{1}{2}bh$ to find the area of a triangle, where *b* is the length of the base and *h* is the height of triangle. Solve the equation for *h*. Show all your work.

$$A = \frac{1}{2}bh$$

$$2A = bh$$

$$\frac{2A}{b} = h$$

5

Post-Test

Name _____ Date _____

1. Is $y = -5x + 3$ a linear function? Use a complete sentence to explain why or why not.

Sample Answer: Yes, because each variable is raised to the first power and each variable only appears once.

2. Is this the graph of a linear function? Use a complete sentence to explain why or why not.

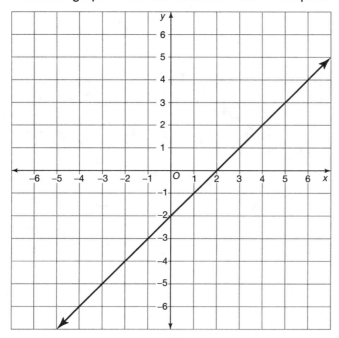

Yes, because the graph is a straight, non-vertical line.

3. Write two sets of ordered pairs that satisfy the equation $y = 2x + 7$.

Answers will vary.

5

Use the graph to identify the intercepts of each line.

4. *x*-intercept: ___5___

   y-intercept: ___−4___

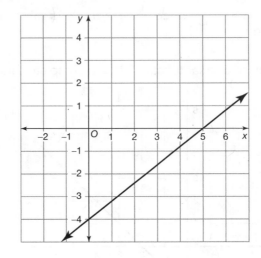

5. *x*-intercept: ___2___

   y-intercept: ___6___

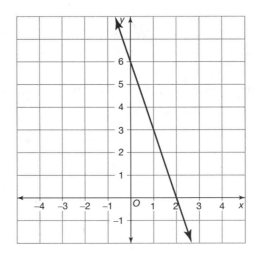

Name _____ Date _____

6. Algebraically find the intercepts of the graph of the equation $y = 2x - 6$. Show all your work.

x-intercept: ___3___

y-intercept: ___12___

$0 = -4x + 12$ $y = -4(0) + 12$

$-12 = -4x$ $y = 0 + 12$

$3 = x$ $y = 12$

7. Determine whether the slope of each line in the graph is positive, negative, zero, or undefined. Use complete sentences in to explain your reasoning.

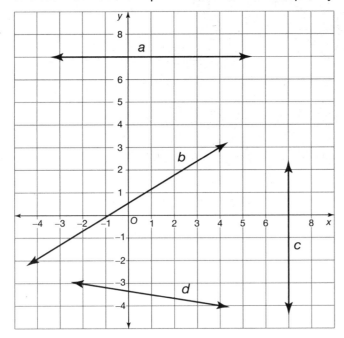

Line *a* is a horizontal line, so its slope is zero. Line *b* rises from left to right, so it has a positive slope. Line *c* is a vertical line, so its slope is undefined. Line *d* falls from left to right, so it has a negative slope.

5

8. Use the coordinates of the points to find the slope of each line. Show all your work.

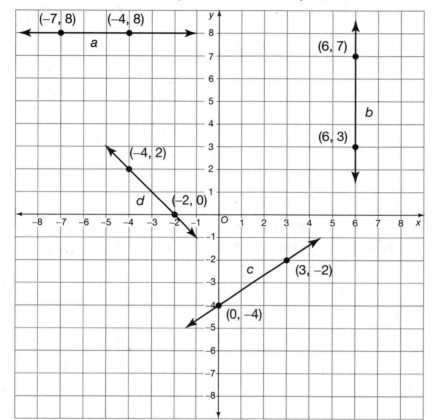

a. Slope of line a: _____0_____

$$m = \frac{8 - 8}{-7 - (-4)}$$

$$m = \frac{0}{-3}$$

$$m = 0$$

b. Slope of line b: __undefined__

$$m = \frac{7 - 3}{6 - 6}$$

$$m = \frac{4}{0}$$

The slope is undefined.

c. Slope of line c: _____$\frac{2}{3}$_____

$$m = \frac{-2 - (-4)}{3 - 0}$$

$$m = \frac{2}{3}$$

d. Slope of line d: _____−1_____

$$m = \frac{2 - 0}{-4 - (-2)}$$

$$m = \frac{2}{-2}$$

$$m = -1$$

5

Post-Test PAGE 5

Name _____ Date _____

9. Which line has the steepest slope? Use a complete sentence to explain how you determined your answer.

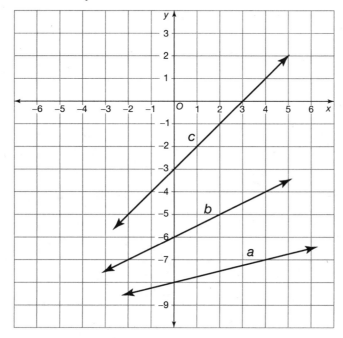

Line *a* has a slope of $\frac{1}{4}$, line *b* has a slope of $\frac{1}{2}$, and line *c* has a slope of 1. Line *c* has the steepest slope because it has the largest slope.

Identify the slope and *y*-intercept of each equation.

10. $y = \frac{3}{5}x + 8$

slope: $\frac{3}{5}$

y-intercept: 8

11. $y = 7x - 4$

slope: 7

y-intercept: −4

5

12. Draw a graph of the equation by using the slope and *y*-intercept.

$$y = -\frac{1}{6}x + 2$$

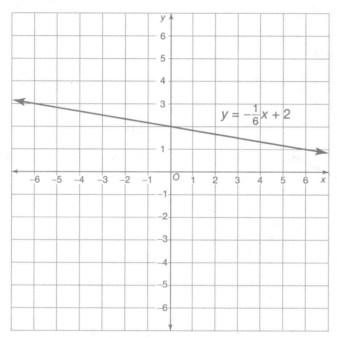

13. Write the equation of the line that has a slope of 5 and passes through the point (4, 3) in slope-intercept form. Show all your work.

$$y - 3 = 5(x - 4)$$
$$y - 3 = 5x - 20$$
$$y = 5x - 17$$

14. Write the equation of the line that passes through the points (3, 1) and (7, 13) in slope-intercept form. Show all your work.

$$m = \frac{13 - 1}{7 - 3} = \frac{12}{4} = 3$$
$$y - 1 = 3(x - 3)$$
$$y - 1 = 3x - 9$$
$$y = 3x - 8$$

5

Post-Test PAGE 7

Name _____ Date _____

15. Write the piecewise function that is represented in the graph below. Use *x* to represent a number from the domain of your function *f*.

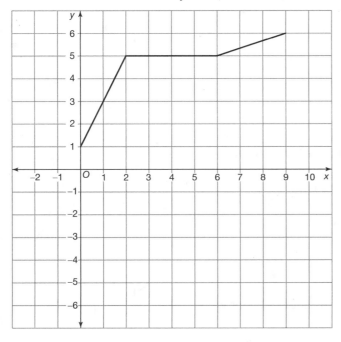

$$f(x) = \begin{cases} 2x + 1, & 0 \le x \le 2 \\ 5, & 2 < x \le 6 \\ \frac{1}{3}x + 3, & 6 < x \le 9 \end{cases}$$

Read the scenario below. Use the scenario to answer Questions 16 and 17.

Your band is selling cheese and pepperoni pizzas to raise money for a trip to Florida. Each cheese pizza costs $8 and each pepperoni pizza costs $10. You made a total of $120 on your pizza sales.

16. Write an equation that represents the total amount you made if you sold *x* cheese pizzas and *y* pepperoni pizzas.

$8x + 10y = 120$

Post-Test PAGE 8

17. Using the equation, write the intercepts of the equation's graph. Show all your work.

x-intercept: __15__

y-intercept: __12__

$8x + 10(0) = 120$ $8(0) + 10y = 120$

$8x = 120$ $10y = 120$

$x = 15$ $y = 12$

18. Write the equation in standard form. Show all your work.

$y = -\dfrac{3}{8}x + 1$

$\dfrac{3}{8}x + y = 1$

$3x + 8y = 8$

19. Write the equation in slope-intercept form. Show all your work.

$2x + 3y = 9$

$3y = -2x + 9$

$y = -\dfrac{2}{3}x + 3$

20. Find the amount of interest earned by depositing $345 into an account that earns 2% interest for 1 year. Show all your work and use a complete sentence in your answer.

$I = 345(0.02)(1)$

$I = 6.9$

The amount of interest earned is $6.90.

21. You can use the formula $A = \dfrac{1}{2}ap$ to find the area of a regular polygon, where a is the length of the apothem and p is the perimeter of the polygon. Solve the equation for a. Show all your work.

$A = \dfrac{1}{2}ap$

$2A = ap$

$\dfrac{2A}{p} = a$

© 2006 Carnegie Learning, Inc.

138   Chapter 5 ■ Assessments

Mid-Chapter Test

Name _____ Date _____

Read the scenario below. Use the scenario to answer Questions 1 through 3.

Your uncle Joe is running for mayor. He orders bumper stickers for his campaign. A local printer has agreed to make them for $.12 each plus a one time set-up fee of $25.

1. Write an equation that gives the total cost in terms of the number of bumper stickers. Use x to represent the number of bumper stickers and use y to represent the total cost.

   $y = 0.12x + 25$

2. Use your equation to find the total cost to print 500 bumper stickers. Show all your work and use a complete sentence in your answer.

   $y = 0.12(500) + 25$

   $y = 60 + 25$

   $y = 85$

   It costs $85 to print 500 bumper stickers.

3. Is the equation you wrote in Question 1 a linear function? Use complete sentences to explain your reasoning.

   Yes, because each variable is raised to the first power and each variable appears once.

Read the scenario below. Use the scenario to answer Questions 4 through 8.

Janine is a marathon runner. She runs the first part of a marathon in 30 minutes. Then she runs at pace of 8 miles per hour, which means it takes her 7.5 minutes to complete each mile.

4. Write an equation that gives the total time in terms of the number of miles after the first part of the race. Use x to represent the number of miles after the first part of the race and use y to represent the total time.

   $y = 7.5x + 30$

5. Complete the three sets of ordered pairs so that they satisfy your equation.

   (–2, _15_)

   (_0_ , 30)

   (8, _90_)

5

6. Use the grid to graph the ordered pairs in Question 5. Then, create a graph of your equation. Complete the table with your bounds and intervals. Be sure to label your graph clearly.

    Answers will vary. A sample is provided below.

Variable quantity	Lower bound	Upper bound	Interval
Distance	–6	24	2
Time	–15	210	15

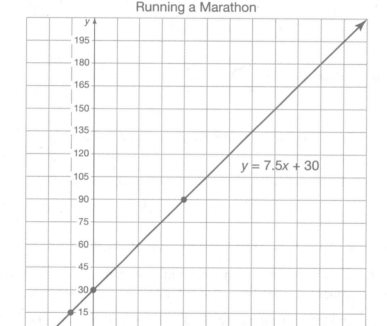

Running a Marathon

$y = 7.5x + 30$

Distance after first part of the race (miles)

7. Is the graph for Question 6 the graph of a linear function? Use a complete sentence to explain your reasoning.

    Yes, because the graph is a straight, non-vertical line.

Name _____   Date _____

8. Use the graph to find the *x*- and *y*-intercepts of the equation. Use complete sentences to explain what these points tell you about the relationship between the number of miles and the total time.

    x-intercept: __–4__   *y*-intercept: __30__

    Sample Answer: The *x*-intercept gives the number of miles Janine has run at zero minutes. It does not make sense in this context because she cannot run a negative number of miles. The *y*-intercept gives the total time it takes Janine to run 0 miles after the first part of the race.

9. Algebraically find the intercepts of the graph of the equation $y = -2x + 6$. Show all your work.

    x-intercept: __3__

    y-intercept: __6__

    $0 = -2x + 6$ $y = -2x(0) + 6$

    $-6 = -2x$ $y = 0 + 6$

    $3 = x$ $y = 6$

10. Use the graph below to find the increase in interest when the principal increases by $1. Use a complete sentence in your answer. Then, write a unit rate that compares the increase in interest to the increase in the principal.

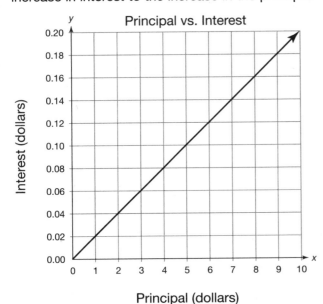

Principal vs. Interest

The interest increases by $.02. Unit rate: $\dfrac{\$.02}{\$1}$.

5

11. Use complete sentences to describe lines that have positive slope, negative slope, zero slope, or undefined slope.

Sample Answer: A line with positive slope rises from left to right; a line with negative slope falls from left to right; a line with zero slope is horizontal; a line with undefined slope is vertical.

12. Find the slope of the line that passes through (–2, 7) and (8, 5). Show all your work.

$$m = \frac{5 - 7}{8 - (-2)} = \frac{-2}{10} = -\frac{1}{5}$$

13.

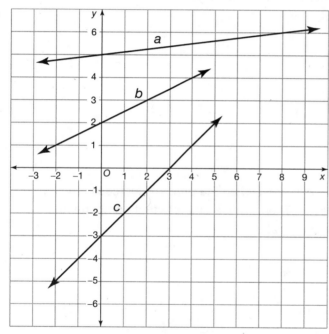

a. For each line, identify the slope and y-intercept.

Line *a*:   slope: $\frac{1}{8}$ y-intercept: 5

Line *b*:   slope: $\frac{1}{2}$ y-intercept: 2

Line *c*:   slope: 1   y-intercept: –3

b. How does the slope of a steep line compare to the slope of a line that is less steep? Use a complete sentence to explain.

Sample Answer: The larger the absolute value of the slope, the steeper the line.

5

Name _____ Date _____

14. Draw a graph of the equation by using the slope and *y*-intercept.

$$y = \frac{1}{4}x - 7$$

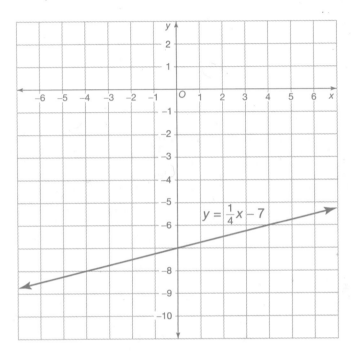

5

15. Write the equation of the line from its graph.

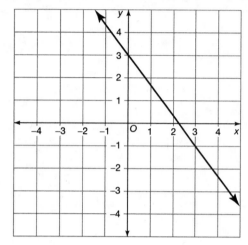

$$y = -\frac{4}{3}x + 3$$

5

End of Chapter Test

Name _____ Date _____

1. You would like to increase the number of CDs in your collection. You currently have 25 CDs. You plan to buy 2 CDs each month. Write an equation that gives the number of CDs in terms of the number of months. Use x to represent the month and use y to represent the total number of CDs. Does the equation you wrote represent a linear function? Use a complete sentence to explain your reasoning.

   $y = 2x + 25$; Yes, because each variable is raised to the first power and appears only once.

Use the graph below to answer Questions 2 and 3.

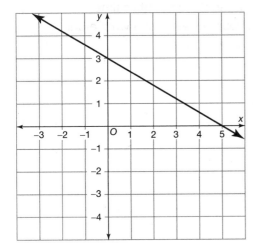

2. Is the graph above the graph of a linear function? Use a complete sentence to explain your reasoning.

   Yes, because the graph is a straight, non-vertical line.

3. Find the x- and y-intercepts of the graph above.

   x-intercept: ___5___

   y-intercept: ___3___

5

4. Algebraically find the intercepts of the graph of the equation $y = 2x - 24$. Show all your work.

x-intercept: ___12___

y-intercept: ___−24___

$0 = 2x - 24$	$y = 2(0) - 24$
$24 = 2x$	$y = -24$
$12 = x$	

5. Use the graph to find the decrease in the height of a candle when the amount of time it burns increases by 30 minutes. Use a complete sentence in your answer. Then write a unit rate that compares the decrease in height to the increase in time.

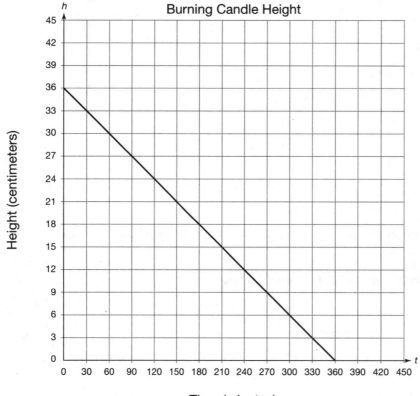

The height decreases by 3 centimeters as the time increases by 30 minutes.

Unit rate: $\dfrac{3 \text{ centimeters}}{30 \text{ minutes}} = \dfrac{0.1 \text{ centimeters}}{1 \text{ minute}}$

Name _____ Date _____

6. Use the coordinates of the points to find the slope of each line. Show all your work.

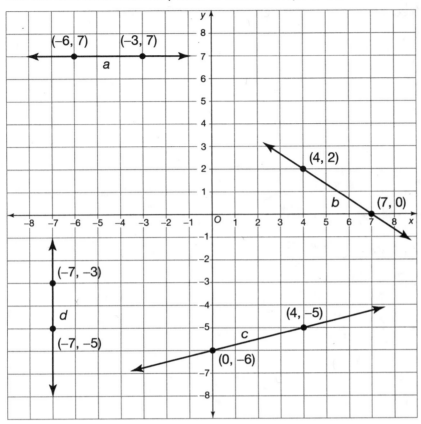

a. slope of line *a*: _____0_____

$$m = \frac{7 - 7}{-3 - (-6)}$$

$$m = \frac{0}{3}$$

$$m = 0$$

b. slope of line *b*: _____$-\dfrac{2}{3}$_____

$$m = \frac{0 - 2}{7 - 4}$$

$$m = \frac{-2}{3}$$

c. slope of line *c*: _____$\dfrac{1}{4}$_____

$$m = \frac{-5 - (-6)}{4 - 0}$$

$$m = \frac{1}{4}$$

d. slope of line *d*: _____undefined_____

$$m = \frac{-5 - (-3)}{-7 - (-7)}$$

$$m = \frac{-2}{0}$$

The slope is undefined.

7. Identify the slope and *y*-intercept of the graph of each equation. Then, use the slope and *y*-intercept to graph each equation on the coordinate grid. Be sure to label each line.

a. $y = \dfrac{3}{8}x - 5$

slope: $\dfrac{3}{8}$

y-intercept: -5

b. $y = -3x + 5$

slope: -3

y-intercept: 5

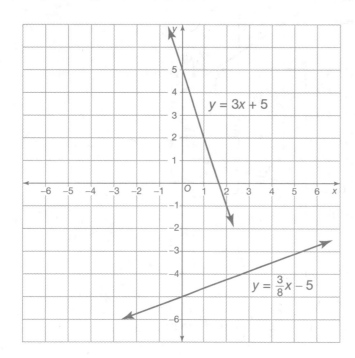

$y = 3x + 5$

$y = \dfrac{3}{8}x - 5$

5

Name _____ Date _____

8. Write the equation of the line from its graph.

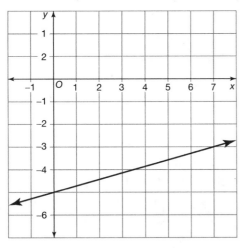

$y = \dfrac{2}{7}x - 5$

9. Write the equation of a line in slope-intercept form that has a slope of $-\dfrac{5}{9}$ and passes through the point (18, 7). Show all your work.

$y - 7 = -\dfrac{5}{9}(x - 18)$

$y - 7 = -\dfrac{5}{9}x + 10$

$y = -\dfrac{5}{9}x + 17$

5

10. Write the equation of a line in slope-intercept form that passes through the points (14, 8) and (−2, 16). Show all your work.

$$m = \frac{16 - 8}{-2 - 14} = \frac{8}{-16} = -\frac{1}{2}$$

$$y - 8 = -\frac{1}{2}(x - 14)$$

$$y - 8 = -\frac{1}{2}x + 7$$

$$y = -\frac{1}{2}x + 15$$

11. Write the equation of the piecewise function given in the graph. Use x to represent a number from the domain of your function f.

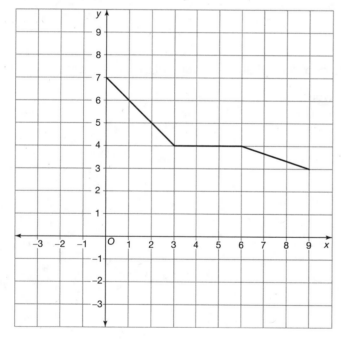

$$f(x) = \begin{cases} -x + 7, & 0 \leq x \leq 3 \\ 4, & 3 < x \leq 6 \\ -\frac{1}{3}x + 6, & 6 < x \leq 9 \end{cases}$$

5

Name _____ Date _____

Read the scenario below. Use the scenario to answer Questions 12 through 15.

As the manager of the school bookstore, you want to order school hats and T-shirts to sell in the bookstore. A company says they will print hats for $5 each and T-shirts for $7 each. You have a budget of $210.

12. Write an equation that represents an order of x hats and y T-shirts whose total cost is equal to the amount of money in your budget.

$5x + 7y = 210$

13. Using the equation you wrote in Question 12, write the intercepts of the equation's graph. Show all your work.

x-intercept: __42__

y-intercept: __30__

$5x + 7(0) = 210$ $5(0) + 7y = 210$
$5x = 210$ $7y = 210$
$x = 42$ $y = 30$

14. What do the intercepts mean in terms of the problem situation? Use complete sentences in your answer.

Sample Answer: The x-intercept is the number of hats that could be ordered if no T-shirts were ordered. The y-intercept is the number of T-shirts that could be ordered if no hats were ordered.

5

15. Use the grid and the intercepts to create a graph of the equation in Question 13. First, choose your bounds and intervals. Be sure to label your graph clearly.

Bounds and intervals may vary. A sample answer is given below.

Variable quantity	Lower bound	Upper bound	Interval
Hats	0	45	3
T-shirts	0	45	3

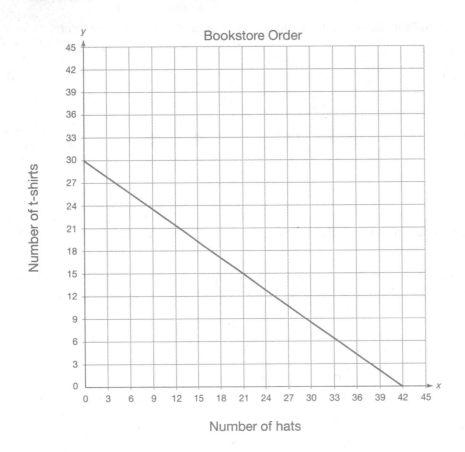

16. Write the equation $3x + 2y = 8$ in slope-intercept form. Show all your work.

$2y = -3x + 8$

$y = -\dfrac{3}{2}x + 4$

Name _____ Date _____

17. Write the equation $y = \dfrac{4}{5}x - 2$ in standard form. Show all your work.

$$-\dfrac{4}{5}x + y = -2$$

$$-4x + 5y = -10$$

18. Find the amount of interest earned by depositing $5430 into an account that earns 3% interest for 1 year. Show all your work and use a complete sentence in your answer.

$I = 5430(0.03)(1)$

$I = 162.9$

The amount of interest earned is $162.90.

19. You can use the formula $I = \dfrac{746P}{V}$ to find the amperage, where I represents amperage, P represents horsepower and V represents voltage. Solve the equation for P. Show all your work.

$$I = \dfrac{746P}{V}$$

$$IV = 746P$$

$$\dfrac{IV}{746} = P$$

5

5

Standardized Test

© 2006 Carnegie Learning, Inc.

Name _____ Date _____

1. What is the *y*-intercept of the graph of $6x + 5y = 30$?

   (a.) 6

   b. 5

   c. −5

   d. −6

2. Which point lies on the line defined by $4x - 3y = 9$?

   a. (3, 7)

   b. (0, 3)

   (c.) $\left(2, -\dfrac{1}{3}\right)$

   d. $\left(2, \dfrac{17}{3}\right)$

3. What is the equation of the line that has a slope of −3 and passes through the point (−6, 9)?

   a. $y = -3x + 21$

   b. $y = -3x - 21$

   c. $y = -3x + 9$

   (d.) $y = -3x - 9$

4. The equation of line *a* is $7x + 2y = 8$, and the equation of line *b* is $2x - 7y = -28$. Which of the following statements is true?

   a. Lines *a* and *b* have the same *x*-intercept.

   (b.) Lines *a* and *b* have the same *y*-intercept.

   c. Lines *a* and *b* have the same slope.

   d. None of the above.

5

5. Which of the following equations shows $y = \dfrac{3}{7}x - 4$ written in standard form?

a. $3x - 7y = 28$

b. $3x + 7y = 28$

c. $-\dfrac{3}{7}x + y = -4$

d. $-\dfrac{3}{7}x - y = 4$

6. Find the slope of the line $3y = 2x + 6$.

a. $-\dfrac{2}{3}$

b. $\dfrac{2}{3}$

c. 2

d. -2

7. Which equation describes a line that has a y-intercept of -10 and a slope of $\dfrac{2}{5}$?

a. $y = \dfrac{2}{5}(10) - x$

b. $y = \dfrac{2}{5}(x - 10)$

c. $y = \dfrac{2}{5}x + 10$

d. $y = \dfrac{2}{5}x - 10$

Standardized Test PAGE 3

Name _____ Date _____

8. What is the slope of the linear function shown in the graph?

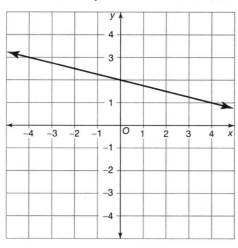

a. −4

b. $-\dfrac{1}{4}$

c. $\dfrac{1}{4}$

d. 4

5

9. Which of the following best describes the slope of the line?

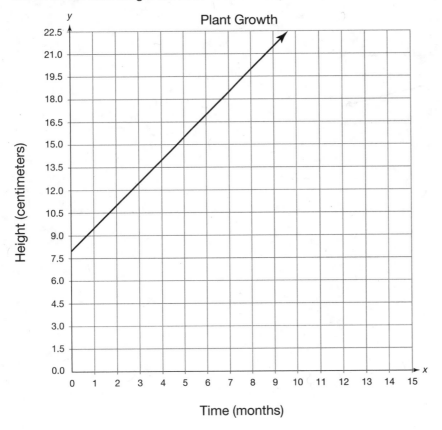

Plant Growth

a. The plant grows 1.5 centimeters every 2 months.

b. The plant grows 1.5 centimeters per month.

c. The plant grows 8 centimeters per month.

d. The plant grows 2 centimeters per month.

10. Which of the following statements about slope is NOT true?

a. The smaller the absolute value of the slope, the steeper the line.

b. The larger the absolute value of the slope, the steeper the line.

c. A vertical line has a slope that is undefined.

d. A horizontal line has a slope of zero.

Name _____ Date _____

11. What are the *x*- and *y*-intercepts of the function that is graphed below?

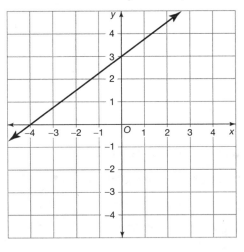

a. (0, 4) and (–3, 0)

b. (0, –4) and (3, 0)

c. (4, 0) and (0, –3)

d. (–4, 0) and (0, 3)

12. You work for a vendor selling bottles of water and lemonade at a baseball stadium. Each bottle of water sells for $2 and each bottle of lemonade sells for $2.50. Your sales for one game total $250. The equation $2x + 2.5y = 250$ represents your sales during that game if you sold *x* bottles of water and *y* bottles of lemonade. What does the *x*-intercept of the graph of the equation represent in terms of this problem situation?

a. The number of bottles of lemonade that were sold if 0 bottles of water were sold

b. The number of bottles of lemonade that were sold if 125 bottles of water were sold

c. The number of bottles of water that were sold if 100 bottles of lemonade were sold

d. The number of bottles of water that were sold if 0 bottles of lemonade were sold

5

13. Which of the following is the equation of the line that passes through (2, 6) and (−8, −14)?

    a. $y = -2x + 2$

    b. $y = 2x - 2$

    (c.) $y = 2x + 2$

    d. $y = -2x - 2$

14. You can use the formula $A = \frac{1}{2}d_1 d_2$ to find the area of a kite, where d_1 is the length of one diagonal and d_2 is the length of the other diagonal. Solve this equation for d_1.

    a. $d_2 = \dfrac{2A}{d_1}$

    (b.) $d_1 = \dfrac{2A}{d_2}$

    c. $d_1 = \dfrac{1}{2}Ad_2$

    d. $2A = d_1 d_2$

15. Which of the following shows $4x - 3y = 18$ written in slope-intercept form?

    a. $y = -\dfrac{4}{3}x + 6$

    b. $y = -\dfrac{4}{3}x + 6$

    (c.) $y = \dfrac{4}{3}x - 6$

    d. $y = \dfrac{4}{3}x + 6$

5

Pre-Test

Name _____   Date _____

Use the data table below for Questions 1 through 4.

The data in the table shows the relationship between a runner's average speed and the average number of steps the runner takes each second.

Speed	Steps
feet per second	steps per second
16.00	3.00
17.00	3.10
17.50	3.20
18.50	3.25
20.00	3.40
21.00	3.50
22.00	3.60
23.00	3.75
24.00	3.80
24.50	3.90

1. Write the ordered pairs from the table that show steps as a function of speed.

   (16.00, 3.00), (17.00, 3.10), (17.50, 3.20), (18.50, 3.25), (20.00, 3.40), (21.00, 3.50), (22.00, 3.60), (23.00, 3.75), (24.00, 3.80), (24.50, 3.90)

2. Create a scatter plot of the ordered pairs on the grid on the next page. First, choose your bounds and intervals. Be sure to label your graph clearly.

   Answers may vary. A sample answer is provided.

Variable quantity	Lower bound	Upper bound	Interval
Speed	0	30	2
Steps	−180	4.5	0.3

© 2006 Carnegie Learning, Inc.

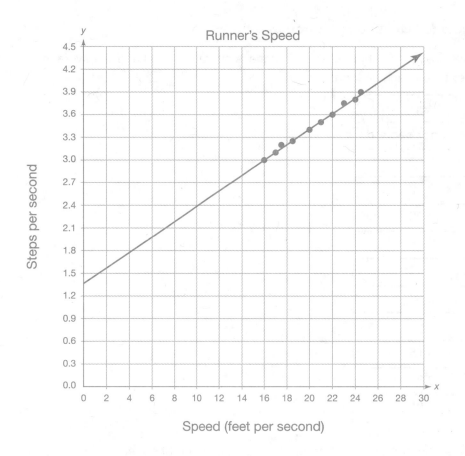

Runner's Speed

3. Use a ruler to draw the line that best fits the data in the graph. Use a complete sentence to explain how you decided where to draw the line.

Sample Answer: I drew a line that followed the pattern of the data points and was close to most of them.

4. What does the *y*-intercept of your line mean in terms of the context of the problem? Use a complete sentence in your answer.

Sample Answer: The *y*-intercept is the number of steps taken at a speed of zero feet per second.

6

Name _____   Date _____

Use the graph below to answer Questions 5 and 6.

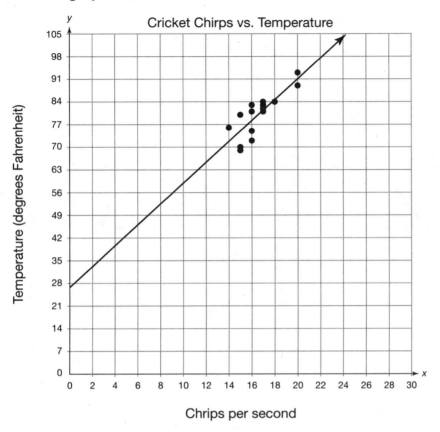

Cricket Chirps vs. Temperature

5. Write the equation of the best fit line shown in the graph above. Show all your work.
   Be sure to define your variables and include units. Mark and label any points on the
   graph that you use to find your answer.

   Answers may vary, but the equation should be close to $y = 3.22x + 26.74$, where x is the
   chirps per second and y is the temperature in degrees Fahrenheit.

6. What does the slope of your line mean in the context of your problem? Use a complete
   sentence in your answer.

   Sample Answer: The slope indicates an increase in temperature of 3.22 degrees
   Fahrenheit for each chirp per second.

Use the graph and best fit line given below to answer Questions 7 and 8.

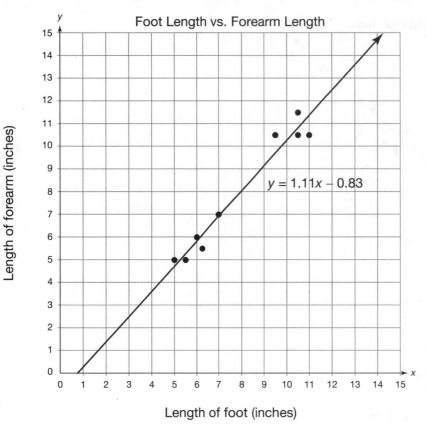

Foot Length vs. Forearm Length

$y = 1.11x - 0.83$

Length of forearm (inches)

Length of foot (inches)

7. Use the equation of the best fit line to predict the length of a person's forearm if the length of their foot is 8 inches. Is your answer reasonable in the context of the problem? Why or why not? Show all your work and use a complete sentence in your answer.

$y = 1.11(8) - 0.83$

$y = 8.88 - 0.83$

$y = 8.05$

This is a reasonable answer because a person with a foot length of 8 inches could have a forearm length of 8.05 inches.

Pre-Test PAGE 5

Name _____ Date _____

8. Use the equation of the best fit line to predict the foot length of a person with a forearm length of 12.25 inches. Show all your work and round your answer to the nearest hundredth. Use a complete sentence in your answer.

$12.25 = 1.11x - 0.83$

$13.08 = 1.11x$

$11.78 \approx x$

The foot length is about 11.78 inches.

9. What is the advantage of using a graph with a break in it? Use a complete sentence in your answer.

Sample Answer: You can see all the data and easily draw a line of best fit. It is also easier to determine the slope.

10. What is the disadvantage of using a graph with a break in it? Use a complete sentence in your answer.

Sample Answer: You cannot see the *y*-intercept.

For Questions 11 through 13, determine whether the points in each scatter plot have a positive correlation, negative correlation, or no correlation. Use a complete sentence to explain your reasoning.

11.

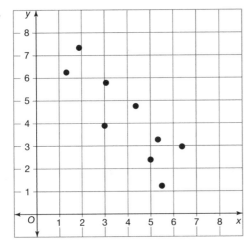

Sample Answer: These data points have a negative correlation, because the line of best fit would have a negative slope.

12.

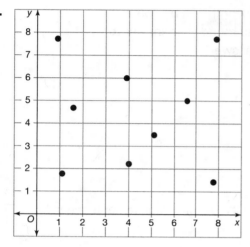

Sample Answer: These data points have no correlation, because the data do not fall in a straight line.

13.

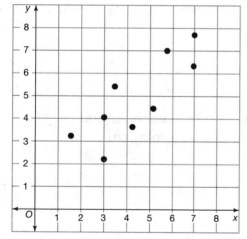

Sample Answer: These data points have a positive correlation, because the line of best fit would have a positive slope.

14. You use a graphing calculator to find a linear regression equation for some data. The calculator also produces a correlation coefficient of 0.9700513659. Use a complete sentence to explain what this value means.

Sample Answer: The data are close to being in a straight line, because the value of *r* is close to 1.

Post-Test

Name _____ Date _____

Use the data table below for Questions 1 through 4.

The data in the table shows the relationship between the number of minutes a basketball player plays in a game and the number of points he scores.

Time	Points
minutes	points
2	3
5	4
8	6
12	9
18	13
22	15
25	16
30	20
32	21
35	24

1. Write the ordered pairs from the table that show points as a function of time.

   (2, 3), (5, 4), (8, 6), (12, 9), (18, 13), (22, 15), (25, 16), (30, 20), (32, 21), (35, 24)

2. Create a scatter plot of the ordered pairs on the grid on the next page. First, choose your bounds and intervals. Be sure to label your graph clearly.

   Answers may vary. A sample answer is provided.

Variable quantity	Lower bound	Upper bound	Interval
Time	0	45	3
Points	0	30	2

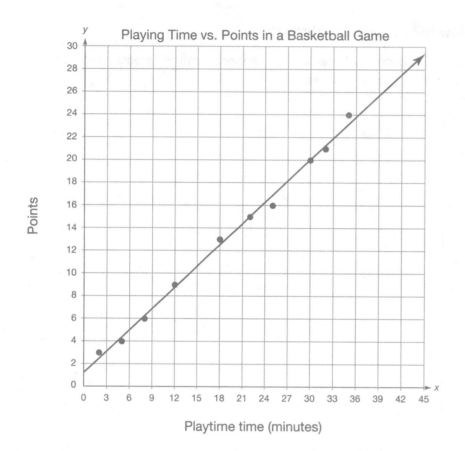

Playing Time vs. Points in a Basketball Game

Points

Playtime time (minutes)

3. Use a ruler to draw the line that best fits the data in the graph. Use a complete sentence to explain how you decided where to draw the line.

    Sample Answer: I drew a line that followed the pattern of the data points and was close to most of them.

4. What does the *y*-intercept of your line mean in terms of the context of the problem? Use a complete sentence in your answer.

    Sample Answer: The *y*-intercept is number of points scored after zero minutes of playing time.

6

Post-Test PAGE 3

Name _____ Date _____

Use the graph below to answer Questions 5 and 6.

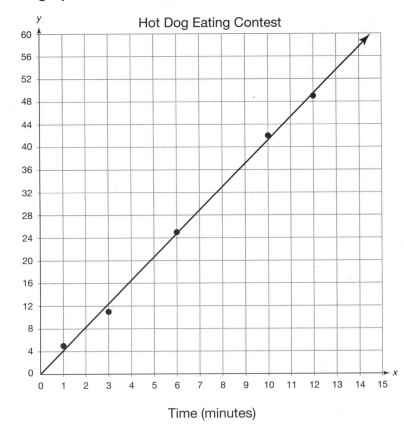

5. Write the equation of the best fit line shown in the graph above. Show all your work. Be sure to define your variables and include units. Mark and label any points on the graph that you use to find your answer.

   Answers may vary, but the equation should be close to $y = 4.12x + 0.02$, where x is the time in minutes and y is the number of hot dogs.

6. What does the slope of your line mean in the context of your problem? Use a complete sentence in your answer.

   Sample Answer: The slope indicates an increase of eating an additional 4.12 hot dogs for each additional minute.

6

Use the graph and best fit line given below to answer Questions 7 and 8.

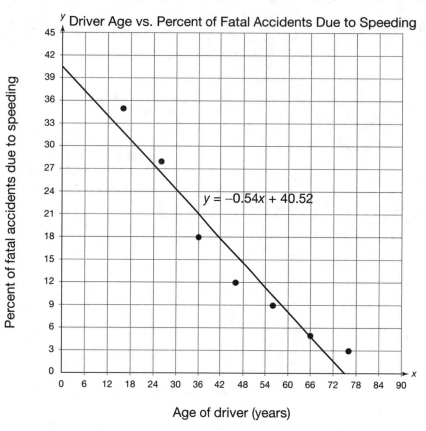

Driver Age vs. Percent of Fatal Accidents Due to Speeding

$y = -0.54x + 40.52$

Percent of fatal accidents due to speeding

Age of driver (years)

7. Use the equation of the best fit line to predict the number of fatal accidents due to speeding if the age of the driver is 84. Is your answer reasonable in the context of the problem? Why or why not? Show all your work and use a complete sentence in your answer.

$y = -0.54(84) + 40.52$

$y = -45.36 + 40.52$

$y = -4.84$

This answer is not reasonable in the context of the problem, because you cannot have a negative number of accidents.

Name _____ Date _____

8. Use the equation of the best fit line to predict the age of the driver with 15% fatal accidents due to speeding. Show all your work and round your answer to the nearest hundredth. Use a complete sentence in your answer.

$$15 = -0.54x + 40.52$$

$$-25.52 = -0.54x$$

$$47.26 \approx x$$

The age of a driver with 15% fatal accidents due to speeding is about 47 years old.

9. What is the advantage of using a graph with a break in it? Use a complete sentence in your answer.

Sample Answer: You can see all the data and easily draw a line of best fit. It is also easier to determine the slope.

10. What is the disadvantage of using a graph with a break in it? Use a complete sentence in your answer.

Sample Answer: You cannot see the y-intercept.

For Questions 11 through 13, determine whether the points in each scatter plot have a positive correlation, negative correlation, or no correlation. Use a complete sentence to explain your reasoning.

11.

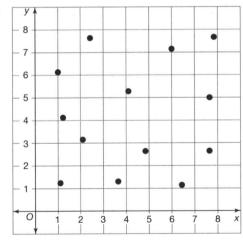

Sample Answer: These data points have no correlation, because the data do not fall in a straight line.

12.

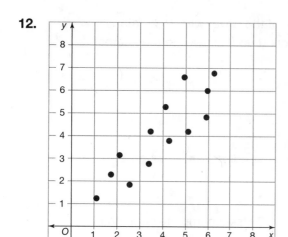

Sample Answer: These data points have a positive correlation, because the line of best fit would have a positive slope.

13.

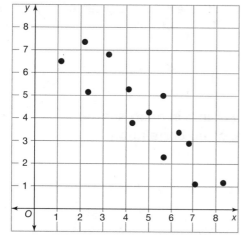

Sample Answer: These data points have a negative correlation, because the line of best fit would have a negative slope.

14. You use a graphing calculator to find a linear regression equation for some data. The calculator also produces a correlation coefficient of 0.9950012875. Use a complete sentence to explain what this value means.

Sample Answer: The data are close to being in a straight line, because the value of *r* is close to 1.

Mid-Chapter Test

Name _____ Date _____

Use the data table below for Questions 1 through 5.

A scientist wonders if you can predict a person's weight at 30 years based on the person's weight at 1 year. She uses some medical files to collect the following data.

Weight at 1 year	Weight at 30 years
pounds	pounds
21	124
25	128
23	130
24	132
20	125
15	122
25	135
21	130
17	128
24	132

1. Write the ordered pairs from the table that show the weight at 30 years as a function of the weight at 1 year.

   (21, 124), (25, 128), (23, 130), (24, 132), (20, 125), (15, 122), (25, 135), (21, 130), (17, 128), (24, 132)

2. Create a scatter plot of the ordered pairs on the grid on the next page. First, choose your bounds and intervals. Be sure to label your graph clearly.

   Answers may vary. A sample answer is provided.

Variable quantity	Lower bound	Upper bound	Interval
Weight at 1 year	0	30	2
Weight at 30 years	0	150	10

© 2006 Carnegie Learning, Inc.

3.

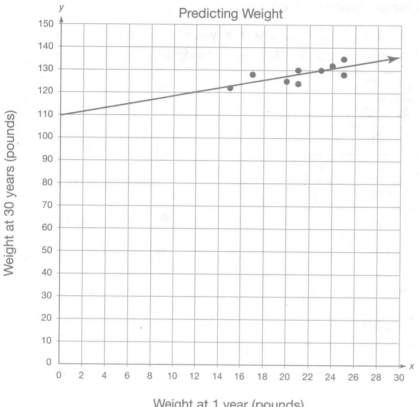

Predicting Weight

Weight at 1 year (pounds)

4. Use a ruler to draw the line that best fits the data in your graph.

Answers will vary, but the graph of the line should be close to $y = 0.8804x + 109.67$.

5. What does the *y*-intercept of your line mean in terms of the context of the problem? Use a complete sentence in your answer.

Sample Answer: The *y*-intercept represents the weight of someone at 30 years who has a weight of 0 at 1 year. It does not really make sense in this problem situation.

6

Mid-Chapter Test   PAGE 3

Name _____   Date _____

**Read the scenario below. Use the scenario and graph to answer Questions 6
through 8.**

The Fast Car dealership tracks its automobile sales based on the type of automobile.
The graph below shows the percent of sales that were SUVs for the years 1995 to 2005.

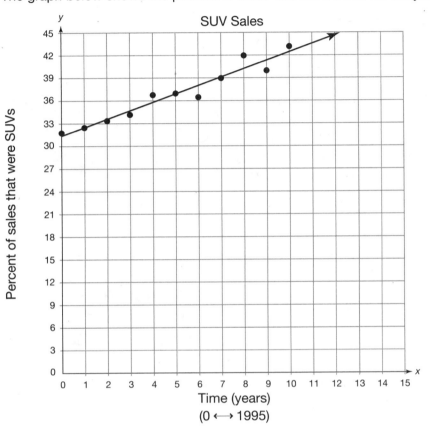

6. Explain what year is represented by 7 on the graph. Use a complete sentence in your
   answer.

   Year 7 represents the year 2002, because it represents 7 years since 1995.

7. Write the equation of the best fit line in the graph. Define your variables and include
   the units.

   Answers will vary, but should be close to y = 1.11x + 31.395, where x is the number of
   years since 1995 and y is the percent of sales that are SUVs.

8. What does the slope of the line represent in this problem situation? Use a complete
   sentence in your answer.

   The slope represents the change in the percent of SUV sales per year.

Read the scenario below. Use the scenario and graph below to answer Questions 9 and 10.

The Fast Car dealership tracks its automobile sales based on the type of automobile. The graph below shows the percent of sales that were compact cars for the years 1995 to 2005.

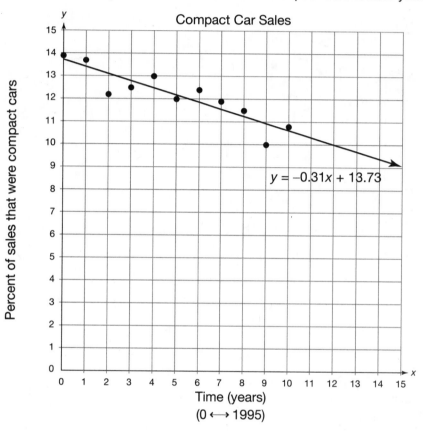

9. Use the equation provided to predict the percent of sales that were compact cars in the year 2006. Show all your work and use a complete sentence in your answer.

$y = -0.31(11) + 13.73 = 10.32$; **The percent should be about 10.3.**

10. Use the equation provided to predict the year in which the percent of sales that were compact cars was 11%. Show all your work and use a complete sentence in your answer.

$$11 = -0.31x + 13.73$$

$$-2.73 = -0.31x$$

$$x \approx 8.8 \qquad 1995 + 8.8 = 2003.8$$

In 2003, the percent of sales that were compact cars was 11%.

6

End of Chapter Test

Name _____ Date _____

Use the data table below to answer Questions 1 through 9.

You just got your ACT scores. Your composite score wasn't exactly what you had expected. You wonder if you could have predicted your composite score using your GPA. You get the following data about 10 students from the counseling office.

GPA	ACT composite score
points	points
3.2	18
3.3	21
3.1	22
3.5	25
3.4	27
3.7	29
3.8	28
3.7	28
3.9	29
4.0	29

1. Write the ordered pairs from the table that show the ACT composite score as a function of the person's GPA.

   (3.2, 18), (3.3, 21), (3.1, 22), (3.5, 25), (3.4, 27), (3.7, 28), (3.8, 28), (3.7, 29), (3.9, 29), (4.0, 29)

2. Create a scatter plot of the ordered pairs on the grid on the next page. Because the data points are clustered together, break the graph on the x-axis. Complete the bounds and intervals table provided below. Be sure to label your graph clearly.

Variable quantity	Lower bound	Upper bound	Interval
GPA	3.1	4.5	0.1
ACT composite score	0	30	2

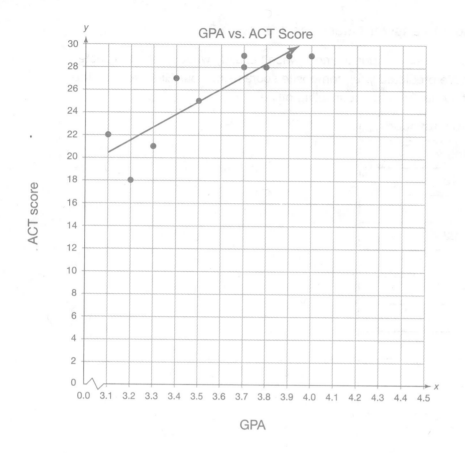

3. What is the advantage of using a graph with a break in it? Use a complete sentence in your answer.

    Sample Answer: You can see all the data and easily draw a line of best fit. It is also easier to determine the slope.

4. What is the disadvantage of using a graph with a break in it? Use a complete sentence in your answer.

    Sample Answer: You cannot see the *y*-intercept.

5. Use a ruler to draw the line of best fit. Then, write the equation of your line. Define your variables.

    Answers will vary, but the graph of the line should be close to *y* = 11.19*x* − 14.22, where *x* is the GPA and *y* is the ACT composite score.

6

End of Chapter Test   PAGE 3

Name _____   Date _____

6. Use your equation to predict the ACT composite score of a student with a GPA of 2.9. Show all your work and use a complete sentence in your answer.

$y = 11.19(2.9) - 14.22$

$= 32.451 - 14.22$

$= 18.231$

A student with a GPA of 2.9 would have an ACT composite score of 18.

7. Use your equation to predict the GPA of a student with an ACT composite score of 20. Show all your work and use a complete sentence in your answer.

$20 = 11.19x - 14.22$

$34.22 = 11.19x$

$3.1 \approx x$

A student with an ACT composite score of 20 would have a GPA of about 3.1.

8. Describe the correlation of the data displayed in the graph in Question 2. Use complete sentences to explain your reasoning.

Sample Answer: The data has a positive correlation, because the line of best fit has a positive slope.

9. Your teacher asks you to use a graphing calculator to find the linear regression equation for this data. In addition to the linear regression equation, the calculator produces a correlation coefficient of 0.8671959024. Use a complete sentence to explain what this number tells you about the data.

Sample Answer: The data are relatively close to being in a straight line because the correlation coefficient is relatively close to 1.

© 2006 Carnegie Learning, Inc.

10. Is a linear model the best model for the data below? Why or why not? Use a complete sentence in your answer.

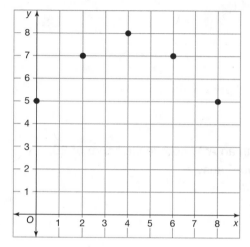

Sample Answer: A linear model is not the best model, because the pattern of the data is a curve.

Standardized Test Practice

Name _____ Date _____

1. The data in the table show the cost of ordering DVDs from an online company, including the flat shipping fee.

Number of DVDs (n)	Cost in dollars (C)
3	11
6	17
10	25

What is the equation of the line that best fits the data if the number of DVDs n is graphed on the horizontal axis and the cost C is graphed on the vertical axis?

a. $C = 2n$

b. $C = 2n - 5$

c. $C = \dfrac{1}{2}n + 5$

d. $C = 2n + 5$

2. Your teacher asks you to make a scatter plot of the data below. He asks you to define time as the number of years since 1996. What number would you use for 2000?

Year	1996	1997	1998	1999	2000
Number of graduates	224	237	219	222	241

a. 2

b. 3

c. 4

d. 5

6

Read the scenario below. Use the scenario and graph to answer Questions 3 through 6.

A baseball coach would like to be able to predict the number of hits his players will get based on the number of times they are at bat. He graphs some data and finds the best fit line. The equation of the best fit line is $y = 0.32x - 20.51$, where x is the number of times at bat and y is the number of hits.

3. How many hits should he expect from a player who is at bat 175 times? Round your answer to the nearest whole number.

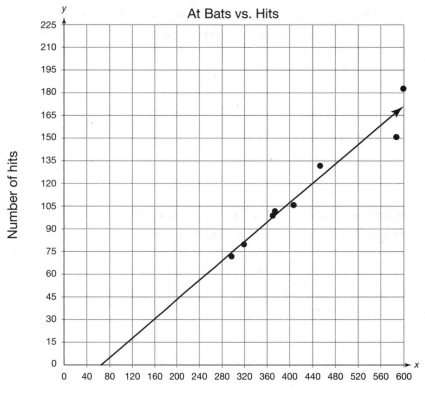

a. 35

b. 36

c. 76

d. 77

Name _____ Date _____

4. How many times is a player at bat if he has 200 hits? Round your answer to the nearest whole number.

   a. 560

   b. 561

   c. 689

   d. 690

5. In the best fit equation $y = 0.32x - 20.51$ from the baseball scenario, what does the slope mean?

   a. The increase in the number of hits for each time at bat

   b. The decrease in the number of hits for each time at bat

   c. The increase in the number of times at bat for each hit

   d. The decrease in the number of times at bat for each hit

6. In the best fit equation $y = 0.32x - 20.51$ from the baseball scenario, what does the y-intercept mean?

   a. The number of times at bat for zero hits

   b. The number of hits for zero times at bat

   c. The number of hits for each time at bat

   d. The number of times at bat before getting one hit

7. Which of the following is NOT an advantage of using a graph with a break in it?

   a. You can see all the data.

   b. You can see the y-intercept.

   c. You can easily draw a line of best fit.

   d. You can more easily determine the slope of the line.

8. Do the points in the scatter plot have a positive correlation, a negative correlation, or no correlation?

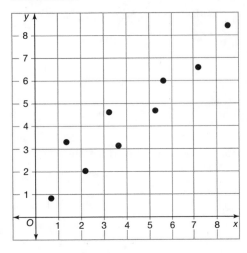

a. positive correlation

b. negative correlation

c. no correlation

9. If a line of best fit models the data very well, what would you expect to see in a graph of the data and the line?

a. The line has a positive slope.

b. The line has a negative slope.

c. The line is very close to all of the points.

d. The line is close to some of the points but not very close to other points.

10. You enter data into a graphing calculator to find the linear regression equation. In addition to producing the equation, the calculator produces a correlation coefficient. Which of the following correlation coefficients would indicate that the data are NOT very close to forming a straight line?

a. −0.897854351

b. 0.089785435

c. 0.897854351

d. 0.978543518

6

Cumulative Test

Name _____ Date _____

Use the sequence below to answer Questions 1 and 2.

Term (n)	1	2	3	4	5
Sequence	–3	–1	1	3	5

1. Write an expression for the nth term and describe the pattern. Use a complete sentence in your answer.

   To find the nth term, start with the previous term and add 2 then subtract 5. The nth term is given by the expression $2n - 5$.

2. Use the expression you wrote in Question 1 to find the 20th term of the sequence. Show all your work.

   $2(20) - 5 = 40 - 5 = 35$

Read the scenario below. Use the scenario to answer Questions 3 through 5.

The student council at your school wants to start an intramural basketball league. During half time of a basketball game, you survey 40 students in each grade to see if they would be interested in playing in an intramural league. You found that 21 freshmen, 37 sophomores, 31 juniors, and 19 seniors said that they would be interested in playing in the intramural league.

3. Write a ratio that shows the relationship between the number of sophomores that are interested in playing in the league and the total number of sophomores that were surveyed.

   $$\frac{37 \text{ sophomores interested in intramural basketball}}{40 \text{ sophomores surveyed}}$$

4. There are 243 sophomores at your school. Use the ratio you wrote in Question 3 to determine how many of them would be interested in playing in the intramural basketball league. Show all your work and use a complete sentence in your answer.

   $$\frac{37 \text{ sophomores interested in intramural basketball}}{40 \text{ sophomores surveyed}} = \frac{x \text{ sophomores interested in intramural basketball}}{243 \text{ total sophomores}}$$

   $$37(243) = 40x$$
   $$8991 = 40x$$
   $$224.775 = x$$

   Sample Answer: Approximately 225 sophomores would be interested in intramural basketball.

1–6

Cumulative Test PAGE 2

5. Was your survey biased? Use a complete sentence to explain your reasoning.

Sample Answer: Yes, the survey was biased. You surveyed students who were at a basketball game, so they might be more interested in basketball than the general student body population.

6. Your uncle takes you and your friends out to eat to celebrate your graduation. The total bill for everyone's dinner is $214.72. Your uncle would like to leave a 20% tip because the service was so good. How much should he leave? Show all your work and use a complete sentence in your answer.

$$\frac{x}{214.72} = \frac{20}{100}$$

$$214.72(20) = 100x$$

$$4294.4 = 100x$$

$$42.944 = x$$

Your uncle should leave a tip in the amount of $42.94.

Solve each equation. Show all your work.

7. $-3x + 4 = -8$

$$-3x + 4 - 4 = -8 - 4$$

$$-3x = -12$$

$$\frac{-3x}{-3} = \frac{-12}{-3}$$

$$x = 4$$

8. $\frac{x}{5} - 7 = 4$

$$\frac{x}{5} - 7 + 7 = 4 + 7$$

$$\frac{x}{5} = 11$$

$$\frac{x}{5} \cdot 5 = 11 \cdot 5$$

$$x = 55$$

9. Evaluate $f(x) = -3x - 9$ at $x = -4$. Show all your work.

$$f(-4) = -3(-4) - 9$$

$$= 12 - 9$$

$$= 3$$

1-6

© 2006 Carnegie Learning, Inc.

186 Chapter 6 ■ Assessments

Name _____ Date _____

10. You recently joined an online book-on-CD club so that you can rent books on CD. The membership fee is $45 and each rental is $4 which covers shipping and handling.

    a. Write an equation that gives the total cost in terms of the number of rentals. Use x to represent the number of rentals and y to represent the total cost.

        $y = 4x + 45$

    b. Does this equation represent a function? If so, identify the domain and range in terms of this real-life situation. If not, explain why. Use complete sentences in your answer.

        Yes, this equation represents a function. The domain is {0, 1, 2, 3, ...} and the range is {45, 49, 53, 57, ...}.

11. Write the repeating decimal 0.2222... as a fraction. Show all your work.

    $10w = 2.2222...$

    $- w = 0.2222...$
    _____

    $9w = 2$

    $w = \dfrac{2}{9}$

12. Solve the following equation. Show all your work.

    $-2(x - 18) = 4(4x - 9)$

    $-2x + 36 = 16x - 36$

    $-18x = -72$

    $x = 4$

13. Solve the following inequality. Then, graph your solution. Show all your work.

$-5x + 8 \geq 43$

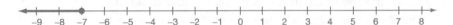

$-5x \geq 35$

$x \leq -7$

14. Solve the following inequality. Then, graph your solution. Show all your work.

$|3x - 6| < 12$

$3x - 6 < 12$	$3x - 6 > -12$
$3x < 18$	$3x > -6$
$x < 6$	$x > -2$

15. Find the x- and y-intercepts of the graph below.

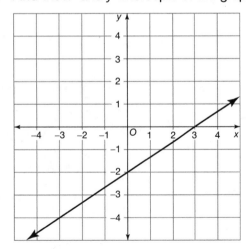

x-intercept: ___3___

y-intercept: ___-2___

1-6

Cumulative Test PAGE 5

Name _____ Date _____

16. Algebraically find the *x*- and *y*-intercepts of the graph of the equation $2x + 7y = 28$. Show all your work.

x-intercept: __14__

y-intercept: __4__

$2x + 7(0) = 28$	$2(0) + 7y = 28$
$2x = 28$	$.7y = 28$
$x = 14$	$y = 4$

Read the scenario below. Use the scenario to answer Questions 17 and 18.

Donna has started her own clowning business. For a fee of $12 per hour, people can hire her to come to a party to make balloon animals and do magic tricks. To get her business started, Donna borrows $20 from her parents for supplies.

17. Write an equation that gives Donna's profit in terms of the number of hours she works. Use *x* to represent the number of hours and use *y* to represent Donna's profit after she pays her parents back.

$y = 12x - 20$

18. What does the *y*-intercept mean in terms of the problem situation? Use a complete sentence in your answer.

Sample Answer: The *y*-intercept represents Donna's profit after working zero hours.

19. Write the equation of a line in slope-intercept form that has a slope of $-\frac{2}{9}$ and passes through the point (18, 5). Show all your work.

$y - 5 = -\frac{2}{9}(x - 18)$

$y - 5 = -\frac{2}{9}x + 4$

$y = -\frac{2}{9}x + 9$

© 2006 Carnegie Learning, Inc.

1-6

Chapter 6 ■ Assessments **189**

20. Write the equation of a line in slope-intercept form that passes through the points (–4, 6) and (8, 12). Show all your work.

$$m = \frac{12 - 6}{8 - (-4)} = \frac{6}{12} = \frac{1}{2}$$

$$y - 12 = \frac{1}{2}(x - 8)$$

$$y - 12 = \frac{1}{2}x - 4$$

$$y = \frac{1}{2}x + 8$$

21. Identify the slope and y-intercept of the equation $y = \frac{2}{5}x - 6$, and use them to graph the equation on the grid below.

slope: $\frac{2}{5}$

y-intercept: -6

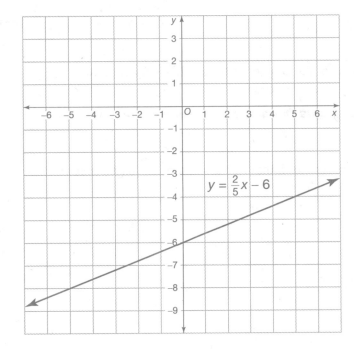

1–6

Name _____ Date _____

22. Write the equation $y = -\dfrac{3}{11}x + 6$ in standard form. Show all your work.

$$y = -\frac{3}{11}x + 6$$

$$\frac{3}{11}x + y = 6$$

$$3x + 11y = 66$$

23. Write the equation $-7x + 9y = 54$ in slope-intercept form. Show all your work.

$$-7x + 9y = 54$$

$$9y = 7x + 54$$

$$y = \frac{7}{9}x + 6$$

Read the scenario below. Use the scenario and data to answer Questions 24 through 29.

Mr. Lane is a new English teacher, and he is deciding which books he would like to have his students read over the course of the year. He wants to predict how long it will take the students to read a book based on the length of the book. Mr. Lane asks several students to read books of varying length and record the amount of time it takes them to read the book.

Number of pages	Time
pages	hours
275	3.4
324	4.5
189	2.5
202	2.75
236	3.4
357	5.5
148	2.2
218	3.2

24. Write the ordered pairs from the table that show time as a function of the number of pages.

(275, 3.4), (324, 4.5), (189, 2.5), (202, 2.75), (236, 3.4), (357, 5.5), (148, 2.2), (218, 3.2)

25. Create a scatter plot of the ordered pairs on the grid below. Break the graph on the x-axis, so that the points will be more spread out. Complete the bounds and intervals table provided below. Be use to label your graph clearly.

Variable quantity	Lower bound	Upper bound	Interval
Number of pages	95	375	20
Time	0.0	6.0	0.4

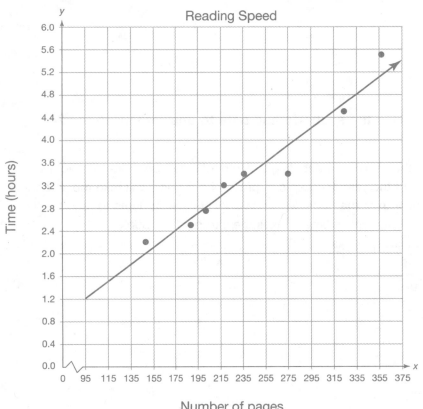

26. Use a ruler to draw a line that best fits the data in your graph. Then, write the equation of the line. Be sure to define your variables and include units.

Answers will vary, but the graph of the line should be close to $y = 0.015x - 0.22$, where x represents the number of pages and y represents the time.

© 2006 Carnegie Learning, Inc.

1-6

Name _____ Date _____

27. What does the slope of the line mean in terms of the problem situation? Use a complete sentence in your answer.

Sample Answer: The slope represents the increase in time for each one page increase in the length of the book.

28. Use the equation you wrote in Question 26 to predict how long it will take to read a book that is 423 pages. Show all your work and round your answer to the nearest tenth, if necessary. Use a complete sentence in your answer.

$y = 0.015(423) - 0.22$

$= 6.345 - 0.22$

$= 6.125$

It will take about 8.2 hours to read a book that is 423 pages long.

29. Use the equation you wrote in Question 26 to predict how many pages a book has if it takes 2.8 hours to read. Show all your work and round your answer to the nearest whole number, if necessary. Use a complete sentence in your answer.

$2.8 = 0.015x - 0.22$

$3.02 = 0.015x$

$201.33 \approx x$

A book that has about 201 pages will take 2.8 hours to read.

1-6

Section 3
Assignments with Answers
Chapters 1–6

Assignment

Name _____ Date _____

Designing a Patio
Patterns and Sequences

Define the term in your own words.

1. sequence

   Sample Answer: A sequence is a set of numbers or objects that change according to a pattern.

2. term

   Sample Answer: A term is an element of a sequence.

You are creating a tile design for your bathroom floor.

3. What are the next two terms of the sequence in your tile design? Draw a separate picture for each term.

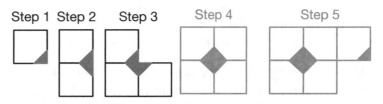

Step 1 Step 2   Step 3   Step 4   Step 5

4. Identify the term from your tile design shown at the right.

   eighth term

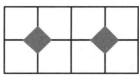

Find the next three terms in the sequence. Use complete sentences to explain how you found your answers.

5. 1, 3, 5, __7__ , __9__ , __11__ , . . .

   Sample Answer: The terms are consecutive odd integers. Add two to the previous term to get the next term.

6. 1, 0.1, 0.01, __0.001__ , __0.0001__ , __0.00001__ , . . .

   Sample Answer: Divide the previous term by 10 to get the next term.

7. 28, 24, 20, __16__ , __12__ , __8__ , . . .

   Sample Answer: Subtract four from the previous term to get the next term.

8. 2, 4, 8, __16__ , __32__ , __64__ , . . .

   Sample Answer: Multiply the previous term by 2 to get the next term.

9. Create your own sequence of numbers or pictures to challenge your classmates. Write or draw the first three terms. Then write a sentence describing the pattern.

   Answers will vary.

1

Name _____ Date _____

Lemonade, Anyone?
Finding the 10th Term of a Sequence

The balance in your savings account is $50. You save $5 each week from your allowance.

1. Complete each statement below to find your savings account balance.

   Balance after 1 week: 50 + 5(_1_) = _$55_   Balance after 3 weeks: 50 + 5(_3_) = _$65_

   Balance after 2 weeks: 50 + 5(_2_) = _$60_   Balance after 10 weeks: 50 + 5(_10_) = _$100_

2. Write the sequence of numbers formed by your savings account balance after 1 week, 2 weeks, 3 weeks, and so on.

   55, 60, 65, 70, . . .

3. Use a complete sentence to explain what the 10th term of the sequence represents.

   The 10th term represents the savings account balance after 10 weeks.

While watching the news, you learn that a major cold front is moving into your region of the country. The temperature is currently 40°F, and dropping at a rate of 2°F per hour.

4. Write the sequence of numbers that represents the temperature in 1 hour, 2 hours, 3 hours, and so on.

   38, 36, 34, 32, . . .

5. What is the 10th term of the sequence? Use a complete sentence to explain what the 10th term of the sequence represents.

   40 − 2(10) = 20; The 10th term represents the temperature in 10 hours.

6. Did you multiply or subtract first when determining the terms of the sequence? How would your sequence change if you reversed the order?

   Sample Answer: I multiplied the rate of change by the time before subtracting. If I had subtracted first, each term of the sequence would have increased by 38 instead of decreasing by 2.

Perform the indicated operations. Show your work.

7. 3 + 4(2)

   3 + 8 = 11

8. 11 − 2(3)

   11 − 6 = 5

9. 42 + 3(2)

   16 + 6 = 22

10. (15 − 3)4 + 2(9)

    12(4) + 18 = 48 + 18

    = 66

11. 15 − 3(4) + 2(9)

    15 − 12 + 18 = 3 +18

    = 21

12. 33 − 5(4 + 1)

    33 − 5(5) = 33 − 25

    = 8

Assignment

Name _____ Date _____

1

Dinner with the Stars
Finding the *n*th Term of a Sequence

While your school is planning the charity dinner, you talk to a friend who recently threw a catered party. She suggests that you hire the caterer she used. Her caterer will serve dinner for only $18 per person, but there is a one-time fee of $25 for renting tablecloths and napkins. You can represent the total catering cost for different numbers of people with the sequence 43, 61, 79, ...

1. Find the total catering costs for 4, 5, and 6 people.

Number of people	1	2	3	4	5	6
Total catering cost (dollars)	43	61	79	97	115	133

2. What is the total catering cost if 10 people attend the event? Use a complete sentence to explain your answer.

   Total cost in dollars: 18(10) + 25 = 205; Sample Answer: To find the total cost, multiply the number of people by the cost of one dinner, and then add the $25 fee.

3. What is the total catering cost if 15 people attend the event? Use a complete sentence to explain your answer.

   Total cost in dollars: 18(15) + 25 = 295; Sample Answer: To find the total cost, multiply the number of people by the cost of one dinner, and then add the $25 fee.

4. What algebraic expression can you write to represent the total catering cost in dollars if *n* people attend?

   $18n + 25$

Evaluate each expression for the given value of the variable.

5. Evaluate $b + 7$ when b is 13.

   $13 + 7 = 20$

6. Evaluate $\frac{p}{5}$ when p is 60.

   $\frac{60}{5} = 12$

7. Evaluate $2m + 4$ when m is 3.

   $2(3) + 4 = 10$

8. Evaluate $8 - 4d$ when d is 0.

   $8 - 4(0) = 8$

Use the *n*th term to list the first five terms of each sequence. Show your work.

9. $a_n = 2.5n$

   $a_1 = 2.5(1) = 2.5$
   $a_2 = 2.5(2) = 5$
   $a_3 = 2.5(3) = 7.5$
   $a_4 = 2.5(4) = 10$
   $a_5 = 2.5(5) = 12.5$

10. $a_n = 6n - 5$

    $a_1 = 6(1) - 5 = 1$
    $a_2 = 6(2) - 5 = 7$
    $a_3 = 6(3) - 5 = 13$
    $a_4 = 6(4) - 5 = 19$
    $a_5 = 6(5) - 5 = 25$

Assignment

1

Name _____ Date _____

Working for the CIA
Using a Sequence to Represent a Problem Situation

A group of engineers is working on a design for a new car. Each member has a separate task that relates to the overall design, but it is important for all group members to understand all parts of the project. The final design is due soon, and it is crucial that all the engineers meet with each other individually to review details before the design is submitted.

1. Find the number of meetings required for 3 engineers to meet with each other individually. What is the number of meetings required for 4 engineers to meet with each other individually? What is the number of meetings redquired for 6 engineers to meet with each other individually?

   3 meetings; 6 meetings; 15 meetings

2. Find the number of engineers involved in the project if a total of 66 meetings were required. Use complete sentences to explain how found your answer.

   12 engineers; Sample Answer: I used guess and check to find my answer. For 12 engineers, it would take 11 + 10 + 9 + 8 + 7 + 6 + 5 + 4 + 3 + 2 +1 = 66 meetings.

3. Describe another problem scenario that can be represented by the sequence in Questions 1 and 2.

   Sample Answer: The number of games that must be played for *n* teams to each play every other team exactly once can be represented by the sequence 1, 3, 6, 15, ...

You are learning about cell division in science class. Suppose a cell divides one time each minute.

4. The sequence of pictures below represents the cell division over time. Draw the 3rd and 4th terms of the sequence.

   1 minute   2 minutes

   3 minutes   4 minutes

   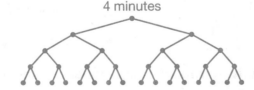

5. Complete the table below to show the number of cells over time.

Time (minutes)	1	2	3	4	5	6	7
Number of cells	2	4	8	16	32	64	128

6. Write a numerical expression for the number of cells in terms of the time.

Number of cells after 1 minute: $2 = \underline{2^1}$

Number of cells after 2 minutes: $4 = \underline{2^2}$

Number of cells after 3 minutes: $8 = \underline{2^3}$

7. Write an algebraic expression for the number of cells in terms of the time t.

Number of cells after t minutes: $\underline{2^t}$

Assignment

1

Name _____ Date _____

Gauss' Formula
Finding the Sum of a Finite Sequence

1. Test to see if Gauss' Formula holds true for the sum of an odd number of numbers.

   Sample Answer: The sum of the numbers from 1 to 9 is $\dfrac{9(10)}{2} = 45$.

A gardener expands a small 4-foot by 6-foot garden that currently exists in his backyard. Each day he increases the length and the width of the garden by two feet each. He then wants to buy fence to surround his garden to protect it from rabbits.

Day	0	1	2	3	4	n
Width	4	6	8	10	12	$2n + 4$
Length	6	8	10	12	14	$2n + 6$
Area	24	48	80	120	168	$(2n + 4)(2n + 6)$
Perimeter	20	28	36	44	52	$2(2n + 4) + 2(2n + 6)$

2. Fill in the width and length of the garden in the chart above to show how the dimensions change for the first four days.

3. Write expressions in the chart for the width and the length of the garden in terms of the number of days n.

4. Fill in the chart for the area of the garden over the first four days.

5. Write an expression in the chart for the area of the garden in terms of the number of days n.

6. Fill in the chart for the perimeter of the garden over the first four days. (*Hint:* The formula for the perimeter of a rectangle is $P = 2l + 2w$.)

7. Explain why the order of operations is important when using the formula for perimeter.

   Sample Answer: It is important to multiply before adding when using the formula for perimeter.

8. Write an expression in the chart for the perimeter of the garden in terms of the number of days n.

9. The gardener has $125 to buy the fence, which costs $1.25 per foot. Use your expression for the perimeter to find the maximum dimensions of the expanded garden.

   24 feet by 26 feet

10. Find the number of days it takes the gardener to expand the garden to its maximum size.

    10 days

© 2006 Carnegie Learning, Inc.

Assignment

Name _____ Date _____

$8 an Hour Problem
Using Multiple Representations, Part 1

After working at Pat-E-Oh Furniture for 6 months, you receive a raise. Your new pay rate is $9.50 per hour.

1. The table below shows the number of hours that you have worked for the first four weeks following your raise. Complete the table.

	Week	Time worked	Earnings
Labels			
Units		hours	dollars
	Week 1	40	380
	Week 2	4	38
	Week 3	8	76
	Week 4	20	190

2. Use the bounds and intervals to label the grid on the next page. Then create a graph of the data in the second and third columns of the table in Question 1.

Variable quantity	Lower bound	Upper bound	Interval
Time worked	0	60	4
Earnings	0	450	30

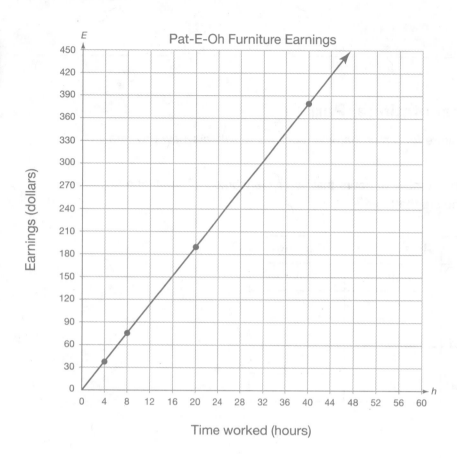

Pat-E-Oh Furniture Earnings

Earnings (dollars)

Time worked (hours)

3. Next week you can work 12 hours. Use the graph to approximate the amount of money that you will earn. Use a complete sentence to explain how you found your answer.

Sample Answer: Start at 12 hours and move up the graph until you reach the line. Then move left and read what the corresponding earnings are. You will earn about $120 for working 12 hours.

4. Write an expression that you can use to find the earnings for any number of hours worked. Let h represent the number of hours worked. Use a complete sentence in your answer.

The earnings for h hours are given by 9.5h.

5. Use the expression to find the exact amount you would earn in 12 hours. Use a complete sentence in your answer.

9.5(12) = 114; You would earn $114 for working 12 hours.

6. Use a complete sentence to explain the difference between an algebraic expression and an algebraic equation. Show an example of each one.

An algebraic expression consists of numbers, variables, and operations, while an algebraic equation is two algebraic expressions set equal to each other.

Expression: 2x Equation: 2x = 10

7. Is $m = 4$ a solution of the equation $m + 10 = 14$? Show your work.

4 + 10 = 14

14 = 14

Assignment

Name _____ Date _____

The Consultant Problem
Using Multiple Representations, Part 2

Complete the conversion.

1. 30 min = __0.5__ hr

2. 150 min = __2.5__ hr

3. 2.75 hr = __165__ min

4. 2.3 mi = __4048__ yds

5. 42 in. = __3.5__ ft

6. 4.2 ft = __50.4__ in.

Write an algebraic equation for each situation. Then identify the dependent and independent variables.

7. A plumber earns $62 for each hour that she works. Let E represent her earnings in dollars for h hours of work.

   $E = 62h$; dependent variable: earnings E; independent variable: number of hours h

8. A marathon runner averages 10 miles per hour. Let m represent the distance in miles run in h hours.

   $m = 10h$; dependent variable: distance m; independent variable: number of hours h

9. A seamstress can hem 3 skirts each hour. Let s represent the number of skirts she hems in h hours.

   $s = 3h$; dependent variable: number of skirts s; independent variable: number of hours h

10. You earn $12 for each yard you mow. Let E represent your earnings in dollars for mowing y yards.

    $E = 12y$; dependent variable: earning E; independent variable: number of yards y

Your aunt was recently hired to work for a large law firm. Over the course of her first year, she will work on several projects. She receives a stipend of $3250 for each completed project.

11. What are the two variable quantities in this problem situation?

    Number of projects completed and money earned

12. Which variable quantity is the independent variable? Write a sentence explaining your answer.

    Number of projects completed is the independent variable because the number of projects determines the money earned.

13. How much money will your aunt make if she completes 5 projects?
    $16,250

14. How many projects did your aunt complete if she earned $32,500?
    10 projects

Assignment

1

Name _____ Date _____

U.S. Shirts
Using Tables, Graphs, and Equations, Part 1

Define the term in your own words.

1. variable quantity

   Sample Answer: A variable quantity is a quantity that does not have a fixed value.

2. constant quantity

   Sample Answer: A constant quantity is a quantity that has a fixed value.

Evaluate each algebraic expression for the value given. Show your work.

3. $8s + 15$ when $s = 20$ 4. $10 - 2m$ when $m = 4$ 5. $\frac{1}{2}r + 30$ when $r = 10$

   $8(20) + 15 = 175$ $10 - 2(4) = 2$ $\frac{1}{2}(10) + 30 = 35$

You want to save money for college. You have already saved $500, and you are able to save $75 each week.

6. If you continue to save money at this rate, what will your total savings be in 3 weeks? What will your total savings be in 10 weeks? What will your total savings be in 6 months? (*Hint:* There are four weeks in one month)

   $725; $1250; $2300

7. Use a complete sentence to explain how you found the total savings in Question 6.

   Sample Answer: The total savings were found by first multiplying the weekly savings rate by the number of weeks and then adding the amount already saved.

8. If you continue to save money at this rate, how long will it take you to save $2000? How long will it take you to save $8000? How long will it take you to save $11,250?

   20 weeks; 100 weeks; 150 weeks

9. Use a complete sentence to explain how you found the answers to the number of weeks in Question 8.

   Sample Answer: The numbers of weeks were found by first subtracting the amount already saved from the amount saved and then dividing the result by the weekly savings rate.

10. Complete the table using the data from Questions 6 and 8. Be sure to fill in your labels and units.

	Time	Total savings
Labels		
Units	weeks	dollars
	3	725
	10	1250
	24	2300
	20	2000
	100	8000
	150	11,250

11. Use the grid below to create a line graph of the data from the table in Question 10. First, choose your bounds and intervals. Be sure to label your graph clearly.

Variable quantity	Lower bound	Upper bound	Interval
Time worked	0	200	10
Earnings	0	15,000	1000

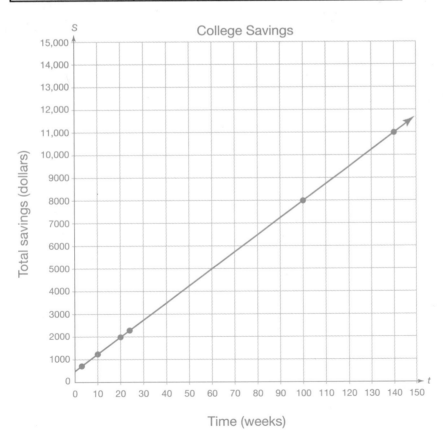

1

12. Write an algebraic equation for the problem situation. Use a complete sentence in your answer.

Sample answer: The equation $S = 75t + 500$, where S represents the total savings in dollars and t represents the time in weeks.

Assignment

Name _____ Date _____

Hot Shirts
Using Tables, Graphs, and Equations, Part 2

Estimate the value of each expression.

1. 118 − 22

   120 − 20 = 100

   118 − 22 ≈ 100

2. 511 + 293

   510 + 290 = 800

   511 + 293 ≈ 800

3. 299 × 0.99

   300 × 1 = 300

   299 × 0.99 ≈ 300

4. 5.26 × 24.74

   5 × 25 = 125

   5.26 × 24.74 ≈ 125

5. 958.16 + 239.85

   958 + 240 = 1198

   958.16 + 239.85 ≈ 1198

6. 39.78 − 14.92

   40 − 15 = 25

   39.78 − 14.92 ≈ 25

7. Give an example from daily life when estimating skills are important.

   Sample Answer: Estimating the total cost of your items in the grocery store

8. Your cousin thinks of a number. He multiplies this starting number by 4 and then adds 12 to get 32. What is the starting number? Use a complete sentence to explain how you found your answer.

   Sample Answer: The starting number is 5. Starting with the result of 32, I subtracted 12 to get 20, and then divided by 4 to get 5.

Great Freights, a local shipping company, bases its charges on the weight of the items being shipped. In addition to charging $.40 per pound, they also charge a one-time fee of $10 to set up a customer's account.

9. How much does Great Freights charge to ship a package that weighs 20 pounds? 50 pounds?

   0.40(20) + 10 = $18; 0.40(50) + 10 = $30

10. Estimate the weight of a package if Great Freights charges the customer $45.

   About 90 pounds

11. Write an algebraic equation for the problem situation. Use a complete sentence in your answer.

   Sample Answer: The equation is $C = 0.40w + 10$, where C represents the total charge in dollars and w represents the weight in pounds.

12. Explain why an equation may be the most useful way to represent the problem situation.

   Sample Answer: An equation is most useful because it allows Great Freights to calculate the exact total shipping charge for any weight.

Assignment

Name _____   Date _____

Comparing U.S. Shirts and Hot Shirts
Comparing Problem Situations Algebraically and Graphically

Two twin brothers, Mike and Mark, are looking for after school jobs. They are both offered jobs at grocery stores. Mike is offered a job at Fresh Foods making $10 per hour. Mark is offered a job at Groovy Groceries making $8 an hour, plus a one-time hiring bonus of $100. Each twin believes that he has been offered the better job.

1. How much does Mike earn at Fresh Foods if he works 20 hours? 40 hours? 60 hours?

    10(20) = $200; 10(40) = $400; 10(60) = $600

2. Use a complete sentence to explain how you found Mike's earnings.

    Sample Answer: I multiplied the hours worked by the hourly rate.

3. How much does Mark earn at Groovy Groceries if he works 20 hours? 40 hours? 60 hours?

    8(20) + 100 = $260; 8(40) + 100 = $420; 8(60) + 100 = $580

4. Use a complete sentence to explain how you found Mark's earnings.

    Sample Answer: I multiplied the hours worked by the hourly rate and then added the hiring bonus.

5. Complete the table using the data from the problem and from Questions 1 and 3. Be sure to fill in your units.

Labels	Time worked	Mike's earnings at Fresh Foods	Mark's earnings at Groovy Groceries
Units	hours	dollars	dollars
	0	0	100
	20	200	260
	40	400	420
	60	600	580

6. Use the grid below to create a graph of the data in the table in Question 5. First, choose your bounds and intervals. Be sure to label your graph clearly.

Variable quantity	Lower bound	Upper bound	Interval
Time worked	0	60	4
Earnings	0	600	40

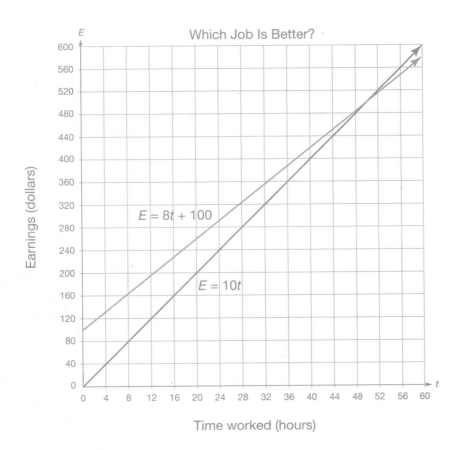

Which Job Is Better?

$E = 8t + 100$

$E = 10t$

Earnings (dollars)

Time worked (hours)

7. After how many hours will the twins earn the same amount of money? Use complete sentences to explain how you found your answer.

Sample Answer: The brothers will earn the same amount of money after working 50 hours. This is the point of intersection on the graph.

8. Whose job is better, Mike's or Mark's? Use complete sentences to explain your reasoning.

Sample Answer: If the twins have worked less than 50 hours, then Mark will make more money and have the better job. Once they work more than 50 hours, however, Mike will make more money and have the better job. In the long run, Mike has the better job.

Assignment

Name _____ Date _____

Left-Handed Learners
Using Samples, Ratios, and Proportions to Make Predictions

Define each term in your own words.

1. ratio   Sample Answer: A ratio compares two quantities with the same units.

2. proportion   Sample Answer: A proportion is two ratios set equal to each other.

3. sample   Sample Answer: A sample is a portion of a population.

4. Explain the difference between a ratio and a proportion. Use a complete sentence in your answer.

   Sample Answer: A ratio is simply an expression while a proportion is an equation.

Use the following scenario to answer Questions 5 through 13.

A class of 30 Algebra students recently took a test on ratios and proportions. Five students received A's, 10 students received B's, 6 students received C's, 4 students received D's, 4 students failed, and 1 student was absent.

Write each ratio by using division and by using a colon. Be sure to include units in your ratios.

5. Number students who received A's to the total number of students

   Sample Answer: $\dfrac{5 \text{ students}}{30 \text{ students}}$; 5 students : 30 students

6. Number of students who received A's to the number of students who failed

   Sample Answer: $\dfrac{5 \text{ students}}{4 \text{ students}}$; 5 students : 4 students

7. Number of students who passed the test to the number of students who failed

   Sample Answer: $\dfrac{25 \text{ students}}{4 \text{ students}}$; 25 students : 4 students

8. Number of students who were absent to the number of students who took the test

   Sample Answer: $\dfrac{1 \text{ student}}{29 \text{ students}}$; 1 student : 29 students

9. A total of 150 students in a school take Algebra. Use a proportion and the results of the sample class to predict the number of Algebra students in the school who received A's. Use a complete sentence in your answer.

Let x represent the number of Algebra students in the school who received A's.

$$\frac{5}{30} = \frac{x}{150}$$

$$30x = 750$$

$$x = 25$$

There should be 25 Algebra students in the school who received A's.

10. A total of 20 Algebra students received A's. Use a proportion and the results of the sample class to predict the total number of students taking Algebra. Use a complete sentence in your answer.

Let x represent the total number of students in the school taking Algebra.

$$\frac{5}{30} = \frac{20}{x}$$

$$600 = 5x$$

$$120 = x$$

There should be 120 students in the school taking Algebra.

11. A total of 20 Algebra students received D's. Use a proportion and the results of the sample class to predict the total number of Algebra students who received C's. Use a complete sentence in your answer.

Let x represent the number of Algebra students in the school who received C's.

$$\frac{6}{4} = \frac{x}{20}$$

$$4x = 120$$

$$x = 30$$

There should be 30 Algebra students in the school who received C's.

12. What sampling method was used to obtain the sample?

convenience sample

13. Describe a sampling method that you could use to obtain a sample of the Algebra students in your school. Is your method biased? Why or why not? Use complete sentences in your answer.

Answers will vary.

Assignment

Name _____ Date _____

Making Punch
Ratios, Rates, and Mixture Problems

Three local grocery stores compete for the same customers. They all offer savings cards that claim to save their customers money. The signs below describe each store's offer.

Stop-N-Shop	Food for Thought	Produce Palace
Save! Save! Save!	*Buy organic and save!*	*Stay lean while your wallet stays fat!*
Buy $80 worth of groceries and receive $8 off your next bill!	For every $50 that you spend, you save $10 off your next shopping trip!	Save $15 off your next purchase when you spend $100!

2

1. For each savings card, write a ratio of the money saved to the money spent on groceries.

    Stop-N-Shop: $\dfrac{\$8 \text{ saved}}{\$80 \text{ spent}}$; Food for Thought: $\dfrac{\$10 \text{ saved}}{\$50 \text{ spent}}$; Produce Palace: $\dfrac{\$15 \text{ saved}}{\$100 \text{ spent}}$

2. For the Stop-N-Shop, how many dollars do you have to spend for every dollar saved? Show your work and use a complete sentence in your answer.

    $\dfrac{\$8 \text{ saved}}{\$80 \text{ spent}} = \dfrac{\$1 \text{ saved}}{\$10 \text{ spent}}$

    You have to spend $10 for every dollar saved.

3. If you shop at Food for Thought, how many dollars do you have to spend for every dollar saved? Show your work and use a complete sentence in your answer.

    $\dfrac{\$10 \text{ saved}}{\$50 \text{ spent}} = \dfrac{\$1 \text{ saved}}{\$5 \text{ spent}}$

    You have to spend $5 for every dollar saved.

4. If you go to the Produce Palace, how many dollars do you have to spend for every dollar saved? Show your work and use a complete sentence in your answer.

    $\dfrac{\$15 \text{ saved}}{\$100 \text{ spent}} = \dfrac{\$1 \text{ saved}}{\$x \text{ spent}}$

    $100 = 15x$

    $x \approx 6.67$

    You have to spend $6.67 for every dollar saved.

5. How much would you have to spend at Stop-N-Shop to save $40? Show all your work and use a complete sentence in your answer.

$$\frac{\$1 \text{ saved}}{\$10 \text{ spent}} = \frac{\$40 \text{ saved}}{\$x \text{ spent}}$$

$$400 = x$$

You would have to spend $400 to save $40 at Stop-N-Shop.

6. How much would you save if you spent $300 on groceries at Food for Thought? Show all your work and write your answer in a complete sentence.

$$\frac{\$1 \text{ saved}}{\$5 \text{ spent}} = \frac{\$x \text{ saved}}{\$300 \text{ spent}}$$

$$5x = 300$$

$$x = 60$$

You would save $60 if you spent $300 at Food for Thought.

7. How much would you have to spend at Produce Palace to save $120? Show all your work and use a complete sentence in your answer.

$$\frac{\$1 \text{ saved}}{\$6.67 \text{ spent}} = \frac{\$120 \text{ saved}}{\$x \text{ spent}}$$

$$800.4 = x$$

You would have to spend about $800 to save $120.

8. Which grocery store offers the best deal? Show all of your work and write your answer in a complete sentence

Sample Answer: Food for Thought offers the best deal, because you have to spend the least amount per dollar saved.

Assignment

Name _____ Date _____

Shadows and Proportions
Proportions and Indirect Measurement

The physics and algebra classes at your school are taking part in an annual paper airplane design competition. Airplanes will be flown from the roof of the school, and a prize will be awarded to the student whose airplane travels furthest from the base of the school building. Before the actual competition, students perform test flights from their classroom windows. Your teacher uses a yardstick, shadows, and a proportion to estimate that the school building is 60 feet tall.

1. Describe how the teacher could have used shadows and proportions to estimate the height of the school building.

   Sample Answer: The teacher could have used a proportion by setting the ratio of his height to his shadow length equal to the ratio of the school's height to the school's shadow length.

2. During a test flight, Jessica throws her airplane from her classroom's first-floor window (10 feet off the ground), and it travels 25 feet. Use a proportion to estimate how far the airplane will travel when she throws it from the roof of the school.

   Let x represent how far the airplane will travel in feet.

   $$\frac{10}{25} = \frac{60}{x}$$

   $$1500 = 10x$$

   $$150 = x$$

   The airplane will travel 150 feet when thrown from the roof of the school.

3. During a test flight, Erica throws her airplane from her classroom's second-floor window (20 feet off the ground), and it travels 20 yards. Use a unit rate and a proportion to convert all units to feet. Then use a proportion to estimate how far the airplane will travel when she throws it from the roof of the school.

   $$\frac{3 \text{ feet}}{1 \text{ yard}} = \frac{? \text{ feet}}{20 \text{ yards}}; ? = 60 \text{ feet}$$

   Let x represent how far the airplane will travel in feet.

   $$\frac{20}{60} = \frac{60}{x}$$

   $$3600 = 20x$$

   $$180 = x$$

   The airplane will travel 180 feet when thrown from the roof of the school.

4. During the actual competition, Andre's airplane flew 120 feet. Estimate the distance that his airplane would have flown during a test flight from his classroom's second-floor window.

Let x represent how far the airplane will travel in feet.

$$\frac{120}{60} = \frac{x}{20}$$

$$60x = 240$$

$$x = 40$$

The airplane will travel 40 feet when thrown from the classroom's second-floor window.

5. If Jessica, Erica, and Andre are the finalists in the competition, who should win? Write an equation that models the distance the winning airplane travels in terms of the height from which it is thrown. Let d represent the distance the airplane travels in feet and let h represent the height from which it is thrown.

Erica; $d = 3h$

6. Jessica ends up winning the competition. Does this agree with your answer from Question 8? If not, what factors might account for an incorrect prediction? Use complete sentences in your answer.

Sample Answer: Wind speed and direction are two factors that can greatly affect the flight of a paper airplane. Because the airplanes are flown outside, these factors are not easily controlled.

Assignment

Assignment for Lesson 2.4

Name _____ Date _____

TV News Ratings
Ratios and Part-to-Whole Relationships

The new superintendent of a local school district states that her main objective is to increase the students' math scores. One initiative to help achieve this goal is to increase the number of students that attend an after-school tutoring program. By the end of the semester, she would like to have three out of every five students attending the program.

1. In order to meet the goal, how many students must attend the tutoring program if the school enrollment is 200? How many students must attend the tutoring program if the school enrollment is 400? How many students must attend the tutoring program if the school enrollment is 800?

   120 students; 240 students; 480 students

2. Describe how you found your answers to Question 1.

   Sample Answer: I wrote a proportion by using the ratio given in the problem and the given school enrollment.

3. One of the elementary schools met their goal when 30 students attended the tutoring program. What is the school's enrollment?

   50 students are enrolled in the school.

4. One of the middle schools has 400 students enrolled. If 230 students attended the tutoring program at the end of the semester, did they meet their goal? Explain your reasoning.

   No. In order to meet their goal, 240 students must attend the tutoring program.

5. Let s represent the number of students enrolled and let t represent the number of students who attend the tutoring program. Write an equation for t in terms of s.

   $t = \dfrac{3}{5}s$

6. One of the high schools has 500 students enrolled and 275 students attending the tutoring program. A second high school has 740 students enrolled and 333 students attending the tutoring program. Has either high school met the goal? If not, which school is closer to meeting the goal? Use complete sentences to explain your reasoning.

   Sample Answer: No. Neither school has met the goal because their ratios of student participation in the tutoring program are less than the goal of $\frac{3}{5} = \frac{12}{20}$. The ratio for the first school is $\frac{11}{20}$, and the ratio for the second school is $\frac{9}{20}$. The first school is closer to meeting the goal because $\frac{11}{20}$ is closer to $\frac{12}{20}$.

© 2006 Carnegie Learning, Inc.

Chapter 2 ■ Assignments **29**

Assignment

Name _____ Date _____

Women at a University
Ratios, Part-to-Part Relationships, and Direct Variation

1. Define *direct variation* in your own words. Use an example in your definition.

   Sample Answer: Direct variation is the relationship between two quantities that have a constant ratio. For example, if I earn $8 per hour, the ratio of my total pay to the number of hours worked will always be 8.

2

Solve each proportion using the means and extremes.

2. $\dfrac{5}{9} = \dfrac{x}{22}$ $x \approx 12.2$

3. $\dfrac{x}{7} = \dfrac{5}{11}$ $x \approx 3.2$

4. $\dfrac{0.32}{x} = \dfrac{1}{3}$ $x = 0.96$

In a college calculus class of 30 students, 6 are pre-med majors, 8 are engineering majors, 5 are mathematics majors, 4 are business majors, and the rest are undecided.

Write each part-to-part ratio.

5. Pre-med majors to mathematics majors

   $\dfrac{\text{6 pre–med majors}}{\text{5 mathematics majors}}$

6. Mathematics majors to undecided students

   $\dfrac{\text{5 mathematics majors}}{\text{7 undecided students}}$

7. Engineering majors to non-engineering majors

   $\dfrac{\text{8 engineering majors}}{\text{22 non–engineering majors}}$

According to a recent survey, 9 out of 10 parents agree with a plan to remove vending machines that sell soda and sugary snacks from the local schools.

8. What is the ratio of the number of parents who agree to the number of parents who disagree?

   $\dfrac{\text{9 parents who agree}}{\text{1 parent who disagrees}}$

9. Let *a* represent the number of parents who agree and let *d* represent the number of parents who disagree. Write an equation for *a* in terms of *d*.

   $\dfrac{a}{d} = \dfrac{9}{1}$

   $9d = a$

10. Complete the table of values at the right that represents the problem situation.

Labels	Number who agree	Number who disagree
Units	parents	parents
Expressions	a	$9d$
	1	9
	50	450
	90	810
	400	3600

11. Use the grid below to create a graph of the data from the table in Question 10. First, choose your bounds and intervals. Be sure to label your graph clearly.

Variable quantity	Lower bound	Upper bound	Interval
Number of parents who disagree	0	450	30
Number of parents who disagree	0	3750	250

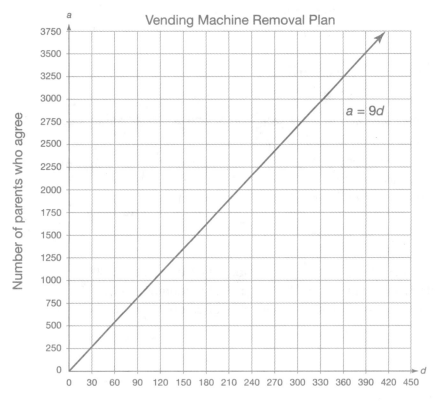

Vending Machine Removal Plan

$a = 9d$

Number of parents who agree

Number of parents who disagree

12. Explain why the equation in Question 9 is a direct variation.

Sample Answer: The equation $a = 9d$ is a direct variation because the quantities a and d have a constant ratio of 9.

Assignment

Name _____ Date _____

Tipping in a Restaurant
Using Percents

Approximately 76% of ninth graders in the Pittsburgh Public Schools will graduate from high school in four years.

2

1. How many students will graduate if the number of students starting in the ninth grade is 8000? How many students will graduate if the number of students starting in the ninth grade is 10,000? How many students will graduate if the number of students starting in the ninth grade is 12,000?

   6080 students; 7600 students; 9120 students

2. Describe how proportions were used to solve Question 1. Use complete sentences in your answer.

   Sample Answer: First, I wrote 76% as the fraction . This fraction represents the ratio of the number of graduates to the number of ninth graders. Then, I set up proportions using the ratio and given numbers of ninth graders. Finally, I solved the proportions by setting the means equal to the extremes and solving for the number of graduates.

3. How many students started in ninth grade if the number of graduates is 25,000? How many students started in ninth grade if the number of graduates is 27,500? How many students started in ninth grade if the number of graduates is 30,000?

   About 32,895 students; about 36,184 students; about 39,474 students

4. Describe how proportions were used to solve Question 3. Use complete sentences in your answer.

   Sample Answer: First, I wrote 76% as the fraction $\frac{76}{100}$. This fraction represents the ratio of the number of graduates to the number of ninth graders. Then, I set up proportions using the ratio and given numbers of graduates. Finally, I solved the proportions by setting the means equal to the extremes and solving for the number of ninth graders.

5. Write an equation that can be used to calculate the number of students who will graduate. Let x be the number of ninth graders and y be the number of graduates.

   $$y = \frac{76}{100}x$$

6. Complete the table of values that represents the problem situation.

Labels	Number of ninth graders	Number of graduates
Units	students	students
Expressions	x	0.76x
	8,000	6080
	10,000	7600
	12,000	9120

7. Use the grid below to create a graph of the data in the table in Question 6. First, choose your bounds and intervals. Be sure to label your graph clearly.

Variable quantity	Lower bound	Upper bound	Interval
Number of ninth graders	0	15,000	1000
Number of graduates	0	12,000	800

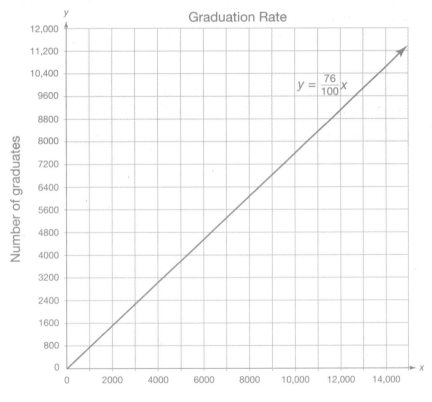

8. Use your graph in Question 7 to estimate the number of graduates if the number of students starting in ninth grade is 7500.

Answers will vary. Sample Answer: about 5700.

Assignment

Name _____ Date _____

Taxes Deducted From Your Paycheck
Percents and Taxes

When purchasing an item at a store, a sales tax is generally added to the price of the item. This sales tax varies from state to state, but generally the price is increased by 4 to 7 percent. For this problem situation, assume that the sales tax rate is 6%.

2

1. How much sales tax will be added to an item that costs $50? How much sales tax will be added to an item that costs $75? How much sales tax will be added to an item that costs $100?

   $3; $4.50, $6

2. Explain how you can use a proportion to solve Question 1. Use complete sentences in your answer.

   Sample Answer: Let x represent the amount paid in sales tax. Write and solve a proportion with one ratio that is the percent written as a fraction and the other ratio that compares the amount paid in sales tax to the given cost of an item.

3. What is the price of an item if the sales tax is $.60? What is the price of an item if the sales tax is $1.20? What is the price of an item if the sales tax is $4.80?

   $10; $20; $80

4. Explain how you can use a proportion to solve Question 3. Use complete sentences in your answer.

   Sample Answer: Let x represent the total price. Write and solve a proportion with one ratio that is the percent written as a fraction and the other ratio that compares the given amount paid in sales tax to the cost of an item.

5. Write an equation that can be used to calculate the sales tax that will be added to the price of an item. Let x be the cost of the item and y be the amount of sales tax paid.

   $y = \dfrac{6}{100}x$

6. Complete the table of values that describes the relationship between the cost of an item and the amount paid in sales tax.

	Number of ninth graders	Number of graduates
Labels		
Units	students	students
Expressions	x	$\dfrac{6}{100}x$
	1.50	0.09
	25	1.50
	45	2.70
	55	3.30

7. What is the total cost after sales tax if the cost of an item is $120? What is the total cost after sales tax if the cost of an item is $200? What is the total cost after sales tax if the cost of an item is $300?

   $127.20; $212; $318

8. Describe how you found your answers in Question 7. Use a complete sentence in your answer.

   Sample Answer: First, I found the amount of sales tax paid, and then I added this amount to the cost of the item.

9. Write an equation that can be used to calculate the total cost after sales tax. Let x be the cost of an item and y be the total cost after sales tax.

   $$y = \dfrac{6}{100}x + x$$

© 2006 Carnegie Learning, Inc.

2

Assignment

Name _____ Date _____

Collecting Road Tolls
Solving One-Step Equations

Solve each one-step equation algebraically. Use mental math to check your answer.

1. $2x = 46$

$$\frac{2x}{2} = \frac{46}{2}$$

$$x = 23$$

2. $\frac{x}{4} = 10$

$$\frac{x}{4} \cdot 4 = 10 \cdot 4$$

$$x = 40$$

3. $3x = 21$

$$\frac{3x}{3} = \frac{21}{3}$$

$$x = 7$$

4. $x - 5 = 32$

$$x - 5 + 5 = 32 + 5$$

$$x = 37$$

5. $x + 7 = 13$

$$x + 7 - 7 = 13 - 7$$

$$x = 6$$

6. $4 + x = 11$

$$4 - 4 + x = 11 - 4$$

$$x = 7$$

You start working part-time after school at a local grocery store. You earn $7.50 per hour.

7. How much money will you earn if you work 1 hour? How much money will you earn if you work 2 hours? How much money will you earn if you work 4 hours? How much money will you earn if you work 5.5 hours?

$7.50; $15; $30; $41.25

8. Use complete sentences to explain how you found your answers in Question 7.

Sample Answer: To find the amount earned, multiply the number of hours worked by $7.50, the amount earned in one hour.

9. Let h represent the number of hours worked. Write an algebraic expression that represents the amount of money earned.

$7.5h$

10. Write an equation that can be used to find the number of hours you must work to earn $105. Solve the equation and write your answer in a complete sentence.

$$105 = 7.5x$$

$$\frac{105}{7.5} = \frac{7.5x}{7.5}$$

$$x = 14$$

I must work 14 hours to earn $105.

11. For this problem situation, what are the independent and dependent variables?

The independent variable is the number of hours worked, and the dependent variable is the dollars earned.

Assignment

Name _____ Date _____

Decorating the Math Lab
Solving Two-Step Equations

Solve each equation algebraically.

1. $3x - 1 = 14$

   $x = 5$

2. $4x + 2 = 22$

   $x = 5$

3. $\dfrac{x}{3} + 4 = 5$

   $x = 3$

4. $1 + 2x = 5$

   $x = 2$

5. $10 = 2x + 4$

   $x = 3$

6. $\dfrac{x}{2} - 3 = 5$

   $x = 16$

Your school district is considering a plan to rent rather than buy a new server for its computer network. A server rents for $2.50 per day with a $25 fee for insurance.

7. What is the total cost of renting a server for 30 days? What is the total cost of renting a server for 180 days? What is the total cost of renting a server for 360 days?

   $100; $475; $925

8. Use complete sentences to explain how you found your answers in Question 7.

   Sample Answer: To find the total cost of renting a server, multiply the time rented in days by $2.50, the cost to rent a server for one day. Then add the insurance fee, $25, to the result.

9. Let d represent the time rented in days. Write an algebraic expression that represents the total cost of renting a server.

   $2.5d + 25$

10. Write and solve an equation to find the number of days for which the school district can rent a server for $250? Use a complete sentence in your answer.

    $2.5d + 25 = 250$

    $2.5d = 225$

    $d = 90$

    The school district can rent a server for 90 days for $250.

11. What inverse operations did you use to solve your equation in Question 10?

    subtraction and division

© 2006 Carnegie Learning, Inc.

12. Write and solve an equation to find the number of days for which the school district can rent a server for $587.50. Use a complete sentence in your answer.

$$2.5d + 25 = 587.5$$
$$2.5d = 562.5$$
$$d = 225$$

The school district can rent a server for 225 days for $587.50.

13. During a school board meeting, the technology coordinator for the district states that it would cost $102.50 to rent a server for the month of February. Algebraically determine if the technology coordinator's statement is true. Use a complete sentence in your answer.

Sample Answer:

$$2.5(28) + 25 \stackrel{?}{=} 102.5$$
$$70 + 25 \stackrel{?}{=} 102.5$$
$$95 \neq 102.5$$

The technology coordinator's statement is not true. Except during a leap year, there are 28 days in February. Twenty eight is not a solution of the equation because the sum of 25 and the product of 2.5 and 28 is not 102.5.

14. Complete the table of values that shows the relationship between the time rented in days and the total cost.

Labels	Time	Total cost
Units	days	dollars
Expressions	d	$2.5d + 25$
	30	100
	90	250
	180	475
	225	587.5
	360	925

15. Use the grid below to create a graph of the data from the table in Question 14.
First, choose your bounds and intervals. Be sure to label your graph clearly.

Variable quantity	Lower bound	Upper bound	Interval
Time	0	900	60
Total cost	0	2500	160

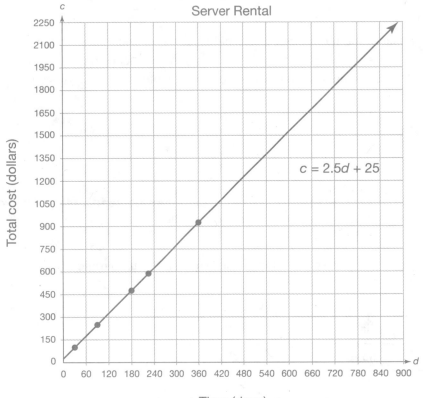

Server Rental

$c = 2.5d + 25$

Total cost (dollars)

Time (days)

16. It costs about $1850 to buy a new server. If the school district must get a new server
every two years, how does the cost of buying a new server compare to the cost of renting
one? Use the graph to determine the cost of renting a server for two years.

Sample Answer: According to the graph, the cost of renting a server for two years
is about $1825. The cost of buying a new server is about the same as renting one.

17. Do you think the school district should buy or rent the new server? Use complete
sentences to explain your reasoning.

Sample Answer: The school district should rent the new server. Although both options
cost about the same, renting saves the district from have to pay for disposal of the
equipment. Also, a rental company may be willing to give the district a new server
more frequently than every two years.

Assignment

Name _____ Date _____

Earning Sales Commission
Using the Percent Equation

Write and solve a percent equation to answer each question. Use a complete sentence in your answer.

1. What is 45% of 400?

   $a = \dfrac{45}{100}(400)$

   $a = 180$

   The number 180 is 45% of 400.

2. 7 is 7% of what number?

   $7 = \dfrac{7}{100}b$

   $b = 100$

   The number 7 is 7% of 100.

3. Define *commission* in your own words.

   Sample Answer: Commission is an amount of money that you get based on a percent of your total sales.

A television salesperson is paid $150 per week, plus a commission of 5% on his total sales for the week.

4. How much money will the salesperson earn if his total sales for the week are $500?
   How much money will the salesperson earn if his total sales for the week are $800?
   How much money will the salesperson earn if his total sales for the week are $1000?

   $175; $190; $200

5. Describe how you found your answers in Question 4. Use complete sentences in your answer.

   Sample Answer: I multiplied the total sales for the week by 0.05. Then, I added the salary of $150 to the result.

6. Let *s* represent the salesperson's total sales for a week and let *E* represent his earnings. Write an equation for *E* in terms of *s*.

   $E = 0.05s + 150$

7. Use your equation to find the salesperson's total sales for the week if his earnings are $300. Show all your work and use a complete sentence in your answer.

   $300 = 0.05s + 150$

   $150 = 0.05s$

   $s = 3000$

   The total sales for the week are $3000.

8. Complete the table of values that represents the relationship between the salesperson's earnings and his total sales for a week.

	Total sales	Earnings
Labels	Total sales	Earnings
Units	dollars	dollars
Expressions	s	$0.05s + 150$
	500	175
	800	190
	1000	200
	3000	300

9. Use the grid below to create a graph of the data from the table in Question 8. First, choose your bounds and intervals. Be sure to label your graph clearly.

Variable quantity	Lower bound	Upper bound	Interval
Total sales	0	3750	250
Earnings	0	600	40

Total Earnings

$E = 0.05s + 150$

Earnings (dollars)

Total sales (dollars)

Assignment

Name _____ Date _____

Rent a Car from Go-Go Car Rentals, Wreckem Rentals, and Good Rents Rentals Using Two-Step Equations, Part 1

You would like to have a cellular phone to use in just case of an emergency, so you compare three pay-as-you-go cellular phone plans. Easy Cell charges a monthly access fee of $5.99 and $.49 per minute for airtime. Emerge-A-Cell charges a monthly access fee of $9.99 and $.29 per minute for airtime. Safety Cell charges $7.99 for monthly access and $.45 per minute for airtime.

1. Determine the cost for the first month for each plan if you use 20 minutes of airtime. Show your work and use complete sentences in your answer.

   Easy Cell: 0.49(20) + 5.99 = $15.79; It will cost $15.79 for the first month.

   Emerge-A-Cell: 0.29(20) + 9.99 = $15.79; It will cost $15.79 for the first month.

   Safety Cell: 0.45(20) + 7.99 = $16.99; It will cost $16.99 for the first month.

2. Use complete sentences to explain how you determined the cost for each plan in Question 1.

   Multiply the number of airtime minutes by the airtime charge for one minute. Then add the monthly access fee to the result.

3. Let t represent the total cost of your first month's cellular phone use in dollars and let m represent the number of airtime minutes used. Write an equation that gives the total cost in terms of the number of airtime minutes used for each of the three cellular phone plans.

   Easy Cell: $t = 0.49m + 5.99$; Emerge-A-Cell: $t = 0.29m + 9.99$; Safety Cell: $t = 0.45m + 7.99$

4. Complete the table of values that shows the relationship between the total cost and the number of airtime minutes used.

Labels		Easy Cell	Emerge-A-Cell	Safety Cell
	Airtime used	Total cost	Total cost	Total cost
Units	minutes	dollars	dollars	dollars
Expressions	m	$0.49m + 5.99$	$0.29m + 9.99$	$0.45m + 7.99$
	0	5.99	9.99	7.99
	10	10.89	12.89	12.49
	20	15.79	15.79	16.99
	45	28.04	23.04	28.24
	50	30.49	24.49	30.49

5. Use the bounds and intervals shown below to create graphs of all three situations on the grid.

Variable quantity	Lower bound	Upper bound	Interval
Airtime used	0	60	4
Total cost	0	45	3

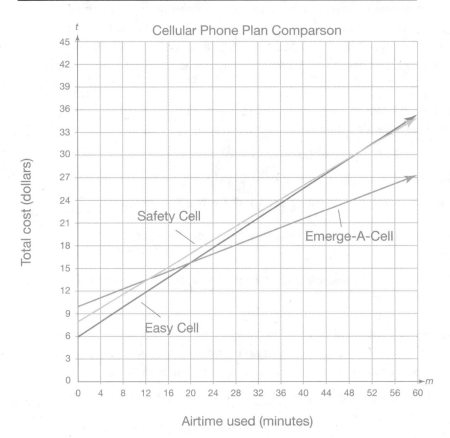

6. Compare the three cellular phone plans. Identify which plan will cost the least and for which number of airtime minutes. Will the cost ever be the same for all three companies? If so, for which number of airtime minutes? Use complete sentences to explain.

Answers should include: Easy Cell costs the least for less than 20 minutes. Emerge-A-Cell costs the least for greater than 20 minutes. The costs for all three companies will never be the same because the three graphs never cross at the same point.

Assignment

Name _____ Date _____

Plastic Containers
Using Two-Step Equations, Part 2

At the start of a new season, three football players decide to compete to see who will reach 10,000 career rushing yards first. The first player currently has 3500 yards and averages 120 yards per game. The second player currently has 4075 yards and averages 95 yards per game. The third player currently has 5575 yards and averages 80 yards per game. Assume that there are 16 games in one season.

1. If each player gains yards at his current average, how many yards will each have at the end of the season? Show your work and use complete sentences in your answer.

   First player: 120(16) + 3500 = 5420; The first player will have 5420 yards.

   Second player: 95(16) + 4075 = 5595; The second player will have 5595 yards.

   Third player: 80(16) + 5575 = 6855; The third player will have 6855 yards.

2. Use complete sentences to explain how you determined the yardage for each player in Question 1.

   Multiply the average yards per game by the number of games in a season. Then add the current number of yards each player has to the result.

3. Let t represent the total rushing yards and let g represent the number of games played. Write an equation that gives the total rushing yards in terms of the number of games played for each of the three players.

   First player: $t = 120g + 3500$; Second player: $t = 95g + 4075$; Third player: $t = 80g + 5575$

4. Complete the table of values that shows the relationship between the total rushing yards and the number of games played.

		First player	Second player	Third player
Labels	Games played	Total yards	Total yards	Total yards
Units	games	yards	yards	yards
Expressions	g	$120g + 3500$	$95g + 4075$	$80g + 5575$
	0	3500	4075	5575
	16	5420	5595	6855
	23	6260	6260	7415
	40	8300	7875	8775
	60	10,700	9775	10,375

5. Use the bounds and intervals shown below to create graphs for all three players on the grid.

Variable quantity	Lower bound	Upper bound	Interval
Games played	0	75	5
Total yards	0	15,000	1000

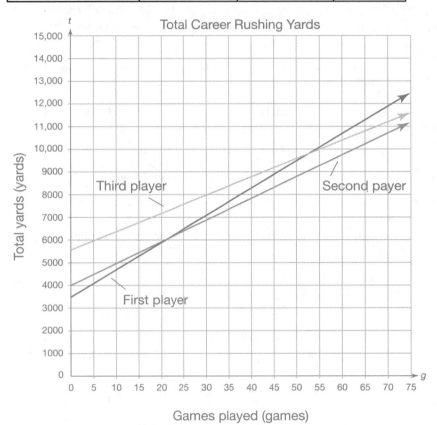

6. Use the graph to estimate after how many games each player will reach 10,000 total yards.

Answers will vary.

7. Check your estimate for each player in Question 6 using algebraic equations to find after how many games each player will reach 10,000 yards. Use complete sentences in your answer.

First player: $10,000 = 120g + 3500$, $g \approx 54.2$; The first player will reach 10,000 total yards after 55 games.

Second player: $10,000 = 95g + 4075$, $g \approx 62.4$; The second player will reach 10,000 total yards after 63 games.

Third player: $10,000 = 80g + 5575$, $g \approx 55.3$; The third player will reach 10,000 total yards after 56 games.

8. Do you think using each player's current average yards per game is a good predictor for determining who will reach the 10,000-yard goal first? Why or why not?

Answers will vary.

Assignment

Name _____   Date _____

Brrr! It's Cold Out There!
Integers and Integer Operations

Perform each indicated operation.

1. –2 + 5

3

2. –3 + (–2)

–5

3. 6 + (–8)

–2

4. 8 – 10

–2

5. –3 – (–5)

2

6. –8 – 2

–10

7. 7(–2)

–14

8. (–3)(–7)

21

9. $(-5)^2$

25

10. –24 ÷ (–3)

8

11. 64 ÷ (–2)

–32

12. –22 ÷ 11

–2

The equation given in the text that relates a temperature C in degrees Celsius to a temperature F in degrees Fahrenheit is $F = \frac{9}{5}C + 32$. By solving for C, another equation that relates these two variable quantities is $C = \frac{5}{9}F - \frac{160}{9}$.

13. Use the second equation above to find the temperature in degrees Celsius that corresponds to a temperature of –4°F. Show all your work and use a complete sentence in your answer.

$C = \frac{9}{5}(-4) - \frac{160}{9} = -24.978$; **The temperature is –24.978°C.**

14. Use the second equation above to find the temperature in degrees Fahrenheit that corresponds to a temperature of –15°C. Show all your work and use a complete sentence in your answer.

$-15 = \frac{5}{9}F - \frac{160}{9}$

$\frac{25}{9} = \frac{5}{9}F$

$F = 5$ **The temperature is 5°F.**

15. Write the second temperature equation above so that the fractions are decimals.

Sample Answer: $C = 0.\overline{5}F - 17.\overline{7}$

16. Which temperature equation is easier to use? Use complete sentences to explain your answer.

Answers will vary. Sample Answer: The first temperature equation is easier to use because the fraction terminates when written as a decimal.

Assignment

Name _____ Date _____

Shipwreck at the Bottom of the Sea
The Coordinate Plane

Define each term in your own words.

1. origin   Sample Answer: the point (0, 0) at which the two axes intersect

2. *x*-axis   Sample Answer: the horizontal axis

3. *y*-axis   Sample Answer: the vertical axis

4. ordered pair   Sample Answer: the notation (*x*, *y*) that represents a point on a graph

5. *x*-coordinate   Sample Answer: the number that indicates how far to the left or right a point is from the *y*-axis

6. *y*-coordinate   Sample Answer: the number that indicates how far up or down a point is from the *x*-axis.

7. Plot and label each point in the coordinate plane.

   A(2, −6)

   B(0, −4)

   C(−4, 0)

   D(2, 0)

   E(2, 6)

   F(−4, 6)

   G(−4, −6)

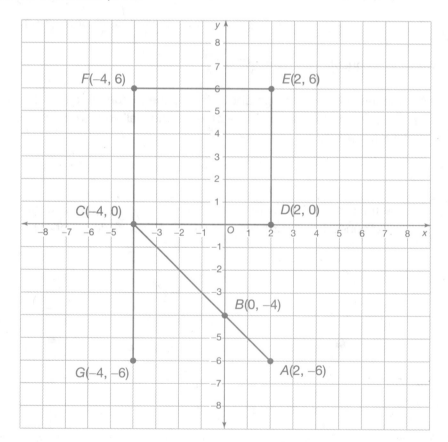

8. What letter is formed when you connect the points you plotted in Question 7 in alphabetical order?   R

Assignment

Name _____ Date _____

Engineering a Highway
Using a Graph of a Two-Step Equation

You are knitting a scarf for your best friend and want to have it finished by 6:00 PM You want the scarf to be 60 inches long when it is complete. At 1:00 PM you have already knit 15 inches of the scarf, and you estimate that from this point on you can knit at the rate of one fourth inch per minute.

1. Write an equation that represents the length of the scarf in inches in terms of the number of minutes.

   $L = \frac{1}{4}m + 15$, where L is the length of the scarf in inches and m in the number of minutes since 1:00 PM

2. Find the length of the scarf at 2:30 PM and at 3:20 PM. Show all your work and use a complete sentence in your answer.

   $L = \frac{1}{4}(90) + 15 = 37.5$; At 2:30 PM, the length of the scarf will be 37.5 inches.

   $L = \frac{1}{4}(140) + 15 = 50$; At 3:20 PM, the length of the scarf will be 50 inches.

3. What time will it be when you complete the scarf? Show all your work and use a complete sentence in your answer.

   $60 = \frac{1}{4}m + 15$

   $45 = \frac{1}{4}m$

   $m = 180$

   Because it will take 180 minutes from 1:00 PM to complete the scarf, it will be finished at 4:00 PM.

4. Assuming you knit at a constant rate, at what time did you begin knitting the scarf? Show all your work and use a complete sentence in your answer.

   $0 = \frac{1}{4}m + 15$

   $-15 = \frac{1}{4}m$

   $m = -60$

   The scarf was started 60 minutes ago, or 12:00 PM.

5. Complete the table of values that shows the relationship between the number of minutes and the length of the scarf in inches.

Labels	Time since 1:00 PM	Scarf length
Units	minutes	inches
Expressions	m	$\frac{1}{4}m + 15$
	0	15
	90	37.5
	140	50
	180	60

6. Use the grid below to create a graph of the data from the table in Question 5. First choose your bounds and intervals. Be sure to label your graph clearly.

Variable quantity	Lower bound	Upper bound	Interval
Time after 1:00 PM	−100	300	20
Scarf length	0	75	5

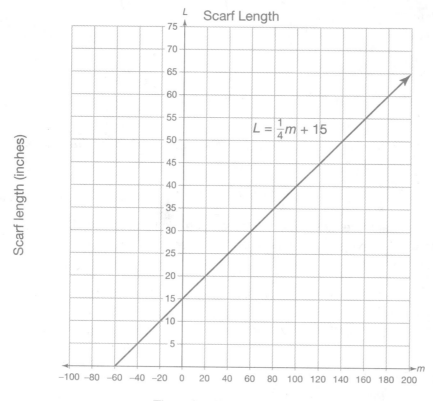

Scarf length (inches)

Time since 1:00 PM (minutes)

7. Use the graph in Question 6 to estimate the length of the scarf at 3:30 PM
   Use a complete sentence in your answer.

   The length of scarf at 3:30 PM will be 52.5 inches.

8. Use the graph in Question 6 to estimate what time it will be when the scarf is
   25 inches long. Use a complete sentence in your answer.

   The scarf will be 25 inches long at 1:40 PM

Solve each equation.

9. $\dfrac{2}{5}x + 100 = 1100$

   $x = 2500$

10. $\dfrac{3}{4}x - 2 = 10$

   $x = 16$

11. $-12 = \dfrac{2}{3}x + 2$

   $x = -21$

3

3

Assignment

Name _____ Date _____

Up, Up, and Away!
Solving and Graphing Inequalities in One Variable

A big Algebra test is coming up, and you are worried about how it will affect your grade. It will have 40 multiple-choice questions and you would like to know how many questions you will need to answer correctly in order to receive each grade. (For a review of percents, see Chapter 2.).

1. What is the number of questions will you need to answer correctly in order to receive a 90%? What is the number of questions will you need to answer correctly in order to receive an 80%? What is the number of questions will you need to answer correctly in order to receive a 70%? What is the number of questions will you need to answer correctly in order to receive a 60%?

    36 questions; 32 questions; 28 questions, 24 questions

2. Let x represent the number of questions answered correctly. Write inequalities for the number of questions that you need to answer correctly in order to receive an A (90%–100%), a B (80%-90%), a C (70%–80%), a D (60%-70%), and an F (0%–59%).

    A: $x \geq 36$; B: $32 \leq x < 36$; C: $28 \leq x < 32$; D: $24 \leq x < 28$; F: $x < 24$

3. Which letter grades are represented by a compound inequality?

    B, C, and D

4

4. Students in one particular class did poorly on the test, so the teacher allowed the students to take the tests home and correct them in order to earn more points. If a student answered 20 questions correctly the first time, what number of additional questions will she need to answer correctly in order to raise her grade to at least a C? Let q represent the number of corrected problems. Show all your work and use a complete sentence in your answer.

    $20 + q \geq 28$

    $q \geq 8$

    She will need to answer at least 8 more questions correctly to raise her test grade to a C.

Solve each inequality and graph the solution.

5. $x - 3 > 7$

$x > 10$

6. $-2x \leq 10$

$x \geq -5$

7. $-3x + 2 \geq 11$

$x \leq -3$

8. $\frac{1}{5}x + 10 < 24$

$x < 70$

Assignment

Name _____ Date _____

Moving a Sand Pile
Relations and Functions

Define each term in your own words.

1. domain   Sample Answer: the set of all input values

2. range   Sample Answer: the set of all output values

3. function   Sample Answer: a relation with exactly one output for every input

Decide whether each relation is a function. If the relation is a function, identify the domain and range. If the relation is not a function, explain why. Use complete sentences in your answer.

4. Relation: (2, 5), (3, 7), (−1, −1), (5, 11)

    The relation is a function. The domain is {2, 3, −1, 5}. The range is {5, 7, −1, 11}.

5. Relation: (1, 1), (2, 1), (3, 2), (3, 3)

    The relation is not a function because the input 3 has two outputs, 2 and 3.

Identify the input and output for each scenario and decide whether or not it represents a function. Use complete sentences to explain your answer.

6. Each student in your class identifies his or her birthday.

    Sample Answer: The inputs are the students' names and the outputs are the corresponding birthdates. This scenario does represent a function because each student can have only one birthday.

7. Each student in your class identifies his or her phone number.

    Sample Answer: The inputs are the students' names and the outputs are the corresponding phone numbers. This scenario does not represent a function because a student can have more than one phone number.

8. At a family reunion, each person writes down his or her home address to create a family directory.

    Sample Answer: The inputs are the family members' names and the outputs are the home addresses. This scenario represents a function because each family member has only one home address.

4

Assignment

Name _____ Date _____

Let's Bowl!
Evaluating Functions, Function Notation, Domain, and Range

1. What is the difference between a relation and a function?

   Sample Answer: A relation and a function both generate a set of ordered pairs, but a function has only one output value for every input value.

2. How do you evaluate a function?

   Sample Answer: Replace the variable in the function with a given value and find the result.

Evaluate each function at the specified value. Show your work.

3. $f(x) = 3 + x$ at $x = -5$

   $f(-5) = 3 + (-5)$
   $= -2$

4. $f(x) = 2x - 15$ at $x = 7$

   $f(7) = 2(7) - 15$
   $= -1$

5. $f(x) = -4 + 3x$ at $x = -1$

   $f(-1) = -4 + 3(-1)$
   $= -7$

You and your friends from Algebra class have volunteered to tutor fifth grade students at the neighborhood elementary school after school. You would like to provide a snack for the fifth graders during tutoring time. You know that you will have to spend $6.50 on napkins and plates. You will be able to buy pretzels and juice at a rate of $.40 per student.

6. Find the total cost of providing snacks if 10 fifth graders come to tutoring. Show your work and use a complete sentence in your answer.

   6.50 + 0.40(10) = 10.50; It will cost $10.50 to provide snacks for 10 students.

7. Find the total cost of providing snacks if 15 fifth graders come to tutoring. Show your work and use a complete sentence in your answer.

   6.50 + 0.40(15) = 12.50; It will cost $12.50 to provide snacks for 15 students.

8. Use function notation to write an equation representing the total cost of providing snacks for any number of students.

   $f(x) = 6.50 + 0.40x$

9. Use complete sentences to explain how to evaluate the function for any number of students.

Sample Answer: Multiply the number of students by the cost of providing snacks per student ($.40) and add the cost of plates and napkins ($6.50).

10. What is the domain of the function in Question 8 if you do not consider the problem situation? Use a complete sentence in your answer.

The domain is {all real numbers}.

11. Suppose there are 65 fifth grade students at the neighborhood elementary school. What is the domain of the function in Question 8 now? Use a complete sentence in your answer.

The domain is all positive integers from 1 to 65, or {1, 2, . . . 64, 65}.

12. Suppose there are only enough tutors for 12 fifth graders to attend tutoring. What is the domain and range of the function in Question 8 now? Use complete sentences in your answer.

The domain is all positive integers from 1 to 12, or {1, 2, 3, 4, 5, 6, 7, 8, 9, 10, 11, 12}.

The range is {$6.90, $7.30, $7.70, $8.10, $8.50, $8.90, $9.30, $9.70, $10.10, $10.50, $10.90, $11.30}.

4

Assignment

Name _____ Date _____

Math Magic
The Distributive Property

Use the distributive property to simplify each algebraic expression.

1. $4(x + 3)$

$4(x + 3) = 4x + 4(3)$
$= 4x + 12$

2. $8(3x - 4)$

$8(3x - 4) = 8(3x) - 8(4)$
$= 24x - 32$

3. $10x - 15x$

$10x - 15x = x(10 - 15)$
$= -5x$

4. $5(9 - 2x)$

$5(9 - 2x) = 5(9) - 5(2x)$
$= 45 - 10x$

5. $\dfrac{36 - 24x}{6}$

$\dfrac{36 - 24x}{6} = \dfrac{36}{6} - \dfrac{24x}{6}$
$= 6 - 4x$

6. $\dfrac{56 + 7x}{7}$

$\dfrac{56 + 7x}{7} = \dfrac{56}{7} + \dfrac{7x}{7}$
$= 8 + x$

Use the distributive property in reverse to rewrite each algebraic expression.

7. $5x + 80$

$5x + 80 = 5x + 5(16)$
$= 5(x + 16)$

8. $7x - 28$

$7x - 28 = 7x - 7(4)$
$= 7(x - 4)$

9. $4x + 18$

$4x + 18 = 2(2x) + 2(9)$
$= 2(2x + 9)$

10. $28x - 49$

$28x - 49 = 7(4x) - 7(7)$
$= 7(4x - 7)$

11. $-5 - 15x$

$-5 - 15x = -5(1) - 5(3x)$
$= -5(1 + 3x)$

12. $4x + 7$

cannot be factored

You and two of your friends have decided to start your own company assembling and selling computers. Suppose that you have already sold the first 20 computers that you assembled for $1800 each. You will then sell each additional computer that you assemble for $1800.

13. What will your company's total sales be if you sell 10 additional computers? What will your company's total sales be if you sell 50 additional computers? What will your company's total sales be if you sell 100 additional computers? What will your company's total sales be if you sell 200 additional computers?

$54,000; $126,000; $216,000; $396,000

14. Write an expression that can be used to calculate your company's total sales. Write your expression in factored form and in simplified form using the distributive property.

Factored: 1800(x + 20)   Simplified: 1800x + 36,000

15. Write two expressions for the total area of the two rectangular sections of garden. Then find the total area. Show all your work.

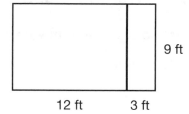

9 ft

12 ft   3 ft

9(15) = 135; Area = 135 square feet

9(12) + 9(3) = 108 + 27 = 135; Area = 135 square feet

4

Assignment

Name _____ Date _____

Numbers in Your Everyday Life
Real Numbers and Their Properties

Define each term in your own words.

1. closure   Sample Answer: When an operation is performed on two numbers in a set, the result is also in that set.

2. rational number   Sample Answer: a number that can be written as a quotient of two integers so that the denominator is not zero.

3. irrational number   Sample Answer: a number that cannot be written as a quotient of two integers

Determine whether each decimal value is rational or irrational number. If it is a rational number, write it as a fraction.

4. 0.5

   rational; $\frac{1}{2}$

5. 0.5555......

   rational; $\frac{5}{9}$

6. 0.151155111555...

   irrational

7. 0.1

   rational; $\frac{1}{10}$

8. 0.152542384...

   irrational

9. 0.151515...

   rational; $\frac{15}{99}$

Identify the property illustrated by each statement.

10. $2 = 2$

    Reflexive Property of Equality

11. $3(7) = 7(3)$

    Commutative Property of Multiplication

12. $(4 + 7) + (-2) = 4 + (7 + (-2))$

    Associative Property of Addition

13. If $\frac{1}{5} = 0.2$ and $0.2 = 20\%$, then $\frac{1}{5} = 20\%$.

    Transitive Property of Equality

14. Identify the property that is used in each step.

$3(5 + 1) - 4 = 5(2 - 8) + 44$	Given problem
$15 + 3 - 4 = 5(2 - 8) + 44$	Distributive Property of Multiplication Over Addition
$15 + 3 - 4 = 10 - 40 + 44$	Distributive Property of Multiplication Over Subtraction
$(15 + 3) - 4 = (10 - 40) + 44$	Grouping
$18 - 4 = -30 + 44$	Add and subtract.
$14 = 14$	Reflexive Property of Equality

Assignment

Name _____ Date _____

Technology Reporter
Solving More Complicated Equations

Solve each equation. Show all your work. Be sure to check your answer in the original equation.

1. $3x = 2x + 5$

$x = 5$

2. $3x + 2 = 2x + 4$

$x + 2 = 4$

$x = 2$

3. $-2x + 1 = 3(x + 2)$

$-2x + 1 = 3x + 6$

$1 = 5x + 6$

$-5 = 5x$

$-1 = x$

4. $5x - 1 = 7(x - 1)$

$5x - 1 = 7x - 7$

$-1 = 2x - 7$

$6 = 2x$

$3 = x$

5. $-x + 4 = -3x + 8$

$2x + 4 = 8$

$2x = 4$

$x = 2$

6. $2(10 + 3x) = 4(x - 4)$

$20 + 6x = 4x - 16$

$20 + 2x = -16$

$2x = -36$

$x = -18$

As a member of the local teen community group, you and your friends take on the responsibility to analyze the most economical option for flooring for the new center. After all the bids are collected, the two most promising bids are for vinyl flooring and carpeting. The vinyl flooring costs $31,000 to install, along with a monthly cleaning and maintenance fee of $175. The carpeting costs $22,500 to install along with a monthly cleaning and maintenance fee of $325.

7. What is the cost of vinyl flooring for 1 month? What is the cost of vinyl flooring for 10 months? What is the cost of vinyl flooring for 50 months? What is the cost of vinyl flooring for 60 months?

$31,175; $32,750; $39,750; $41,500

8. Write an expression for the cost of vinyl flooring.

Sample Answer: 31,000 + 175*m*, where *m* is the number of months

9. What is the cost of carpeting for 1 month? What is the cost of carpeting for 10 months? What is the cost of carpeting for 50 months? What is the cost of carpeting for 60 months?

$22,825; $25,750, $38,750; $42,000

10. Write an expression for the cost of carpeting.

Sample Answer: 22,500 + 325*m*, where *m* is the number of months

11. Complete the table below.

	Time	Cost of vinyl flooring	Cost of carpeting
Labels			
Units	months	dollars	dollars
Expressions	m	$31{,}000 + 175m$	$22{,}500 + 325m$
	1	31,000	22,825
	10	32,750	25,750
	50	39,750	38,750
	60	41,500	42,000

12. Based on the table, estimate when the cost of the vinyl flooring will equal the cost of the carpeting. Use complete sentences to explain your answer.

Sample Answer: The costs will be equal at some point between 50 and 60 months. At 50 months, the vinyl flooring is more expensive, but at 60 months, the carpeting is more expensive.

13. Write and solve an equation to find when the two flooring options cost same. Use a complete sentence in your answer.

$$175m + 31{,}000 = 325m + 22{,}500$$
$$31{,}000 = 150m + 22{,}500$$
$$8500 = 150m$$
$$56.7 \approx m$$

The two flooring options cost the same after about 56.7 months.

14. Why is it helpful to isolate the variable m on the right side of the equation in Question 13, instead of the left side? Use a complete sentence in your answer.

Sample Answer: It is helpful to isolate the variable m on the right side of the equation because the resulting variable term will be positive instead of negative.

15. Your group must determine the best option over time. Consider the fact that both products carry a 10-year warranty. Justify your recommendation using your calculations above.

I would recommend the vinyl flooring option. You can see from the equation in Question 13 that the two options will be equal after about 57 months. From the table, you can see that after that point, the vinyl flooring option will be less expensive. Based on the fact that both have a 10-year warranty, they will both last over time. However, after 10 years (120 months), the carpeting will cost $61,500 and the vinyl will cost $52,000. We will save almost $10,000 over a 10-year period by choosing the vinyl flooring option.

© 2006 Carnegie Learning, Inc.

Assignment

Name _____ Date _____

Rules of Sports
Solving Absolute Value Equations and Inequalities

Evaluate each expression. Show all your work.

1. $|-13 + 5|$

$|-13 + 5| = |-8|$
$= 8$

2. $|6 - 10| \cdot (-2)$

$|6 - 10| \cdot (-2) = |-4| \cdot (-2)$
$= 4 \cdot (-2)$
$= -8$

3. $|(-5)(2)|$

$|(-5)(2)| = |-10|$
$= 10$

4. $|-2| + |3|$

$|-2| + |3| = 2 + 3$
$= 5$

5. $|-2 + 3|$

$|-2 + 3| = |1|$
$= 1$

6. $\left|\dfrac{-24}{4}\right|$

$\left|\dfrac{-24}{4}\right| = |-6|$
$= 6$

7. Complete the table below for the functions $y = x + 2$ and $y = |x + 2|$.

x	$x + 2$	$|x + 2|$
−4	−2	2
−3	−1	1
−2	0	0
−1	1	1
0	2	2
1	3	3
2	4	4

8. Graph both functions from Question 7 on the grid at the right.

9. How does the absolute value change the graph of the function?

Sample Answer: Any negative output values of the function $y = x + 2$ will be positive for the function $y = |x + 2|$. So, the negative part of the line $y = x + 2$ reflects above the x-axis and forms a V for the function $y = |x + 2|$.

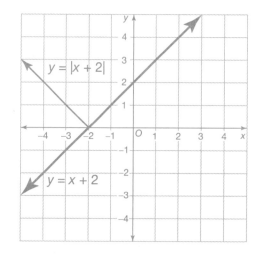

4

Assignment

Name _____ Date _____

Widgets, Dumbbells, and Dumpsters
Multiple Representatives of Linear Functions

Widgets cost $7 each, with a shipping charge of $11 per order.

1. Write an equation for the problem situation. Use w to represent the number of widgets ordered and use c to represent the total cost of an order in dollars.

    $c = 7x + 11$

2. What is the total cost of an order for 12 widgets? What is the total cost of an order for 257 widgets? Show all your work and use a complete sentence in your answer.

    $c = 7(12) + 11 = 95$; The total cost of an order for 12 widgets is $95.

    $c = 7(257) + 11 = 1810$; The total cost of an order for 257 widgets is $1810.

3. How many widgets can you order for $88? Show all your work and use a complete sentence in your answer.

    $88 = 7x + 11$

    $77 = 7x$

    $x = 11$ Eleven widgets can be ordered for $88.

4. How many widgets can you order for $1488? Show all your work and use a complete sentence in your answer.

    $1488 = 7x + 11$

    $1477 = 7x$

    $x = 211$ Two hundred eleven widgets can be ordered for $1488.

5. How many widgets can you order for $6472? Show all your work and use a complete sentence in your answer.

    $6472 = 7x + 11$

    $6461 = 7x$

    $x = 923$ Nine hundred twenty three widgets can be ordered for $6472.

5

Assignment

Name _____ Date _____

Selling Balloons
Finding Intercepts of a Graph

Overnight, a huge blizzard dumped 10 inches of snow on the ground. When the sun comes out, it melts the snow at a rate of about 1 inch per hour.

1. Write an equation for the problem situation. Use h to represent time in hours and use s to represent the amount of snow on the ground in inches.

   $s = 10 - h$

2. Complete the table of values that shows the relationship between the amount of snow in inches on the ground and the time in hours.

Labels	Time	Snow on the ground
Units	hours	inches
Expressions	h	$10 - h$
	–2	12
	1	9
	5	5
	10	0
	11	–1

3. Does an h-value of –2 make sense in the problem situation? Use complete sentences to explain.

   Sample Answer: An h-value of –2 can be interpreted as 2 hours before the sun comes out. This makes sense as far as time is concerned, but it does not make sense for the problem situation. The snow was not melting before the sun came out.

4. Use the grid to create a graph of the data from the table in Question 2. Use the bounds and intervals given below. Be sure to label your graph clearly.

Variable quantity	Lower bound	Upper bound	Interval
Time	–3	12	1
Snow on the ground	–3	12	1

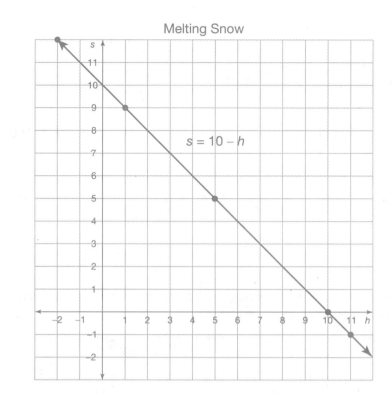

Melting Snow

Snow on the ground (inches)

Time (hours)

$s = 10 - h$

5. Use the graph in Question 4 to find the h- and s-intercepts. What do these points tell you about the relationship between the amount of snow on the ground and the time in hours. Use complete sentences in your answer.

Sample Answer: The graph crosses the h-axis at the point (10, 0). This point tells you that 10 hours after the sun comes out, all of the snow is gone. The graph crosses the s-axis at the point (0, 10). This point tells you that when the sun came out, there were 10 inches of snow on the ground.

6. Algebraically verify the h- and s-intercepts you found in Question 5.

$s = 10 - h$ $s = 10 - (0) = 10$

$0 = 10 - h$ h-intercept: 10

$10 = h$ s-intercept: 10

7. Does the graph in Question 4 increase or decrease from left to right? Why? Use complete sentences in your answer.

Sample Answer: The graph decreases from left to right. Because the snow is melting, the amount of snow on the ground is decreasing as time goes on.

Assignment

Name _____ Date _____

Recycling and Saving
Finding the Slope of a Line

The student council is selling heart-shaped lollipops to help raise money for the Valentine's Day dance. They earn $.25 for each lollipop sold.

1. Write an equation that relates the number of lollipops sold to the amount of money earned. Use x to represent the number of lollipops sold and y to represent the amount of money earned.

   $y = 0.25x$

2. Use the grid below to create a graph of the equation in Question 1. Use the bounds and intervals given below. Be sure to label your graph clearly.

Variable quantity	Lower bound	Upper bound	Interval
Number of lollipops sold	0	75	5
Money earned	0	30	2

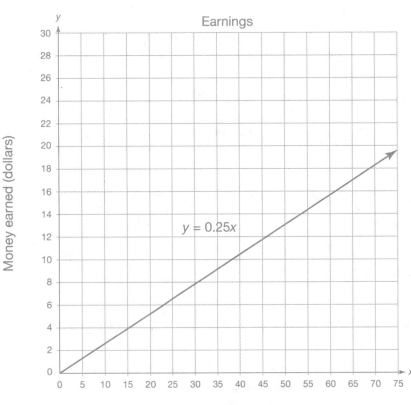

3. Use your graph to find the increase in earnings when the number of lollipops sold increases by one. Use a complete sentence in your answer.

The earnings increase by $.25.

4. Use your graph to find the increase in earnings when the number of lollipops sold increases by 20. Use a complete sentence in your answer.

The earnings increase by $5.

5. Use your graph to find the increase in earnings when the number of lollipops sold increases by 45. Use a complete sentence in your answer.

The earnings increase by $11.25.

6. Write a unit rate that compares the increase in earnings to the increase in the number of lollipops sold.

$$\frac{\$.25}{1\ \text{lollipop}}$$

7. Determine whether the slope of the line in Question 2 is positive, negative, zero, or undefined. Complete each sentence to explain.

The rise of the line is a _____ positive _____ number and the run of the line is _____ positive _____ number. So, the slope is _____ positive _____.

8. Use the slope formula and two points on the line in Question 2 to verify the slope in Question 6.

Sample Answer: Using (20, 5) and (45, 11.25), $m = \dfrac{11.25 - 5}{45 - 20} = \dfrac{6.25}{25} = \dfrac{1}{4} = 0.25$.

Find the slope of the line that goes through the given points. Show all your work.

9. (5, 7) and (6, 5)

$$m = \frac{5 - 7}{6 - 5} = \frac{-2}{1} = -2$$

10. (20, 50) and (60, 90)

$$m = \frac{90 - 50}{60 - 20} = \frac{40}{40} = 1$$

Assignment

Name _____ Date _____

Running a Marathon
Slope-Intercept Form

Write each equation in slope-intercept form, if necessary. Then identify the slope and *y*-intercept.

1. $y = 2x + 3.5$

Slope: 2; *y*-intercept: 3.5

2. $y = -3(x - 5)$

$y = -3x - 15$

Slope: –3; *y*-intercept: –15

3. $y = \frac{1}{4}x - 10$

Slope: $\frac{1}{4}$;

y-intercept: –10

Two families are competing on a reality TV show. The goal of the show is to race across the country from Los Angeles, California to New York, New York. The families are taking indirect routes and have different tasks to complete along the way. The family that accomplishes all of their tasks and finishes the race in the least amount of time wins.

4. The race has begun and the first family has traveled 450 miles. They are averaging 300 miles per day. Write an equation that gives the total distance the first family has traveled in terms of the number of days that have passed after the first 450 miles were completed. Use *x* to represent the number of days and *y* to represent the total distance traveled in miles.

$y = 450 + 300x$

5. If the first family continues traveling at this rate, how far will they have traveled 4 days after the first 450 miles are completed? Show all your work and use a complete sentence in your answer.

$y = 450 + 300(4) = 1650$; The first family will have traveled 1650 miles.

6. If the first family continues traveling at this rate, how many additional days will it take them to travel 1950 total miles after the first 450 miles are completed? Show all your work and use a complete sentence in your answer.

$1950 = 450 + 300x$

$1500 = 300x$

$5 = x$ It will take 5 days after the first 450 miles for the first family to travel 1950 miles.

7. The race has begun and the second family has traveled 1100 miles. They are currently traveling at an average rate of 150 miles per day. Write an equation that gives the total distance the second family has traveled in terms of the number of days that have passed after the first 1100 miles were completed. Use *x* to represent the number of days and *y* to represent the total distance traveled in miles.

$y = 1100 + 150x$

8. If the second family continues traveling at this rate, how far will they have traveled 5 days after the first 1100 miles are completed? Show all your work and use a complete sentence in your answer.

   y = 1100 + 150(5) = 1850; The second family will have traveled 1850 miles.

9. If the second family continues traveling at this rate, how many additional days will it take them to travel 1700 total miles after the first 1100 miles are completed? Show all your work and use a complete sentence in your answer.

   1700 = 1100 + 150x

   600 = 150x

   4 = x   **It will take 4 days after the first 1100 miles for the second family to travel 1700 miles.**

10. Identify the slope and y-intercept for each line in Questions 1 and 4.

    First family: **slope: 300**   **y-intercept: 450**

    Second family: **slope: 150**   **y-intercept: 1100**

11. Use the grid below to create graphs of the equations in Questions 4 and 7 using the slopes and y-intercepts from Question 10.

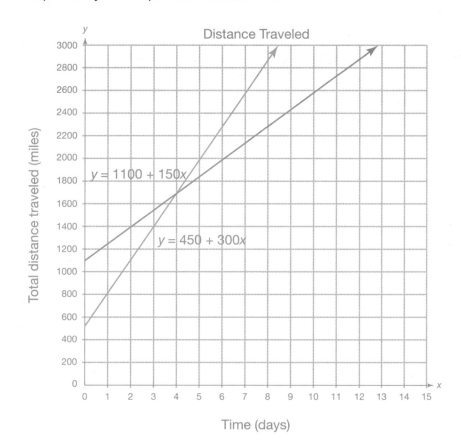

5

Assignment

Name _____ Date _____

Saving Money
Writing Equations of Lines

A marathon runner checks his watch at the halfway point (13 miles) of the Boston Marathon and sees that he has been running for about 100 minutes. He realizes that in order to match his personal best he will have to run faster. His personal best time for 26 miles is 191 minutes.

1. In this scenario, what are the two variable quantities? Let the time in minutes be the dependent variable and let the distance in miles be the independent variable. Use a complete sentence in your answer.

    Sample Answer: The two variable quantities are the distance in miles x and the time in minutes y.

2. Identify the two points given in the problem statement.

    (13, 100) and (26, 191)

3. What is the runner's rate (slope) during the second half of the race in minutes per mile? Show all your work and use a complete sentence in your answer.

    $m = \dfrac{191 - 100}{26 - 13}$

    $m = \dfrac{91}{13}$

    $m = 7$ The runner's rate for the second half of the race is 7 minutes per mile.

4. Write an equation in slope-intercept form that gives the time in terms of the distance. Use x to represent the distance in miles and y to represent the time in minutes. Show all your work.

    $y - 100 = 7(x - 13)$

    $y - 100 = 7x - 91$

    $y = 7x + 9$

Find an equation of the line that passes through each given set of points. Write your equation in slope-intercept form. Show all your work.

5. (1, 2) and (2, 0)

    $m = \dfrac{0 - 2}{2 - 1}$ $y - 2 = -2(x - 1)$

    $m = \dfrac{-2}{1}$ $y - 2 = -2x + 2$

    $m = -2$ $y = -2x + 4$

6. (4, 100) and (6, 200)

    $m = \dfrac{200 - 100}{6 - 4}$ $y - 100 = 50(x - 4)$

    $m = \dfrac{100}{2}$ $y - 100 = 50x - 200$

    $m = 50$ $y = 50x - 100$

© 2006 Carnegie Learning, Inc.

Assignment

Name _____ Date _____

Spending Money
Linear and Piecewise Functions

1. Explain the difference between a linear function and a piecewise function. Use complete sentences in your answer.

   Answers will vary. Sample Answer: For a linear function, every input value in the domain uses the same rule to determine its corresponding output value. For a piecewise function, different parts of the domain can use different rules (functions) to determine the corresponding output values.

The college library pays its student workers every two weeks. On payday, one of the workers receives a $270 check for the hours that he spends shelving books. The first week (7 days) after payday the student generally does the majority of his shopping and spends an average of about $25 per day. The next 5 days he spends an average of $15 per day, and the last 2 days before the next payday he spends only $10 per day.

2. Complete the table below that shows the amount of money left after different numbers of days.

Time since payday	Money left
days	dollars
0	270
1	245
2	220
3	195
4	170
5	145
6	120
7	95
8	80
9	65
10	50
11	35
12	20
13	10
14	0

3. Use the grid below to create a graph of the table in Question 2. First, choose your bounds and intervals. Be sure to label your graph clearly.

Variable quantity	Lower bound	Upper bound	Interval
Time since payday	0	15	1
Money left	0	300	20

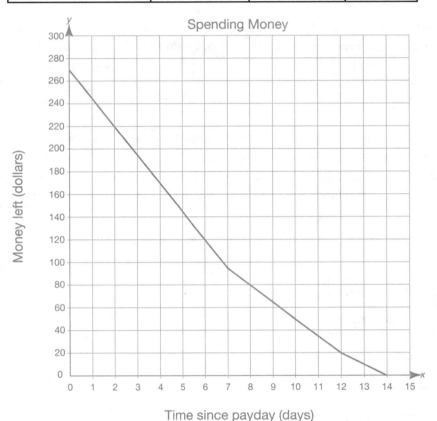

Spending Money

4. Write a piecewise function *f* for the graph in Question 3. Use *x* to represent a number from the domain of your function *f*.

$$f(x) = \begin{cases} 270 - 25x & 0 \le x \le 7 \\ 200 - 15x & 7 < x \le 12 \\ 140 - 10x & 2 < x \le 14 \end{cases}$$

5. Does the domain of the function *f* accurately represent the domain when you consider the problem situation? Use complete sentences in your answer.

Answers will vary. Sample Answer: The domain of the function *f* does not accurately represent the domain when considering the problem situation. The domain of *f* is all real numbers from 0 to 14, but the problem only makes sense for the whole numbers from 0 to 14.

Assignment

Name _____ Date _____

The School Play
Standard Form of a Linear Equation

The athletic department will raise money by charging admission to an upcoming football game. The price will be different for students and adults. Student tickets cost $3 each and adult tickets cost $5 each.

1. Write an expression that represents the total amount of money the athletic department will raise from the sale of x student tickets and y adult tickets.

   $3x + 5y$

2. The goal is to raise $5000 from the sale of tickets to the game. Write an equation that can be used to find the number of student and adult tickets sold if the goal is reached.

   $3x + 5y = 5000$

3. Using the equation from Question 2, write the intercepts of the equation's graph. Show all your work.

   x-intercept: **$3x + 5(0) = 5000$**   **y-intercept:**   **$3(0) + 5y = 5000$**

                             $3x = 5000$ **$5y = 5000$**

                              $x = 1666.\overline{6}$ **$y = 1000$**

4. What do the intercepts mean in terms of the problem situation? Use complete sentences in your answer.

   The x-intercept represents the number of student tickets sold if no adult tickets were sold. The y-intercept represents the number of adult tickets sold if no student tickets were sold.

5. Use the grid to create a graph of the equation in Question 2. First, choose your bounds and intervals. Be sure to label your graph clearly.

Variable quantity	Lower bound	Upper bound	Interval
Student tickets	0	2250	150
Adult tickets	0	2250	150

5

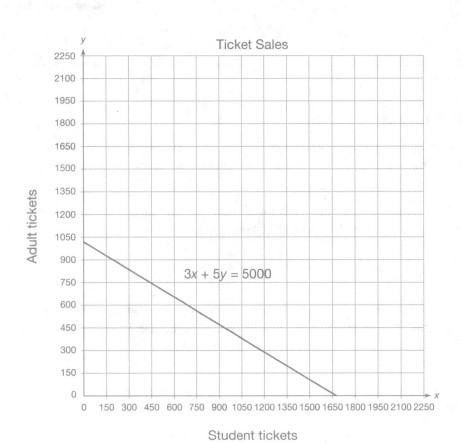

Ticket Sales

Adult tickets (y-axis): 0, 150, 300, 450, 600, 750, 900, 1050, 1200, 1350, 1500, 1650, 1800, 1950, 2100, 2250

Student tickets (x-axis): 0, 150, 300, 450, 600, 750, 900, 1050, 1200, 1350, 1500, 1650, 1800, 1950, 2100, 2250

$3x + 5y = 5000$

6. Assuming the athletic department met its goal of $5000, find the number of student tickets sold if 600 adult tickets sold. Use complete sentences to explain your reasoning.

Sample Answer: According to the graph, when $y = 600$, $x = 640$. If 600 adult tickets sold, then 640 student tickets sold.

7. Assuming the athletic department met its goal of $5000, find the number of adult tickets sold if 400 student tickets sold. Use complete sentences to explain your reasoning.

Sample Answer: According to the graph, when $x = 400$, $y = 760$. If 400 student tickets sold, then 760 adult tickets sold.

8. Write the equation in Question 2 in slope-intercept form. Show all your work.

$3x + 5y = 5000$

$5y = -3x + 5000$

$y = -\dfrac{3}{5}x + 1000$

Assignment

Name _____ Date _____

Earning Interest
Solving Literal Equations

1. A formula for the area of a rectangle is $A = bh$, where b is the length of the base of the rectangle and h is the height of the rectangle. Solve the equation for h. Show all your work. Then use a complete sentence to explain how you can find the height when you know the area and length of the base.

    $A = bh$

    $h = \dfrac{A}{b}$ To find the height, divide the area by the length of the base.

2. The formula for the area of a triangle is $A = \dfrac{1}{2}bh$, where b is the length of the base of the triangle and h is the height of the triangle. Solve the equation for b. Show all your work. Then use a complete sentence to explain how you can find the length of the base when you know the area and the height.

    $A = \dfrac{1}{2}bh$

    $2A = bh$

    $b = \dfrac{2A}{h}$ To find the length of the base, divide twice the area by the height.

3. The formula for the diameter of a circle is $d = 2r$, where r is the radius of the circle. Solve the equation for r. Show all your work. Then use a complete sentence to explain how you can find the radius when you know the diameter.

    $d = 2r$

    $r = \dfrac{d}{2}$ To find the radius, divide the diameter by two.

4. The formula for the perimeter of a rectangle is $P = 2l + 2w$, where l is the length of the rectangle and w is the width of the rectangle. Solve the equation for w. Show all your work.

    $P = 2l + 2w$

    $P - 2l = 2w$

    $w = \dfrac{P - 2l}{2}$

5

5

© 2006 Carnegie Learning, Inc.

Assignment

Name _____ Date _____

Mia's Growing Like a Weed
Drawing the Line of Best Fit

The typical gestational period (time from conception to birth) for a human baby is about 40 weeks. Recent developments in ultrasound scanning allow doctors to make measurements of parts of a baby's body while it is still in the womb. The table below contains data about the length of a baby's femur (thigh bone) during gestation.

Gestation time	Femur length
weeks	centimeters
14	1.5
14.5	1.6
15	2.0
16	2.1
20	3.3
25	4.8
30	6.2
40	8.0

1. Write unit rates that compare the baby's change in femur length to the change in gestation time from 14 weeks to 14.5 weeks, from 16 weeks to 20 weeks, and from 30 weeks to 40 weeks. Show all your work.

14 weeks to 14.5 weeks: $$\frac{1.6 \text{ cm} - 1.5 \text{ cm}}{14.5 \text{ weeks} - 14 \text{ weeks}} = \frac{0.1 \text{ cm}}{0.5 \text{ weeks}} = \frac{0.2 \text{ cm}}{1 \text{ week}}$$

16 weeks to 20 weeks: $$\frac{3.3 \text{ cm} - 2.1 \text{ cm}}{20 \text{ weeks} - 16 \text{ weeks}} = \frac{1.2 \text{ cm}}{4 \text{ weeks}} = \frac{0.3 \text{ cm}}{1 \text{ week}}$$

30 weeks to 40 weeks: $$\frac{8 \text{ cm} - 6.2 \text{ cm}}{40 \text{ weeks} - 30 \text{ weeks}} = \frac{1.8 \text{ cm}}{10 \text{ weeks}} = \frac{0.18 \text{ cm}}{1 \text{ week}}$$

2. Do all the data points lie on the same line? What does this tell you about the baby's femur length change over time? Use complete sentences to explain your reasoning.

No. The baby's femur length is not changing at the same rate over time.

3. Write ordered pairs from the table that show the baby's femur length as a function of gestation time.

(14, 1.5), (14.5, 1.6), (15, 2), (16, 2.1), (20, 3.3), (25, 4.8), (30, 6.2), (40, 8)

4. Create a scatter plot of the ordered pairs in Question 3 on the grid below. First, choose your bounds and intervals. Be sure to label your graph clearly.

Variable quantity	Lower bound	Upper bound	Interval
Student tickets	0	45	3
Adult tickets	0	15	1

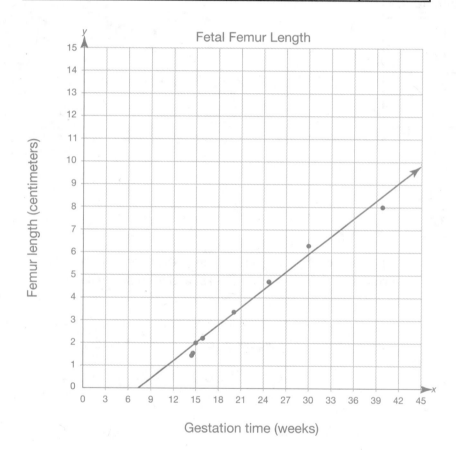

5. Use a ruler to draw the line that best fits your data on your graph in Question 4. Then write the equation of your line. Be sure to define your variables and include the units.

Answers will vary, but the equation should be close to $y = 0.26x - 1.9$, where x is the gestation time in weeks and y is the femur length in centimeters.

6. According to your line, approximately how many centimeters did the femur grow each week from 14 weeks to 40 weeks? How did you find your answer? Use complete sentences in your answer.

Sample Answer: The baby's femur grew about 0.26 centimeter each week. The answer is given by the slope of the line in Question 5.

7. According to your line, approximately how long would the baby's femur have been when the gestation time is 7 weeks? Show all your work and use a complete sentence in your answer.

$y = 0.26(7) - 1.9 = -0.08$; The baby's femur length would have been -0.08 centimeter.

8. According to your line, approximately how long would the baby's femur have been when the gestation time is 8 weeks? Show all your work and use a complete sentence in your answer.

$y = 0.26(8) - 1.9 = 0.18$; The baby's femur length would have been 0.18 centimeter.

9. Do your answers to Questions 7 and 8 make sense? Use complete sentences in your answer.

Sample Answer: No. The length of a baby's femur cannot be negative, and it is unlikely that the femur bone is even identifiable at 8 weeks gestation time.

10. What can you conclude about the accuracy of your model? Use a complete sentence in your answer.

Sample Answer: The model seems to only be accurate for gestation times from 14 weeks to birth.

6

Assignment

Name _____ Date _____

Where Do You Buy Your Music?
Using Lines of Best Fit

The table below shows the percent of voter participation in U.S. presidential elections for the years 1956 to 2000.

Election year	Voter participation
year	percent
1956	59.3
1960	62.8
1964	61.9
1968	60.9
1972	55.2
1976	53.5
1980	54.0
1984	53.1
1988	50.2
1992	55.9
1996	49.0
2000	50.7

1. Because the *x*-coordinates represent time, we can define time as the number of years since 1956. So, 1956 would become 0. What number would you use for 1960? What number would you use for 1964? What number would you use for 1968? Use complete sentences to explain your reasoning.

   Sample Answer: I would use four because 1960 is four years since 1956. Similarly, 1964 can be represented by 8 and 1968 can be represented by 12.

2. Write the ordered pairs that show the percent of voter participation as a function of the number of years since 1956.

   (0, 59.3), (4, 62.8), (8, 61.9), (12, 60.9), (16, 55.2), (20, 53.5), (24, 54.0), (28, 53.1), (32, 50.2), (36, 55.9), (40, 49), (44, 50.7)

3. Looking at the data, do you think your line of best fit will have a positive slope or a negative slope? Use a complete sentence to explain your reasoning.

   Sample Answer: The line of best fit will have a negative slope because overall voter participation is decreasing.

6

4. Create a scatter plot of the ordered pairs in Question 2 on the grid below. First, choose your bounds and intervals. Be sure to label your graph clearly.

Variable quantity	Lower bound	Upper bound	Interval
Time	0	60	4
Voter participation	0	75	5

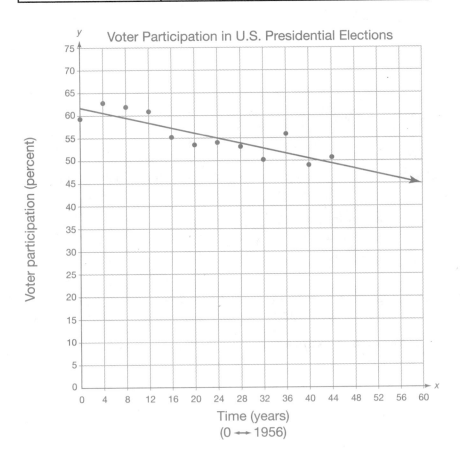

5. Use a ruler to ruler to draw the line that best fits the data on the graph in Question 4. Then write the equation of the line. Define your variables and include the units.

Answers will vary, but should be close to $y = -0.28x + 61.7$ where x is the number of years since 1956 and y is the percent of voter participation.

6. Use your equation to predict the percent of voter participation in 2008. Show all your work and use a complete sentence in your answer.

$y = -0.28(52) + 61.7 = 47.14$; The percent of voter participation should be about 47.

7. Considering the problem situation, what is the domain of your function? Use a complete sentence to explain your reasoning.

Sample Answer: The domain is {0, 4, 8, 12, 16, . . ., 220} because U.S. presidential elections occur every four years and voter participation cannot be negative.

8. Use your equation to predict the year in which the voter participation will be 45%. Show all your work and use a complete sentence in your answer.

$$45 = -0.28x + 61.7$$

$$-16.7 = -0.28x$$

$$59.6 \approx x \qquad\qquad 1956 + 59.6 = 2015.6$$

Voter participation will be 45% for the 2016 election.

9. Use your equation to determine what the voter participation was in 1980. Show all your work and use a complete sentence in your answer.

$y = -0.28(24) + 61.7 = 54.98$; **The percent of voter participation should be about 55.**

10. How close is your answer to Question 9 to the actual data? Use a complete sentence in your answer.

The answer, about 55% is fairly close to the actual data, 54%.

11. Consider a line of best fit for the percent of non-voters over time. Would this line increase or decrease from left to right? How would the line's steepness compare to the steepness of the line in Question 4? Use complete sentences in your answer.

Sample Answer: A line of best fit for the percent of non-voters over time would increase from left to right. The steepness of the lines should be the same because the percent is changing at the same rate.

6

Assignment

Name _____ Date _____

Stroop Test
Performing an Experiment

The goal of a word recall experiment is to see how many words from a list that is read aloud that a person can memorize and repeat back. Five word lists are given below.

5-Word List: chair, shoe, horse, suitcase, lamp

7-Word List: animal, sweater, cheetah, avocado, back, desk, plant

10-Word List: stereo, basketball, violin, teacher, pear, baby, table, zoo, curtains, ox

15-Word List: cup, barn, paper, book, fire, comb, glass, vacuum, cloud, road, suit, stereo, computer, trunk, television

20-Word List: football, hair, pizza, scarf, sandwich, T-shirt, microphone, screen, clock, fingers, coat, watch, tires, candles, cushions, earrings, heater, picture, keyboard, soda

1. If you were to perform a word recall experiment, what results would you expect to see as the number of words increases? Do you expect people to remember more words or fewer words? Do you think people will remember the same percent of words as the length of the list increases? Use complete sentences in your answer.

   Answers will vary.

2. What are the two variable quantities in a word recall experiment? Which variable quantity depends on the other? Use complete sentences in your answer.

   Sample Answer: The two variable quantities are the length of the word list and the number of words that a person can recall. The number of words recalled depends on the length of the list.

3. Perform the experiment for each word list. Read each list of words slowly and clearly to someone, but do not repeat any of the words. After you have finished reading each list, the person should repeat any words he or she remembers back to you. Do not allow the person to write anything down. Keep track of how many words the person correctly repeats back to you by filling in the table on the next page. Repeat this experiment two more times and average the results.

List length (words)	Trial 1 (words recalled)	Trial 2 (words recalled)	Trial 3 (words recalled)	Average (words recalled)
5-word list				
7-word list				
10-word list				
15-word list				
20-word list				

4. Write the ordered pairs from the from the table that show the average number of words recalled as a function of the number of words in the list.

Answers will vary.

5. Create a scatter plot of the ordered pairs in Question 4 on the grid below. First, choose your bounds and intervals. Be sure to label your graph clearly.

Variable quantity	Lower bound	Upper bound	Interval
Time	0	30	2
Voter participation	0	30	2

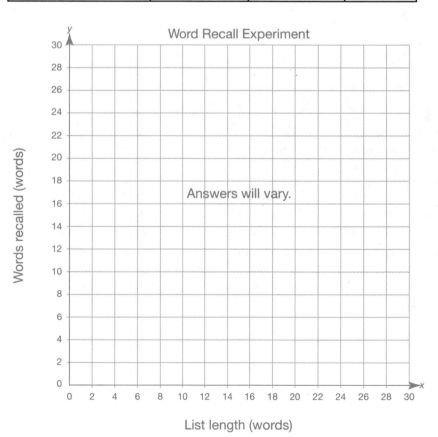

Word Recall Experiment

Answers will vary.

Words recalled (words)

List length (words)

6

6. Use a ruler to draw a line of best fit. Then write the equation of your line.

   Answers will vary.

7. Find the *y*-intercept of your line. What does the *y*-intercept represent in this situation? Use complete sentences in your answer.

   Answers will vary for the y-intercept depending on the line of best fit. Sample Answer: The y-intercept represents the number of words recalled when the number of words in the list is zero.

8. Find the slope of your line. What does the slope represent in this situation? Use complete sentences in your answer.

   Answers will vary for the y-intercept depending on the line of best fit. Sample Answer: The slope represents the increase in the number of words recalled as the length of the list increases by one word.

9. What is the average number of words that should be recalled from a list of 25 words? What is the average number of words that should be recalled from a list of 35 words? What is the average number of words that should be recalled from a list of 50 words? Show all your work and use complete sentences in your answer.

   Answers will vary.

10. What length should the word list be if a person recalls 20 words? Show your work and use a complete sentence in your answer.

    Answers will vary.

Assignment

Name _____   Date _____

Jumping Correlation

Define each term in your own words.

1. correlation   **Sample Answer: a relationship between two variables**

2. positive correlation   **Sample Answer: As *x*-values increase, *y*-values increase.**

3. negative correlation   **Sample Answer: As *x*-values increase, *y*-values decrease.**

Decide whether each set of data most likely has a positive correlation, a negative correlation, or no correlation. Use a complete sentence in your answer.

4. The number of hours you study compared to your test score

   Sample Answer: The set of data most likely has a positive correlation because the longer you study, the better you should be prepared for the test.

5. Your running speed compared to the time that it takes you to run the 100-meter dash

   Sample Answer: The set of data most likely has a negative correlation because the faster you go, the less time it will take you to run the 100-meter dash.

6. The number of calories that you eat compared to your weight

   Sample Answer: The set of data most likely has a positive correlation because the more calories you eat, the more weight you gain.

7. The number of computers sold compared to the amount of rainfall in inches

   Sample Answer: The set of data has no correlation because the amount of rainfall should not influence the purchasing of computers.

8. Give examples of two variable quantities that are positively correlated, two variable quantities that are negatively correlated, and two variable quantities that are not correlated.

   Answers will vary.

6

Assignment

Name _____ Date _____

Human Chain: Wrist Experiment
Using Technology to Find a Linear Regression Equation, Part 1

The table below shows the number of students per computer in U.S. public schools.

School year	Students per computer
year	students
1984	125
1985	75
1986	50
1987	37
1988	32
1989	25
1990	22
1991	20
1992	18
1993	16
1994	14
1995	10.5
1996	10
1997	7.8
1998	6.1
1999	5.7
2000	5.4

1. Because the x-coordinates represent time, we can define time as the number of years since 1984. So, 1984 would become 0. What number would you use for 1990? What number would you use for 1996? What number would you use for 2000? Use complete sentences to explain your reasoning.

    Sample Answer: I would use six because 1990 is six years since 1984. Similarly, 1996 can be represented by 12 and 2000 can be represented by 16.

© 2006 Carnegie Learning, Inc.

2. Write the ordered pairs that show the number of students per computer as a function of the number of years since 1984.

(0, 125), (1, 75), (2, 50), (3, 37), (4, 32), (5, 25), (6, 22), (7, 20), (8, 18), (9, 16), (10, 14), (11, 10.5), (12, 10), (13, 7.8), (14, 6.1), (15, 5.7), (16, 5.4)

3. Use a graphing calculator to find the linear regression equation. You can round the values of the slope and the y-intercept to the nearest hundredth.

$y = -4.91x + 67.48$

4. What is the value of r for your linear regression equation? Does this indicate a positive or negative correlation? Use a complete sentence in your answer.

$r = -0.8023097383$; Because the value of r is negative, it indicates a negative correlation.

5. What is the slope of your linear regression equation? What does the slope mean in this problem situation? Use a complete sentence in your answer.

−4.91; Sample Answer: The slope indicates the change in the number of students per computer each year.

6. What is the y-intercept of your linear regression equation? What does the y-intercept mean in this problem situation? Use a complete sentence in your answer.

67.48; The y-intercept represents the number of students per computer in 1984.

7. How does the y-intercept of your linear regression equation compare to the actual data? Why or why not? Use complete sentences in your answer.

Sample Answer: The y-intercept 67.48 is not close to actual data of 125 for 1984. In the mid-1980s, the number of students per computer was decreasing at a much faster rate than it did later, so the y-intercept of the linear regression equation is influenced more by the later data.

8. Is your linear regression equation a good model of the data? Show all your work use complete sentences to explain your reasoning.

Answers will vary, but students should make a comparison of the y-values determined by the linear regression equation to the actual data values in the table. They should come to the conclusion that the data is not really modeled well by a line.

6

Assignment

Name _____ Date _____

Human Chain: Shoulder Experiment
Using Technology to Find a Linear Regression Equation, Part 2

The table below shows the yearly cost of tuition at a private four-year college.

School year	Cost of tuition
year	dollars
1993	10,294
1994	10,952
1995	11,481
1996	12,243
1997	12,881
1998	13,344
1999	13,973
2000	14,588
2001	15,531

1. Because the x-coordinates represent time, we can define time as the number of years since 1993. So, 1993 would become 0. What number would you use for 2000? Use a complete sentence in your answer.

   I would use seven because 2000 is seven years since 1993.

2. Write the ordered pairs that show the yearly tuition cost as a function of the number of years since 1993.

   (0, 10,294), (1, 10,952), (2, 11,481), (3, 12,243), (4, 12,881), (5, 13,344), (6, 13,973), (7, 14,588), (8, 15,531)

3. Use a graphing calculator to find the linear regression equation. You can round the values of the slope and y-intercept to the nearest dollar.

   $y = 632x + 10{,}280$

4. Why is it more appropriate to round the slope and y-intercept of the linear regression equation in Question 3 to nearest dollar instead of to the nearest cent? Use complete sentences in your answer.

   Sample Answer: It is appropriate to round the slope and y-intercept to the nearest dollar because the values are rather large. It is not important to know the change in tuition to nearest cent.

5. What is the value of r for your linear regression equation? Does this indicate a positive or negative correlation? Use a complete sentence in your answer.

   $r = 0.9982115308$; **Because the value of r is positive, it indicates a positive correlation.**

6. What is the slope of your linear regression equation? What does the slope mean in this problem situation? Use a complete sentence in your answer.

   632; Sample Answer: The slope indicates the amount the cost of tuition increases each year.

7. Use your linear regression equation to predict the cost of tuition in 2005. Show all your work and use a complete sentence in your answer.

   $y = 632(12) + 10{,}280 = 17{,}864$; **The cost of tuition in 2005 will be $17,864.**

8. Use your linear regression equation to determine in which year the cost of tuition will be $25,000. Show all your work and use a complete sentence in your answer.

   $25{,}000 = 632x + 10{,}280$

   $14{,}720 = 632x$

   $x \approx 23.29$ $1993 + 23.29 = 2016.29$

   The cost of tuition will be $25,000 in about 2016.

Assignment

Name _____ Date _____

Making a Quilt
Scatter Plots and Non-Linear Data

An automatic sprinkler system includes ground-level sprinkler heads that rotate to water a circular area. The radius of the circular area can be adjusted at installation to accommodate the shape of any yard.

1. Complete the table below that shows the watering area for different sprinkling radii. Recall that the area of a circle is $A = \pi r^2$, where $\pi \approx 3.14$.

Radius	Area
feet	square feet
0	0
1	3.14
2	12.56
3	28.26
4	50.24
5	78.50
6	113.04
7	153.86

2. Write the ordered pairs that show the area as a function of the watering radius.

(0, 0), (1, 3.14), (2, 12.56), (3, 28.26), (4, 50.24), (5, 78.5), (6, 113.04), (7, 153.86)

3. Create a scatter plot of the ordered pairs on the grid. First, choose your bounds and intervals. Be sure to label your graph clearly.

Variable quantity	Lower bound	Upper bound	Interval
Radius	0	7.5	0.5
Area	0	225	15

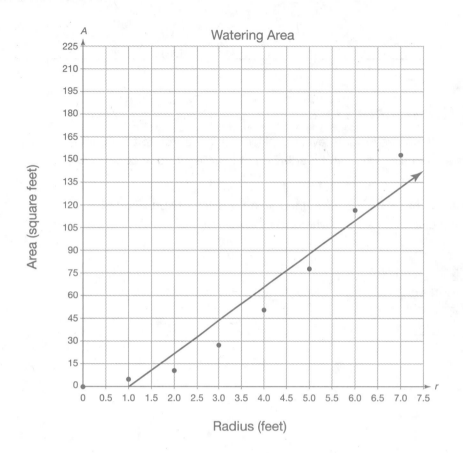

Watering Area

4. Use a graphing calculator to find the linear regression equation.

A = 21.98*r* – 21.98

5. Find the watering area when the sprinkler radius is 10 feet as you did when you filled in the chart in Question 1. Then use the equation in Question 4 to find the area. What can you conclude about your linear model? Use complete sentences in your answer.

Sample Answer: 314 square feet; 197.82 square feet; Because the data is shaped more like curve than a line, the linear model is not an accurate predictor of the watering area.

6